Bob Penber.

STRUCTURAL
PROCESSES
IN CREEP

STRUCTURAL PROCESSES IN CREEP

Report of a symposium organized by
The Iron and Steel Institute and
The Institute of Metals
London 3 and 4 May 1961

1961   THE IRON AND STEEL INSTITUTE

Special Report no. 70
© 1961 The Iron and Steel Institute
4 Grosvenor Gardens London SW1

*The photomicrograph on the dust-jacket
is from Fig. 20d on page 313*

Made and printed in England by
Percy Lund, Humphries & Co. Ltd, London and Bradford

Contents

Foreword

During the last two or three decades, research in physical metallurgy has led to a much better understanding of the reasons why metals and alloys behave as they do. There is, nevertheless, a considerable gap between the results of fundamental research and technological applications. The gap is probably narrower in the field of creep than in most branches of metallurgy, but even here there is plenty of scope for improvement. There is a growing feeling that those concerned with practical aspects of creep and those whose interest lies mainly in reaching an understanding of creep processes should both make a more serious effort to understand each other's points of view and outstanding problems. The Iron and Steel Institute and The Institute of Metals found that they had been independently planning meetings to contribute in this direction, and they therefore decided to organize a joint symposium on 'Structural processes in creep'. The symposium was very well attended, but unfortunately not all who wished to take part in the discussions were able to do so, due to limitations of time.

It is hoped that the publication of the papers and discussions in book form will make a further contribution to the advance of knowledge in this field, and will help those concerned with engineering aspects of creep to understand the approach of the physical metallurgist, and vice versa.

October 1961   A. G. Q.

Intercrystalline creep fractures

A. H. Cottrell

A survey is made of present knowledge and understanding of fractures produced at grain boundaries in metals by prolonged loading at high temperatures. Conditions for the formation of spreading cracks and spheroidal cavities are discussed. Grain boundary sliding appears important for nucleating the fractures, and atomic migration for growing spheroidal cavities at low stresses. The ease with which the fractures can be nucleated is still not fully understood, but particles of non-wetting substances on the grain boundaries may be important as nucleating agents. Strongly adherent particles may improve creep ductilities by supporting some of the load otherwise relaxed on sliding grain boundaries. The practical implications of these deductions are briefly discussed.

THE EQUICOHESIVE TEMPERATURE

ONE OF THE OLDEST IDEAS in physical metallurgy is that grain boundaries strengthen metals at low temperatures and weaken them at high temperatures. Figure 1 shows how the strengths of grains and their boundaries are usually considered to change with temperature. The strength of the boundaries falls rapidly with rising temperature, becoming virtually zero before the melting point of the material, T_m, is reached. The grains also become weaker, but more gradually.

Professor Cottrell is Goldsmiths' Professor of Metallurgy in the University of Cambridge.

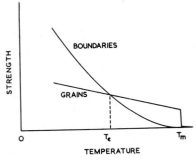

1 *Effect of temperature on the strengths of grains and grain boundaries*

Except at abnormally low rates of strain they retain some strength even at the melting point. The two strength curves intersect at the 'equicohesive temperature' T_e, commonly about $0.6T_m$ (°K). Below T_e ductile metals generally fail by plastic tearing in the grains after an elongation of usually 20–60% in a tensile test. Above T_e the fracture becomes localized in the grain boundaries and usually occurs before the elongation reaches 10%; the metal then appears brittle, not because of any inherent brittleness of the grains, but because this intercrystalline fracture occurs under applied stresses below the creep strength of the grains.

Rosenhain emphasized many years ago that their non-crystalline structures would cause grain boundaries to behave mechanically like amorphous materials such as glass: soft and fluid at high temperatures, hard at low temperatures. The modern view is that adjoining grains in pure metals maintain their crystal structures up to within one or two atomic distances of one another, only the almost monatomic layer of the interface itself being highly disordered in structure. Atoms in this interface have two crystal surfaces on which to crystallize, but they fail to do so on either because of the rival forces from the other. They thus have a choice of alternative possible positions, between which they can move to some extent independently of their neighbours. Normally such movements occur randomly to and fro, but a shear stress applied along the interface preferentially encourages those movements that cause the interface to slide with the stress. This process is quite different from slip on a crystal plane; there the orderliness of the crystal structure prevents atoms from moving independently (apart from atomic diffusion) but allows them to move collectively whenever dislocations glide along the plane.

The rate of shear, $\dot{\gamma}$, due to any process such as these can be expressed generally in the form

$$\dot{\gamma} = A_e^{-\dfrac{V(\sigma_o - \sigma)^n}{kT}} \qquad \cdot \quad \cdot \quad \cdot \quad \cdot \quad \cdot \quad \cdot \quad (1)$$

which takes account of the way that the thermal motion (T=absolute temperature, k=Boltzmann's constant) of the material can help the applied stress σ ($<\sigma_o$) to produce the necessary atomic movements. The values of the parameters A, V, σ_o, and n, depend on the particular material and process concerned. In the simplest cases $n=1$; V is then a characteristic volume which measures the size of a single creep event. For example, when a dislocation line is gliding between the particles of a dispersion-hardened alloy, some thousands of atoms slip each time one such obstacle is passed. Measured on an atomic

2

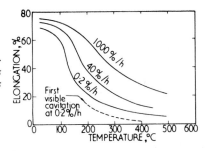

2 *Effect of strain rate on the ductility of alpha brass at various temperatures, based on the results of Greenwood et al.[1]*

scale, V is then very large and the rate of slip remains negligible until σ approaches σ_0 closely. There is thus a well defined yield stress, at $\sigma \simeq \sigma_0$, that is fairly insensitive to temperature and rate of straining. By contrast, a single slip event in a grain boundary involves so few atoms that the exponent in (1) remains small at high temperatures even at the lowest applied stresses. In the limit of small stresses (setting $n=1$, taking $V\sigma/kT$ out of the exponent, and subtracting the flow in the reverse direction) this leads to Newtonian viscosity,

$$\dot{\gamma} = \left(\frac{2AV}{kT} \, e^{-\frac{V\sigma_0}{kT}}\right) \sigma, \quad \cdot \quad \cdot \quad \cdot \quad \cdot \quad \cdot \quad (2)$$

with an activation energy $V\sigma_0$.

We can thus explain the curves of Fig.1 if these refer to flow stresses. As regards the grains it is clear that flow stress or creep strength is the relevant property. However, the grain boundary curve in Fig.1 refers to fracture, not flow, and it is not immediately obvious that these properties are related. We can take two points of view about this: (i) that grain boundary sliding leads directly to fracture; (ii) that the grain boundary curve in Fig.1 is a reflection of the increase in atomic mobility at high temperatures, this mobility leading to both sliding and fracture without these being necessarily related.

The explanation of Fig.1 in terms of thermal activation implies that the equicohesive temperature should be higher in quick tests than slow. The thermally activated jumps of the atoms in the boundaries provide a 'thermal clock' that runs faster at higher temperatures. The equicohesive temperature is that at which this clock is just fast enough to run to failure in the time allowed. A given material at the same temperature can thus fail in a ductile transcrystalline manner when pulled quickly, and in a brittle intercrystalline manner when pulled slowly. Figure 2 shows an example of this, obtained by Greenwood et al.[1] on alpha brass. At 200°C,

3

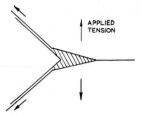

3 *Triple point crack produced on a transverse grain boundary as a result of sliding on an inclined boundary*

APPLIED
TENSION

for example, quickly strained (1 000 %/h) specimens elongated (60 %) in the typical manner of ductile brasses whereas the slowly strained (0·2 % h) ones broke along grain boundaries after 20 % elongation; the respective times to failure were 3·6 and 6 000 min.

This effect of time and strain rate has led to the generalized concept of the 'equicohesive point' θ,

$$\theta = T(C_1 - \log \dot{\gamma}), \qquad \cdot \quad \cdot \quad \cdot \quad (3)$$
$$\text{or} \qquad \theta = T(C_2 + \log t), \qquad \cdot \quad \cdot \quad \cdot \quad (4)$$

in place of the equicohesive temperature, where t is the duration of loading or the rupture time.[2] The logarithmic factor expresses the relation between temperature and strain rate as given in (1).

TYPES OF FRACTURE

Zener[3] emphasized some years ago that when slip occurs along an interface severe stress concentrations can be produced at the ends where it is held up by an obstacle. The interface acts like a 'shear crack' and the stress at its ends can in principle become large enough to nucleate fracture there. This idea has become the starting point for theories of several types of fractures in solids. Eborall[4] and Chang and Grant[5] have applied it in particular to a commonly observed form of intercrystalline cracking which starts at and spreads from 'triple points' where three grain boundaries meet, as shown in Fig.3. Many examples of this type of fracture have now been observed in various materials[6] and there can be no doubt that this is a major cause of high-temperature brittleness in polycrystals.

Although it is an obvious direct cause of such intercrystalline fractures, grain boundary sliding does not always lead to fracture. Servi and Grant[7] have shown that pure aluminium resists intercrystalline fracture and remains very ductile at all temperatures up to the melting point, even though grain boundary sliding occurs copiously. It has often been observed that the ductility of metals improves when the temperature becomes sufficiently high, or the time of loading sufficiently long, to allow the grain boundaries to migrate, as in grain growth, during the deformation.[6] Presumably

4

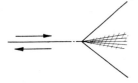

this migration disperses the stress or strain concentrations produced by the sliding.[8] Another mode of dispersal, which was observed in Servi and Grant's aluminium, is by plastic deformation in the grain at the end of the sliding boundary, which gives a plastic 'fold' as shown in Fig.4.

This last observation shows that hardening the grains, to improve their creep resistance, is likely to promote intercrystalline fracture. Experience with commercial creep-resistant alloys certainly supports this conclusion. Bailey[9] emphasized some years ago that brittle intergranular failures occur mainly when the grains are made too strong in relation to the boundaries. Glen[10] has shown that the hot tensile strength (400–600°C) of low carbon steel can be increased considerably by the addition of alloys (e.g. 1·5%Mn or Mo) that promote strain age hardening but that this increase leads to brittleness and a markedly intercrystalline fracture. Another example is provided by the niobium-bearing austenitic steels (e.g. 18%Cr, 12%Ni, 1%Nb) used for high temperature steam plant.[11,12] These are strong but have low rupture ductilities in long-term tests and also tend to crack in the heat-affected zones of restrained welds. It seems that in this case the grains become very hard, due to the precipitation of niobium carbide on dislocations, and that this leads to brittle, intercrystalline, fractures; the ductility can be restored by overageing the precipitates but this softens the grains again.

Intergranular brittleness is also sometimes observed when soft zones occur in the grains alongside the boundaries, due for example to local overaging and solute denudation effects in precipitation hardening alloys. Alloys of the Al–Mg–Zn (DTD 683) type tend to fracture in a brittle manner along grain boundaries when aged to maximum hardness. Thomas and Nutting[13] showed that the state of precipitation in the grain boundaries of such alloys is always well ahead of that in the grains and that zones about 0·5 μin wide alongside boundaries remain free from precipitates. Plastic deformation occurs preferentially along these zones at stresses well below the general yield stress of the material. In such cases the fracture no longer depends on grain boundary sliding in the strict sense, but on plastic shear along the soft zones lining the boundary. Since a

5 *Stages in the formation, growth, and coalescence of creep on a grain boundary*

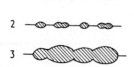

difference in yield strengths between the surface layers and insides of the grains is now involved, this type of intercrystalline brittleness can persist to low temperatures where the usual conditions for creep fractures do not hold.

An interesting similar effect at high temperatures has been observed by Lozinsky and Simeonova.[14] They produced rapid plastic flow in iron by thermally cycling the specimen repeatedly through the a–γ transformation while it was under stress. In pure iron this led to general deformation and a necking failure, but in commercial iron intercrystalline fracture occurred at the sides of the heated region, where the temperature ranged between the limits 720–850°C. It appears that carbon segregates to the grain boundaries and locally enriches the metal enough to make it transform from a–γ when heated just above A_1. Very soft zones, due to the repeated a–γ transformation, are then produced along the boundaries by thermal cycling in a critical temperature range and these lead to rapid intercrystalline fracture.

All the types of fracture described above are clearly related to grain boundary shear and the Zener mechanism. In 1954 Greenwood, *et al.*[1] reported an apparently quite different type of intercrystalline fracture which is now usually called 'cavitation'. In this the fracture starts by the formation of many small spheroidal cavities along the grain boundaries, spaced usually at intervals of a few microns. As shown in Fig.5, these cavities slowly grow, giving the appearance of a string of beads, and eventually coalesce to form cracks with wavy edges. Figure 6 shows an example.

This type of creep fracture has been studied intensively in recent years and has been observed in a wide variety of metals and alloys.[6] The cavities form predominantly though not exclusively on boundaries transverse to applied tensile stress. They appear to be distributed almost at random along such boundaries and are not obviously concentrated at or near triple points. They form at an early stage of deformation simultaneously on a large number of boundaries and then grow slowly, the life of the specimen being determined mainly by the time for the bridges of material between them to 'neck down' to zero cross-section. Cavitation fracture generally occurs at higher temperatures and lower applied stresses

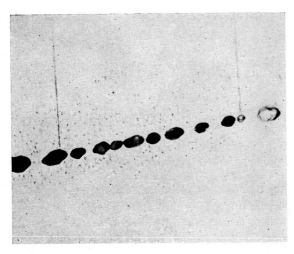

6 *Cavities formed along a grain boundary in copper subjected to a stress of 5 000 lb/in² at 450°C* ×500

than triple-point cracking. For example, McLean[15] showed that cavities were formed in Nimonic 90 at tensile stresses below 5 tons/in² and temperatures above 800°C; triple point cracks at stresses above 10 tons/in² and temperatures below 900°C; and both types of fracture at intermediate conditions.

The part played by grain boundary sliding in cavitation fracture is not immediately obvious. The facts that the cavities form mainly on transverse boundaries and are not particularly associated with triple points suggest that the sliding might not be important in this case. However, Chen and Machlin[16] showed in experiments on copper bicrystals that sliding was necessary to produce cavities. A shear stress alone, applied to the bicrystal boundary, produced cavities; a tensile stress alone, applied normal to the boundary, failed to produce cavities; and a shear stress followed by a tensile stress produced many cavities. We shall return to this point when we discuss the nucleation of intercrystalline fracture. The effects of other variables have been studied less completely. Reid and Greenwood[17] used vacuum-cast copper to prove that varying the hydrogen content of the metal did not alter the rate of cavity formation. On the other hand, vacuum melting is known to improve the stress-rupture life of some high-temperature alloys considerably.[18] Resnick and Seigle[19] have made important observations on 70–30 brass. They showed that specimens containing 0·28% oxygen, probably as ZnO,

7

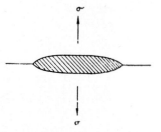

7 *Elongated cavity on a grain boundary subjected to a tensile stress*

broke after 6% elongation in slow tension at 400°C whereas specimens containing only 0·07% oxygen survived until 14·5% elongation.

MECHANICS OF INTERCRYSTALLINE FRACTURE

The high tensile strengths of transverse grain boundaries are proved by the mechanical properties of ductile metals at low temperatures; except when certain impurities are present it is usually impossible to produce intercrystalline fractures even in tensile necks where the stress may reach as high as $E/100$ ($E=$Young's modulus). The ideal tensile strength of a grain boundary can be estimated by the same general method as is used for crystals and amorphous solids. The work required to break the atomic bonds across the boundary can be deduced approximately in terms of other physical properties and from this the ideal tensile strength σ_f

$$\sigma_f \simeq \sqrt{\frac{E\gamma_s}{a}} \qquad \cdot \quad \cdot \quad \cdot \quad \cdot \quad \cdot \quad (5)$$

can be estimated. Here a is the atomic spacing and γ_s the effective surface energy per unit area of fractured surface. The effective surface energy is slightly ($\simeq 20\%$) smaller than the true surface energy because the energy originally belonging to the fractured grain boundary is released by the fracture. The values of E and a generally also differ slightly from those for the grains. However, the order of magnitude of σ_f is not affected and remains comparable with the ideal tensile strength ($\simeq E/10$) of the crystal.

The problem of how such a high cohesive strength as this is overcome by the small stresses used in high-temperature creep tests is best approached by considering first the growth of already existing cracks and cavities. Figure 7 shows an elongated cavity on a grain boundary subjected to a tensile stress σ. There are several ways in which this cavity can change at high temperatures, of which the following are particularly important:

(i) by spreading along the boundary, like a cleavage crack, through the breaking of atomic bonds by the concentrated stress at its ends

(ii) by changing in volume through elastic deformation, as a result of changes in the applied stress or in the length of the cavity

(iii) by spreading along the boundary at constant volume (apart from elastic deformation) through the migration of atoms, mainly by surface diffusion, from the ends to the sides of the cavity

(iv) by spreading along the boundary, with changing volume, through the removal of atoms from the ends by atomic migration along the boundary or into the grains.

For the cavity to grow by processes (i) or (iii) it is necessary that energy be released through elastic deformation more rapidly than it is consumed as surface energy of the new fracture faces.[22] This condition is expressed by Griffith's formula,

$$\sigma_G \simeq \sqrt{\frac{E\gamma_s}{c}} \quad . \quad . \quad . \quad . \quad . \quad . \quad (6)$$

for the *minimum* tensile stress σ_G to enable a crack of length $2c$ to grow. This is not a sufficient condition for the crack to grow by process (i) however, since in this case the concentrated stress at the tip must also reach the value σ_f, which requires the crack to be sharp. Some sharpness will be maintained at the tip of even a stationary cavity on a grain boundary at high temperatures, since the equilibrium of surface tensions at the triple point require a certain dihedral angle to exist at the tip, but it is not clear whether this sharpness is sufficient to ensure cleavage at the Griffith stress. In practice intercrystalline creep fractures spread slowly and not at the high speeds expected from the cleavage process, except possibly during the last stages of fracture.

The Griffith criterion is, however, always a sufficient condition for the slow growth of a cavity by process (iii) because in this case the atomic bonds at the tip are overcome by thermal agitation and a high stress concentration is not necessary. Such a process of growth could continue even if the cavity were blunt. Strictly, however, the Griffith criterion is sufficient only for an infinitesimally slow growth. A higher stress (or longer cavity) would be needed for growth at a finite rate. This is because the atomic migration producing the growth is a form of viscous creep which occurs at a rate proportional to $\sigma - \sigma_G$ when $\sigma \simeq \sigma_G$.

As regards numerical magnitudes we take $E \simeq 2 \times 10^{12}$ dyn/cm^2, $\gamma_s \simeq 1\,500$ erg/cm^2, and $\sigma \simeq 1 \cdot 5 \times 10^9$ dyn/cm^2 ($\simeq 10$ tons/in^2) for a Nimonic alloy, in which case the Griffith criterion is satisfied when $c \simeq 0 \cdot 013$ mm. In McLean's experiments,[15] spreading triple-point

9

cracks of lengths comparable with the grain size (0·08–0·016 mm) were produced mainly at stresses above 10 tons/in², so that Griffith's criterion appears to have been satisfied under these conditions. However, fractures can be produced by the spheroidal cavitation process at stresses far below the Griffith stress for any reasonable crack length. Some magnesium alloys, for example, can fracture in this manner under stresses only about 100 lb/in² at 450°C.[20,21] At this stress level, with $E \simeq 5 \times 10^{11}$ dyn/cm,² $\gamma_s \simeq 500$ erg/cm,² and $\sigma \simeq 10^7$ dyn/cm,² very long cracks ($c \simeq 2·5$ cm) would be needed to satisfy Griffith's criterion. Clearly, although small strings of linked cavities in such cases may appear geometrically to be 'cracks', they do not in fact satisfy the mechanical conditions usually associated with a true crack. In particular the energy of elastic deformation and the stress concentration at the tip are of minor importance for their growth.

When the applied stress is smaller than the Griffith stress, for a given length of cavity, processes (i) and (iii) tend to make the cavity contract. We shall not consider closure by process (i) since this could occur only if the cavity were a true elastic crack which owed its volume to elastic deformation and not to missing atoms. Contraction by surface migration can occur at constant cavity volume (apart from elastic deformation); the tendency then is for the cavity to *spheroidize*, i.e. to take up a lenticular shape as nearly spherical as possible which satisfies the requirements of minimum total surface energy and preserves the correct dihedral angles at the grain boundary. Since surface diffusion is generally faster than the other diffusion processes (grain boundary and lattice) that can change the shape of a cavity, we expect small cavities to take up this spheroidal shape, as is observed in practice. Presumably coalesced cavities maintain their cracklike shapes (cf. Fig.5) only because the large amount of matter that would need to be transported by surface diffusion makes their rate of spheroidization small compared with the rate at which other cavities add themselves to their ends.

A spheroidal cavity, though small and well below the Griffith size, can nevertheless grow by processes of type (iv) because these allow the applied stress to do more work than is possible through elastic deformation alone. One such process, suggested by Greenwood,[23] is the migration to the grain boundaries of lattice vacancies created by plastic deformation within the grains. The process we shall particularly consider, however, is the migration of atoms, through the lattice or along the grain boundary (with a corresponding counterflow of lattice vacancies or grain boundary voids), from a cavity on to its nearby grain boundary. This is important for two reasons: (a) the diffusion path is short so that the process can operate rapidly, especially at temperatures where grain boundary diffusion is much faster than lattice diffusion; (b) the deposition of atoms on grain boundaries provides a means for enabling tensile stresses across those boundaries to do work. It is known from experiments on sintering,[24,25] on the growth of gas bubbles in irradiated metals,[26] and on the annealing of vacancies in quenched metals,[27] that a grain boundary is a very effective source and sink of vacancies. This is of course the condition that such a boundary be capable of accepting atoms removed from a cavity.

The extra atoms deposited in the boundary crystallize on the faces of the adjoining crystals and cause these crystals to grow perpendicularly to the boundary. The work done by the tensile stress σ in this direction is $\sigma\Omega$ per atomic volume Ω deposited (this can be seen by considering the element of tensile force $\sigma\Omega^{\frac{2}{3}}$ which acts through one such atom to be displaced through a distance $\Omega^{\frac{1}{3}}$ by the addition of this atom to the boundary). This work is additional to any work of elastic deformation and it is large enough to enable very small cavities to grow. The surface area of a spherical cavity of radius r increases by $2\Omega/r$ per atom removed from its surface. The condition for growth is that the work $\sigma\Omega$ exceed the increase in surface energy $2\Omega\gamma_s/r$; thus a stress greater than

$$\sigma = \frac{2\gamma_s}{r} \qquad \cdots \cdots \quad (7)$$

enables the cavity to grow. If $r = 10^{-4}$ cm and $\gamma_s = 1\,000$ erg/cm^2 this is only about 300 lb/in^2. The critical importance of this process of cavity growth is evident; if small cavities exist on transverse boundaries a creep specimen *must* ultimately fail at high temperatures, even under applied stresses far below the creep strength of the grains.

This theory of creep cavitation has been developed by several people, particularly by Baluffi and Seigle.[28] Estimates of the rate of cavity growth have been made by McLean[29] and Gifkins,[6] using lattice diffusion, and by Hull and Rimmer,[30] using grain boundary diffusion. Grain boundary diffusion is faster but can occur only along a narrow channel, whereas lattice diffusion can occur through a diffusion zone as wide as the cavity itself. Hull and Rimmer have shown that the grain boundary process is generally the dominating one in copper at 500°C.

A simplified, approximate form of Hull and Rimmer's calculation is as follows. Consider a regular array of equal, spherical cavities of spacing a between centres, on a grain boundary under a tensile stress σ. The rate of growth alters with the growth but, for

11

simplicity, we shall evaluate an approximate average rate at the stage where the radius r of the cavities is $a/4$. At this stage the distance between neighbouring cavities is $a/2$. To produce uniform crystal growth over the regions between cavities an atom has to migrate on average a distance rather less than one-half of $a/2$; let us say $a/6$. We suppose that $\sigma > > 2\gamma_s/r$ so that $\sigma\Omega$ is the only important factor controlling the atomic movements. The work $\sigma\Omega$ done through the migration of an atom by a distance $a/6$ along the boundary is equal to that done by a force

$$F \simeq \frac{6\sigma\Omega}{a} \qquad . \qquad . \qquad . \qquad . \qquad . \qquad (8)$$

acting on that atom. Einstein's relation gives the velocity v of an atom moving with a diffusion coefficient D under the action of such a force as

$$v = \frac{DF}{kT} = \frac{6D\sigma\Omega}{akT} \qquad . \qquad . \qquad . \qquad . \qquad (9)$$

The area over which the cavity is joined to the grain boundary, which is where this migration starts, is $2\pi r\delta$ where δ is the thickness of the boundary. The volume V of the cavity thus increases at the rate

$$\frac{dV}{dt} = 2\pi rv\delta \simeq \frac{12\pi r\sigma\Omega D\delta}{akT} \qquad . \qquad . \qquad . \qquad (10)$$

and the corresponding rate at which the radius increases is given by

$$\frac{dr}{dt} = \frac{1}{4\pi r^2}\frac{dV}{dt} = \frac{3\sigma\Omega D\delta}{arkT} \qquad . \qquad . \qquad . \qquad (11)$$

For an order of magnitude estimate we suppose this rate to hold over the entire rupture process, from $r = r_0$ to $r \simeq a/2$. The rupture time t_r is then given by

$$t_r \simeq \frac{akT}{3\sigma\Omega D\delta}\int_{r_0}^{a/2} r\,dr \simeq \frac{a^3kT}{24\sigma\Omega D\delta,} \qquad . \qquad . \qquad . \qquad (12)$$

assuming that $r_0 < < a$. The leading term in the more exact formula obtained by Hull and Rimmer is the same as this but with 16π in place of the factor 24.

To test their formula, Hull and Rimmer made creep/rupture experiments on copper. Typically, at $T = 410°C$ and $\sigma = 5\,050$ lb/in², failure occurred in $7\,000$ s by the coalescence of voids at a spacing $a \simeq 3 \times 10^{-4}$ cm on transverse boundaries. The value of $D\delta$ is unknown but, exploiting the similarity between copper and silver, Hull and Rimmer used a value $D\delta = 3 \times 10^{-15}$ cm³/s obtained from grain boundary self-diffusion experiments on silver. Accepting this value, and taking $\sigma = 3\cdot4 \times 10^8$ dyn/cm², $\Omega = 1\cdot2 \times 10^{-23}$ cm³, $a^3 = 27 \times 10^{-12}$

cm³, and $kT = 10^{-13}$ erg, we obtain $t_r \simeq 4\,500$ s. Except for the uncertainty due to the assumed value of $D\delta$ it thus appears that the process can operate fast enough to produce the observed rate of cavitation and fracture.

We can also use the theory to estimate the minimum creep ductility. It is clear from Fig.5 that the crystal growth process causes a grain to elongate by an amount of order a as the cavities coalesce. If the grain size is L the *minimum* tensile ductility is thus given by

$$\varepsilon_r \simeq \frac{a}{L} \qquad . \qquad . \qquad . \qquad . \qquad . \qquad (13)$$

This is a minimum since it excludes other processes of deformation, e.g. creep in the grains, that may also occur. Some of the observed creep ductilities at low stresses appear to be of this order. McLean's published photographs of cavitation in Nimonic alloys[15] suggest that $L/a \simeq 10$ to 15 in this case, i.e. $\varepsilon_r \simeq 6$ to 10%, which compares with some of the observed elongations. In the experiments of Greenwood et al.[1] fracture at the lowest strain rates occurred at about 5% elongation after cavities were first seen. This would correspond to $L/a \simeq 20$ which is reasonably consistent with the observed microstructures. These comparisons are very approximate since no systematic observations to test the point have been made but they do show that at low strain rates and applied stresses the deformation due to this process can account for much and possibly all of the observed rupture ductility.

The smallness of observed rupture ductilities in brittle creep fractures makes it difficult in fact to accept any processes of cavitation other than this. If, for example, the process consisted of the production of lattice vacancies by dislocations moving in the grains, these vacancies then migrating to cavities on grain boundaries, much higher ductilities would be expected. Many atoms would have to glide to produce one vacancy and only a few of these vacancies could be expected to find their way to grain boundary cavities.

NUCLEATION OF INTERCRYSTALLINE FRACTURE

As with most processes, it is much harder to understand how creep fractures nucleate than how they develop afterwards. When the material in the grain boundaries is fully coherent a stress concentration approaching the ideal tensile strength, as given by (5) is needed to start such a fracture. At a triple point where grain boundary sliding is obstructed, Zener's mechanism[3] can in principle produce this stress. Stroh[31] has shown that a necessary condition to

8 *Cavities (dark) associated with particles of precipitate on a sliding grain boundary*

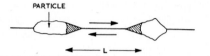

start a fracture at the end of a sliding interface of length L is that the applied shear stress σ must exceed the value

$$\sigma_s = \sqrt{\frac{12\mu\gamma_s}{\pi L}} \qquad \cdot \qquad \cdot \qquad \cdot \qquad \cdot \qquad \cdot \qquad (14)$$

where μ is the shear modulus. This is the equivalent of Griffith's criterion, the interface acting in effect as a shear crack; when $L \simeq 2c$ it gives $\sigma_s \simeq \sigma_G$.

McLean[15] and Weaver[32] have applied this formula to inter-crystalline creep fractures in Nimonic and other commercial creep-resistant alloys. Taking the minimum shear stress at which triple-point cracks were seen as 2·5 tons/in² (i.e. a tensile stress of 5 tons/in²), and taking $\mu = 8 \times 10''$ dyn/cm² and $L = 10^{-2}$ cm, McLean showed that this stress is equal to σ_s if $\gamma_s = 450$ erg/cm². This value of the surface energy is comparable with but distinctly lower than the expected one ($\simeq 1\,500$ erg/cm²). Using the same values of μ and γ_s Weaver showed that the Stroh-McLean analysis can explain the effect of precipitates, mainly carbides, on grain boundaries in raising the creep rupture stress of a Nimonic alloy. These precipitates occur at intervals along the boundaries and interrupt the free sliding length, as shown in Fig. 8; L is then no longer determined by the grain size but by the distance between precipitates. In a typical case this observed distance gave $2\sigma_s = 17$ tons/in² in agreement with the observed breaking stress.

McLean has suggested that the low value of γ_s may be due to segregated impurities that lower the surface energy of the fracture. Such an effect is known to be responsible for the critical embrittling action of certain impurities in metals, e.g. lead in copper[33] and sodium in aluminium-magnesium alloys.[34] Without appealing to some such effect as this it is hard to understand why intercrystalline fractures ever occur; why plastic deformation in the adjoining grains, as shown in Fig.4, does not always disperse the stress concentrations at grain boundary obstacles. The idea that segregated impurities may reduce the cohesion at grain boundaries has been advanced in several forms. Bleakney[35] has made experiments on copper which support his view that oxygen is gradually absorbed from the atmosphere and becomes concentrated in grain boundaries. Another view is that the fractures may start at inclusions on the boundaries.[19,30,36] Non-wetting inclusions should be particularly

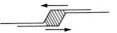

effective, and it is known that the contact angles between metals and oxides are frequently high.[37] It is interesting that aluminium, one of the metals least susceptible to intercrystalline creep fracture, adheres to its own oxide particularly well.[38]

Various suggestions have been made to explain the nucleation of spheroidal cavities.[6] The idea that these might be caused by the spontaneous coalescence of lattice vacancies created by deformation in the grains has generally been abandoned; in addition to the difficulty that an extremely high supersaturation of vacancies would be needed to produce a cavity in the absence of a pre-existing nucleus[28,29] it is also difficult to see why such vacancies should not be annihilated at grain boundaries, which are good vacancy sinks. The weight of the evidence supports the view that the cavities are nucleated by grain boundary sliding. The observations of Chen and Machlin[16] on copper bicrystals have already been mentioned. Hull and Rimmer[30] were also led by their experiments to consider sliding as a nucleating process. They subjected their copper specimens to the combined effect of uniaxial tension σ and hydrostatic compression p. The effect of this, in (12), should be to replace σ by σ-p. In experiments where p was varied at constant σ the rupture time t_r changed inversely with σ-p as expected from eqn. (12), but when σ was varied at constant p, t_r became much more sensitive to σ-p and more cavities were produced at higher levels of σ. Now the only difference between two experiments with the same value of σ-p, one with small σ and p, the other with large σ and p, is in the *shear* stress in the material. Hull and Rimmer thus concluded that increasing the shear stress component of the total stress state increases the number of cavities produced. It seems likely then that shear processes such as grain boundary sliding (also slip in the grains) cause the cavities to form.

One view of how grain boundary sliding may nucleate cavities is that foreign particles on the boundaries may obstruct the sliding and lead to fractures, in the manner of Fig.8.[30,36] The observations of Weaver [39] certainly show that cavities sometimes form at such particles. Another view is that jogs or steps on sliding grain boundaries may open up to form holes, as shown in Fig.9. Several people have suggested mechanisms of this type.[8,16,22,40,41,42] In particular, Gifkins[40] has pointed out that some metallographic observations indicate that cavities are formed where crystal slip bands meet the grain boundaries and has proposed that these slip bands may produce jogs in the boundaries.

A general problem with all such processes is that mechanically they are not greatly different from the process of triple-point fracture discussed above. We might expect them to require nucleating stresses determined by a criterion of the Griffith-Stroh type, whereas in practice cavitation fractures generally occur at lower stresses than triple-point fractures.[15] There are several comments to make about this. Very small cavities may exist *ab initio* in the grain boundaries, as suggested by Ivanova and Oding,[43] and the function of the grain boundary sliding may be to enlarge these until they can begin to grow by an atomic migration process. It is difficult to see why such cavities should not sinter up when they are very small, but this difficulty would not apply if the nuclei consisted of small non-wetting inclusions. Another possibility is that if a grain boundary jog is sufficiently small, e.g. one or two atomic diameters high, thermal fluctuations may help a relatively small stress to form a cavity there.[41] A third point is that when a sliding grain boundary is held up by isolated spheroidal inclusions it can impose a higher stress concentration at these inclusions than it can at a line obstacle (such as a triple point) since the slip can pass all round; the state of stress developed at such obstacles is essentially the same as that discussed by Fisher, Hart, and Pry, in their theory of dispersion hardening.[44]

CONCLUSION

Although we are still some way from fully understanding intercrystalline creep fractures, the following factors are beginning to emerge as particularly important:

1. Grain boundary sliding, because it produces stress concentrations at triple points and other obstacles.
2. Adherent particles on grain boundaries, because they can obstruct the sliding and take some of the load off the triple points.
3. Non-wetting particles on grain boundaries, because cavities can form easily on them.
4. Atomic diffusion along or near grain boundaries, because this enables cavities to grow under very small stresses at high temperatures.

These points enable some deductions to be drawn about the design of alloys with improved creep ductilities. Where only uniaxial tension is to be supported, an elongated grain structure in the direction of the tensile axis is an obvious advantage in increasing the load-carrying area of the grain boundaries. The use of particles in the boundaries to support the stresses relaxed by the boundaries and to take the load off the triple points has important possibilities, as is shown by the work of Betteridge and Franklin[45] and Weaver.[32,39] For this method to succeed it is essential that these particles adhere strongly to the surrounding material. Non-wetting particles are obviously harmful; if they cannot be eliminated they should be kept as coarse as possible, to make the cavitation distance (a in (13)) large. It is important that the adherent particles introduced to hold up the boundaries should be present in sufficient abundance to ensure that the load supported by each is too small to start a fracture there.

REFERENCES

1. J. N. GREENWOOD, et al.: Acta. Met., 1954, 2, 250.
2. See for example: E. E. UNDERWOOD: J. Inst. Metals, 1959–60, 88, 266–271.
3. C. ZENER: 'Fracturing of metals', 1: 1948, Cleveland, Ohio, USA, Amer. Soc. Metals.
4. R. EBORALL: Proc. NPL Symposium on creep and fracture of metals at high temperatures, 229; 1956, London, National Physical Laboratory.
5. H. C. CHANG and N. J. GRANT: Trans. AIME, 1956, 206, 544.
6. See for example: R. C. GIFKINS: 'Fracture' (Ed. B. L. AVERBACH et al.), 579; 1959, New York, Wiley.
7. I. S. SERVI and N. J. GRANT: Trans. AIME, 1951, 191, 909.
8. B. J. NIELD and A. J. QUARRELL: J. Inst. Metals, 1956–57, 85, 480–488.
9. R. W. BAILEY: J. Jun Inst. Eng., 1935, 46, (1) 1.
10. J. GLEN: JISI, 1958, 190, 30–39.
11. K. J. IRVINE et al.: ibid., 1960, 196, 166–179.
12. R. N. YOUNGER and R. G. BAKER: ibid., 188–194.
13. G. THOMAS and J. NUTTING: J. Inst. Metals, 1959–60, 88, 81–90.
14. M. G. LOZINSKY and I. S. SIMEONOVA: Acta Met., 1959, 7, 709.
15. D. McLEAN: J. Inst. Metals, 1956-7, 85, 468–472.
16. C. W. CHEN and E. S. MACHLIN: Acta Met., 1956, 4, 655.
17. B. J. REID and J. N. GREENWOOD: Trans. AIME, 1958, 212, 503.
18. F. T. CHESTNUT: Met. Prog., 1955, 68, 118.
19. R. RESNICK and L. SEIGLE: Trans. AIME, 1957, 209, 87.
20. G. C. E. OLDS and G. M. MICHIE: J. Inst. Metals, 1959–60, 88, 493–499.
21. P. E. BROOKES et al.: ibid., 500–508.
22. C. CRUSSARD and J. FRIEDEL: Proc. NPL Symposium on creep and fracture of metals at high temperatures, op. cit., 243.
23. J. N. GREENWOOD: J. Inst. Metals Bull., 1952, 1, 104–121.
24. J. E. BURKE: J. Amer. Ceram. Soc., 1957, 40, 80.
25. B. CLAPSON and D. A. ROBBINS: Powder Met., 1959, 3, 72.
26. R. S. BARNES et al.: Phil. Mag., 1958, 3, 97.
27. P. B. HIRSCH et al.: ibid., 897.
28. R. W. BALUFFI and L. L. SEIGLE: Acta Met., 1957, 5, 449.
29. D. McLEAN: Symposium on vacancies and other point defects in metals and alloys, 187; 1957, London, Inst. Metals.
30. D. HULL and D. RIMMER: Phil. Mag., 1959, 4, 673.
31. A. N. STROH: Proc. Roy. Soc., 1954, 223(A), 404.
32. C. W. WEAVER: Acta Met., 1960, 8, 343.

33. R. EBORALL and P. GREGORY, *J. Inst. Metals*, 1955–6, **84**, 88–90.
34. C. E. RANSLEY and D. E. J. TALBOT: *ibid.*, 1959–60, **88**, 150–158.
35. H. H. BLEAKNEY: *Canad. J. Technology*, 1952, **30**, 340.
36. C. W. CHEN and E. S. MACHLIN: *Trans. AIME*, 1957, **209**, 829.
37. M. HUMENICK and W. D. KINGERY: *J. Amer. Ceram. Soc.*, 1954, **37**, 18.
38. R. D. CARNAHAN *et al.*: *ibid.*, 1958, **41**, 343.
39. C. W. WEAVER: *J. Inst. Metals*; 1959–60, **88**, 296–300.
40. R. D. GIFKINS: *Acta Met.*, 1956, **4**, 98.
41. D. MCLEAN: 'Grain boundaries in metals'; 1957, Oxford, Clarendon Press.
42. P. W. DAVIES and J. P. DENNISON: *J. Inst. Metals*, 1959–60, **88**, 471–476.
43. V. S. IVANOVA and L. A. ODING: *Dokl. Acad. Nauk. USSR*, 1955, **103**, 77.
44. J. C. FISHER *et al.*: *Acta. Met.*, 1953, **1**, 336.
45. W. BETTERIDGE and A. W. FRANKLIN: *J. Inst. Metals*, 1956–7, **85**, 473.

The stress sensitivity of creep

D. McLean, D.Sc., and K. F. Hale, B.Sc., Ph.D.

A considerable amount of data confirms that under high-temperature creep conditions the strain rate varies as a power function of the stress, the activation energy being independent of stress. Experiments are under way in which dislocation densities are being measured after creep. So far such measurements have been made on a series of iron specimens which had been subjected to creep at stresses between $\frac{1}{2}$ and $5 \cdot 6$ tons/in² at temperatures of 550° or 700°C, from which were determined the separate contributions to the stress sensitivity of the dislocation density and the mean dislocation velocity; the latter makes the larger contribution. These initial results are consistent with a recent theory of the flow stress and suggest modifications to the structure of precipitation-hardened alloys that should raise their creep resistance.

INTRODUCTION

THIS PAPER is mostly about pure metals, but it leads to some conclusions concerning modifications which are expected to improve the creep resistance of complex alloys.

Dorn[1] and Weertman[2] have obtained evidence which shows that the creep rate of pure metals is affected by stress, not mainly through an influence of stress on the activation energy, but as a power function of the stress. This and other evidence is collected together in Fig.1, in which $\log_{10} \sigma/G$ is plotted against $\log_{10} \dot{\epsilon} + Q/2.3RT$, where σ is the applied tensile stress, G the shear modulus,* $\dot{\epsilon}$ the creep rate in %/h, and Q the known or accepted activation energy for diffusion except in the case of copper. In the case of copper the creep experiments give an activation energy of 33 400 cal/mol, which is very different from the self-diffusion activation energy of

---

*Ideally, the modulus at the temperature of the test should be used. As reliable values at temperature are scarce, the most uniform procedure seems to be to use the room temperature values, and this was done except for β thallium, for which Köster's[3] value at the transformation temperature was used. For γ iron the room temperature value for 18–8 stainless steel was used; this is very close to that of α iron.

The authors are with the Metallurgy Division of the National Physical Laboratory, Teddington, Middlesex.

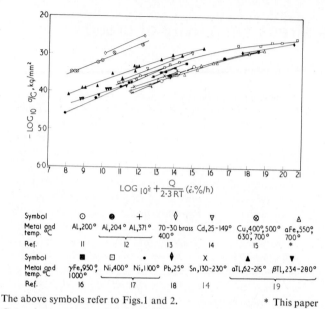

Symbol	$\odot$	$\bullet$	$+$	$\Diamond$	$\triangledown$	$\otimes$	$\triangle$
Metal and temp. °C	Al,200°	Al,204°	Al,371° 400°	70–30 brass 400°	Cd,25–149°	Cu,400°,500° 630°,700°	αFe,550° 700°
Ref.	11	12		13	14	15	*

Symbol	$\blacksquare$	$\square$	$\bullet$	$\blacklozenge$	X	$\blacktriangle$	$\blacktriangledown$
Metal and temp. °C	γFe,950° 1000°	Ni,400°	Ni,1100°	Pb,25°	Sn,130–230°	αTl,62–215°	βTl,234–280°
Ref.	16	17		18	14	19	

The above symbols refer to Figs.1 and 2.   * This paper

1 *Creep data on 12 metals plotted in accordance with eqn. (1)*

47 100 cal/mol, and the creep value has been used. The method of plotting used in Fig.1 is of course derived from an equation for the creep rate $\dot{\epsilon}$ of the form

$$\dot{\epsilon} = A \left(\frac{\sigma}{G} \right)^n e^{-Q/RT} \qquad . \quad . \quad . \quad . \quad . \quad (1)$$

where A and n are constants and the stress is 'normalized' by dividing by the shear modulus. It can be seen from Fig.1 that provided neither the stress is too high nor the temperature too low, i.e., provided the conditions are those of high temperature creep, the metals, Al, Cu, αFe, γFe, Cd, Ni, αTl, βTl, and Sn all give straight lines and therefore obey the Dorn-Weertman power law. The index n is about 5 (5·4 for α iron) and the constant A about 10^{28} with $\dot{\epsilon}$ in %/h. At tensile stresses greater than about $10^{-3}G$ the stress sensitivity begins to increase still further and a relation like equation (1) ceases to describe the situation. One possibility, supported by experiments on aluminium,[4] is that the stress is now large enough to affect the activation energy. It is interesting to note that this normalized plot brings all the metals except copper fairly close together, which is an indication that at a given normalized stress the mechanism of creep is the same for all the metals except copper.

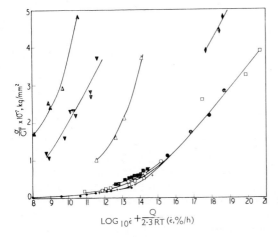

See Fig.1 for
key to symbols

2 *Creep data on 7
metals plotted
according to
eqn. (2)*

In order to demonstrate that the most likely alternative to equation
(1) does not describe high-temperature creep, most of the results
that are plotted in Fig.1 are replotted in Fig.2 as σ/GT against
$\log_{10} \dot{\epsilon} + Q/2 \cdot 3RT$. This kind of plot is derived from the equation

$$\dot{\epsilon} = Be^{-\left(\frac{Q - \beta\sigma/G}{RT}\right)} \qquad . \qquad . \qquad . \qquad . \qquad . \qquad (2)$$

In Fig.2, towards the left, i.e. where the conditions are those of
high temperature creep, all the lines are curves, so that equation (2)
does not hold in this range. Towards the right, at higher stresses,
however, equation (2) does begin to apply.

The creep rate can also be written

$$\dot{\epsilon} = \rho b v \qquad . \qquad . \qquad . \qquad . \qquad . \qquad . \qquad (3)$$

where ρ is the density of active dislocations, v their average velocity,
and b their Burgers vector. As there is some possibility of measuring
ρ with the electron microscope thin foil technique, the way in which
ρ and v separately vary with the stress can be determined. Some
preliminary results of such an investigation are now available.

ELECTRON MICROSCOPE INVESTIGATION

The specimens which have so far been tested and examined were of
NPL iron–carbon alloy of the percentage analysis:

C	N	O	Si	S	P	Mn	Al	Ni	Cr	Cu	Mo	Total
0·051	0·0005	0·0005	0·013	0·0026	0·001	0·001	0·006	—	—	—	—	0·035*

*Excluding carbon

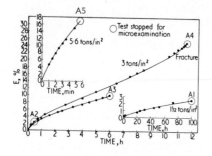

3 *Creep curves at 550°C*

The gauge length was about 10 cm, the width about 2·5 cm, and the thickness about 0·03 cm. They were strained in a vacuum at 550°C or 700°C, using stresses in the range 0·5–6 tons/in². The specimens had previously been normalized and recrystallized below A_1, by cold working 50% and heating at 650°C (in a vacuum) for 1 h, followed by air cooling, in order to eliminate the usual veining structure. The grain size after this treatment was 0·025 mm.

The extension during creep was measured from the movement of the shackle outside the furnace and included any stretching outside the gauge length. When it was decided to stop a test, the specimen was cooled under load in order to maintain the dislocation structure. After measuring the elongation of each of four 2·5 cm lengths into which the 10 cm length was divided, the gauge length was cut into 2·5 cm lengths, some examination of the polished faces was made with an optical microscope, and foils were prepared for examination in the electron microscope.

The creep curves are shown in Figs.3 and 4, in which are also indicated the points at which specimens were stopped for microexamination, repeat specimens being stressed under the same conditions to different elongations where necessary. In the micrographs and in Table I the elongation of the particular 2·5 cm length is quoted, and does not coincide exactly with the values at the

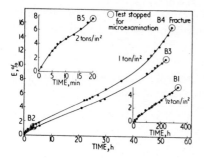

4 *Creep curves at 700°C*

TABLE I Results of dislocation counts
The starting material contained 6.3×10^7 cm of dislocation line per cm^3

Test temperature		550°C			
Stress, tons/in^2	1.5		3		5.6–4*
Elongation, %	2.4	2.7	10	50†	20
Specimen no.	A_1	A_2	A_3	A_4	A_5
$\dot{\varepsilon}$ %/h	0.015	4.36	1.73	4.54	153
Dislocation density ρ, cm/cm^3	7.0×10^8	1.5×10^9	1.6×10^9	1.2×10^9	2.8×10^9
Av. dislocation spacing x, cm	0.38×10^{-4}	0.26×10^{-4}	0.25×10^{-4}	0.29×10^{-4}	0.19×10^{-4}
Av. dislocation speed v, cm/s	2.4×10^{-7}	3.3×10^{-5}	1.2×10^{-5}	4.2×10^{-5}	6.1×10^{-4}
$v' = ve^{Q/kt}$, cm/s	1.5×10^9	2.1×10^{11}	7.6×10^{10}	2.7×10^{11}	3.9×10^{12}

Test temperature		700°C			
Stress, tons/in^2	0.5		1		2
Elongation, %	3.0	1.2	8	10	8
Specimen no.	B_1	B_2	B_3	B_4	B_5
$\dot{\varepsilon}$ %/h	0.0145	0.309	0.56	0.64	22.8
Dislocation density ρ, cm/cm^3	1.6×10^8	3.5×10^8	3.4×10^8	4.9×10^8	7.6×10^8
Av. dislocation spacing x, cm	0.81×10^{-4}	0.54×10^{-4}	0.55×10^{-4}	0.46×10^{-4}	0.37×10^{-4}
Av. dislocation speed v, cm/s	1.0×10^{-6}	9.9×10^{-6}	1.9×10^{-5}	1.5×10^{-5}	3.4×10^{-4}
$v' = ve^{Q/kt}$, cm/s	2.6×10^7	2.5×10^8	4.6×10^8	3.7×10^8	8.4×10^9

*This specimen stretched so fast that it was unloaded during cooling from 5.6 tons/in^2 to 4.0 tons/in^2.
†Section near to fracture.

points marked in Figs.3 and 4 because the elongation varied somewhat along the length of each specimen. Examination with the optical and electron microscopes showed the following qualitative features:

    (i) A sub-crystal structure developed and the misorientation at the sub-boundaries evidently increased with extension; the sub-boundaries became more marked under optical examination as illustrated by Figs.5 and 6, the specimens for which were subjected to an etch-pitting attack, and the network composing them rapidly became too fine to resolve with the electron microscope, except for occasional sub-boundaries. A sub-boundary which could be resolved with the electron microscope is shown in Fig.7.

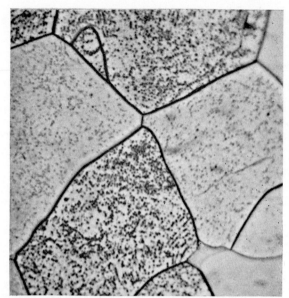

5 *Creep specimen B2, 1 ton/in² at 700°C for 3·5 h: elongation 0·8%*   × 1 500

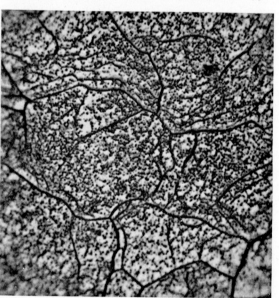

6 *Creep specimen B4, l ton/in² at 700°C for 54 h, area near fracture; elongation about 20%*   × 1 500

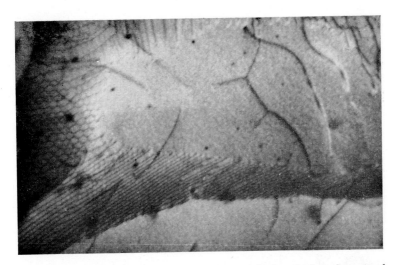

7 *Sub-boundaries in which dislocations are resolved and three-dimensional network. Elongation 50% (near fracture): specimen A4, iron loaded with 3 tons/in² at 550°C* × 30 000

8 *Three-dimensional network of dislocations, the density of which is about twice average. Elongation 12%, specimen A3, iron loaded with 3 tons/in² at 550°C* × 30 000

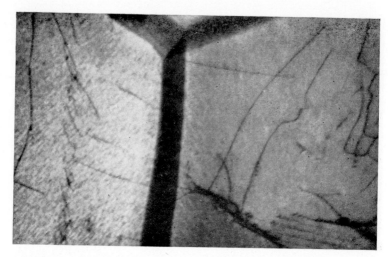

9 *Three-dimensional network of average density, and triple grain boundary junction. Elongation 50%, specimen A4, iron loaded with 3 tons/in² at 550°C*
× 30000

10 *Three-dimensional network of density below average, and sub-boundaries in which the dislocation density is too high to be resolvable. Elongation 12%, specimen A3, iron loaded with 3 tons/in² at 550°C*
× 30000

(ii) The sub-grain contained a three-dimensional network of dislocations, examples of which are shown in Figs.8–10; the network is seen alone in Fig.8, close to a triple grain boundary junction in Fig.9, and close to a sub-boundary in Fig.10. The three-dimensional network must consist of active dislocations which move across a sub-crystal, intersecting each other on their way. They eventually join a sub-boundary, which acts as a sink for dislocations. It might be added that, according to network theory, as far as geometry and conservation of Burgers vector are concerned, there is always some way in which any dislocation can join any sub-boundary network.

(iii) The density of the three-dimensional network varied a great deal in any given foil. Figure 8 shows a region where the dislocation density of the three-dimensional network is about twice the average for this specimen, and Fig.10 a region where it is almost zero. This variation can also be seen in the optical micrographs, Figs.5 and 6, in which dislocations are evidently revealed by etch-pits. Creep is clearly a statistical effect.

In spite of (iii) it was possible to make counts of dislocation density that have so far been reproducible to within $\pm$ 10 to 20%. We define the density as the total length of dislocation line per unit volume of crystal. Let n be the number of dislocations apparently intersected by a line of unit length lying parallel to the surface of the foil. If the foil thickness is t, the number of dislocations intersecting unit area is then n/t. This would be equal to the defined density of dislocations if the dislocations were all normal to the plane of intersection. However, the dislocations lie along all possible directions and so the true density is approximately given by $\rho = 3n/t$ cm/cm³, while the true spacing x between dislocations will be about $\frac{1}{\sqrt{\rho}} = \sqrt{\frac{t}{3n}}$. The actual procedure of making the measurements was to use a line of length L (9 cm) scribed on the viewing screen of the microscope and to count the number of dislocations intersecting this line when the image was viewed at a magnification M ($\times 22\,000$). The dislocation density was then given by $\rho = \dfrac{3NM}{Lt}$ and the true dislocation spacing by $x = \sqrt{\dfrac{Lt}{3NM}}$. Starting at an arbitrary area, after each count the specimen was moved on a further 9 cm along the viewing screen. Several groups of 25 counts were made independently by two observers, on each specimen. Usually several hundred

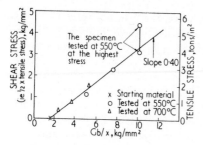

11 *Plot of dislocation spacing x according to eqn. (4). (Note: The specimen tested at 550°C at the highest stress stretched so fast that it was unloaded during cooling from 5·6 tons/in² (upper point) to 4·0 tons/in² (lower point))*

dislocations were counted in all (maximum 2 500) for each of the values reported below, although in the specimen with the lowest density only 50 groups were counted.

The results are collected in Table I. To assist a comparison between the results at the different temperatures, a dislocation velocity corrected for temperature is included, i.e., $v' = v e^{-Q/kt}$, where Q is the activation energy for self-diffusion for α iron and is 60 000 cal/mol.

According to these initial results, the dislocation density hardly varies from halfway through primary creep onwards as is shown by the data for different elongations under similar conditions, the points at which specimens were examined being marked in Figs. 3 and 4. This constant dislocation density can be seen to vary somewhat more slowly than (stress)² and v' varies somewhat faster than (stress).[3] According to these initial results, therefore, the increase in dislocation density with stress makes a substantial contribution to the stress sensitivity, but a larger contribution comes from the concomitant increase in average dislocation speed.

The variation of dislocation density with stress is reasonably consistent with recent theories of the flow stress, which emphasize that attractive and repulsive junctions form on intersection.[5-10]

a unstressed   b stressed

12 *Part of 3-dimensional dislocation net*

28

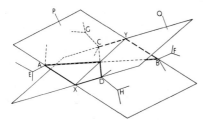

13 *Intersection of dislocations with opposite Burgers vectors*

From these theories the shear flow stress is calculated to be

$$\tau = aGb/x \qquad \cdot \quad \cdot \quad \cdot \quad \cdot \quad \cdot \quad \cdot \quad \cdot \qquad (4)$$

where x is the average dislocation spacing (assumed uniform) and a is a constant ~ 0.3 for a bcc metal. The experimental values of τ (taken as half the applied tensile stress) and Gb/x are plotted against each other in Fig.11. They fall close to a straight line of slope $a = 0.4$ and so agree numerically quite well with these theories, except that the line does not pass through the origin.

This agreement suggests a model for creep in a pure metal which provides some reason for the variation of dislocation speed with applied stress. The model is as follows; the three-dimensional network which provides the strength, shown diagrammatically in the unstrained state in Fig.12a, is strained as in Fig.12b by the stress sufficiently that thermal agitation can break it; this means that individual junctions are then within ~ 1 eV of breaking, compared with the energy released when an attractive junction forms of several hundred eV.[7] The junction dislocations such as A in Fig.12b are therefore only a few atoms long. When a junction breaks the subsequent movement is presumably accompanied as usual by strain hardening; i.e. there is an increase in dislocation line length and the average value of x decreases. In second-stage creep there must be a recovery process reducing the dislocation line length at an equal rate. One recovery process is depicted in Fig.13, which represents part of the three-dimensional network of dislocations in the metal. The dislocation of which AB is a part lies in the plane P. In common with other dislocations, after breaking the junctions which hold it momentarily, it moves on until stopped again by strong enough junctions. In the fleeting situation depicted in Fig.13, it is connected to attractive junctions AE and BF at A and B respectively. CD is part of a dislocation moving similarly in plane Q which at the same moment is connected to attractive junctions CG and DH at C and D respectively. Since planes P and Q intersect, the two dislocations must intersect at some time, and are shown at the instant of doing so.

29

Suppose that dislocations AB and CD have equal but opposite Burgers vectors along XY, the line of intersection of the planes P and Q. On intersecting there is then no junction dislocation along XY, and the dislocations will glide into positions AXD, CYB, i.e. the shortest lines lying in planes P and Q joining AD and CB respectively. This process is the analogue of that in which two dislocations of opposite sign move towards and meet each other in the same plane. They then annihilate each other completely. When they lie in different planes as in Fig.13, complete annihilation is impossible, but some reduction in dislocation line length occurs. Since the Burgers vectors of the dislocations AXD and CYB lie along XY, the dislocations AXD and CYB are largely edge type. As they can climb at the elevated temperatures which exist during creep testing, they will try to straighten along AD and CB. There is a reasonable probability that this climb will increase the angles at the holding junctions at A, B, C, and D, whereupon AXD can glide and climb until A and D become coincident with E and H respectively and similarly C and B can become coincident with G and F respectively, thereby reducing the total length of dislocation. This is therefore a recovery process, the rate controlling step in which is the climb of AXD (and CYB). The whole process is analogous to pricking a bubble in a foam; there would be some readjustment and an increase in average bubble size; similarly, if a link in the three-dimensional network of dislocations is cut, there is some readjustment and increase in average mesh size, and thus a reduction in total length of dislocation line.

In steady-state creep the rate of hardening or rate of increase in dislocation line length, and the rate of recovery, or rate of reduction in dislocation line length, must be equal. The balance is accomplished in this model by the network automatically adjusting its size to such a point that the thermal agitation required to break a junction has the right magnitude to produce the balance.

Two ways can be seen in which stress increases the rate of recovery and therefore average dislocation speed. The applied stress has already shortened the junctions at A, B, C, and D in Fig.13 nearly to breaking point, so that the amount of climb required is small. Thus an applied stress greatly accelerates the recovery process without affecting the activation energy. In addition, a stress will exert the usual directing effect on climb, which for normal creep stresses gives a term in σ outside the exponential in equation (1).

Temperature therefore affects the time scale of events through the factor $e^{-Q/kt}$, but has no influence on the size or geometry of the

30

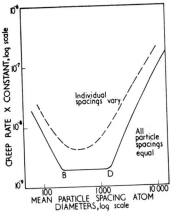

14 *Calculated variation of creep rate with particle spacing, assuming that the precipitate occupies 0·1 of the volume*

network apart from certain effects not considered here. Consequently in a plot of dislocation spacing against stress it is approximately correct to include results for different temperatures, and the results in Fig.11 bear this out.

Some things have been neglected in the foregoing. There is the fact that in Fig.11 the line does not pass through the origin; possibly at low stress only the weaker links of the network are active at any one moment, but more experiments are necessary to decide this point. It also seems rather likely that the sub-boundaries have not settled fully into minimum energy positions, and may therefore exert a long ranging stress which will add on to that given by equation (4). The grain boundaries, on the other hand, presumably dissolve dislocations in effect and so eliminate any source of long-range stress near them; this is perhaps a reason why fine-grained pure metals creep faster than coarse-grained ones.

PRECIPITATION-HARDENED ALLOYS

In precipitation-hardened alloys there seems to be a fresh source of stress-sensitivity which makes a uniform structure look very desirable. Unpublished calculation of the creep rate as a function of particle spacing, for a given total volume of precipitate, gives the kind of result shown as the full line in Fig.14. The principle behind the calculation is simple: a dislocation moves quickly until it meets a particle, which it either has to climb over or push along. The creep rate is therefore governed by the rate of climb, the distance to be climbed (the particle dimension), and the freely slipping distance (the particle spacing), or by the speed at which the particles can be pushed along. Along *BD*, as the mean slip distance between particles

31

increases, so does the distance to be climbed over each particle, and the average speed of a dislocation is unaffected by particle spacing. To the left of B, in the region of very tiny particles, a dislocation can push particles ahead of itself faster than it can climb over them, although this only happens with particles too small to be of practical importance. The important thing is the limit at D. Here, the particle spacing is large enough for two things to begin more or less simultaneously, and both accelerate the creep rate: (a) the dislocations need no longer be considered as effectively rigid, only a piece of dislocation near the particle need climb: (b) several dislocations can be wrapped round the precipitates and pressed into the space between them, and can climb together. The combined effect is that the creep rate increases rather rapidly beyond the point D. As this spacing l is given by

$$1 \sim Gb/\tau \qquad \cdot \qquad \cdot \qquad \cdot \qquad \cdot \qquad \cdot \qquad \cdot \qquad (5)$$

a deduction is that for a given uniform structure the creep rate will increase with stress very rapidly beyond the stress represented by equation (5). The non-uniform structure that is likely in practice has a mean particle spacing about which the actual spacings are scattered, probably rather widely as a rule. In Fig.14 it would give a curve like the dashed line. Increasing the stress now increases the proportion of particles around which the critical spacing is exceeded. A uniform structure should then eliminate this source of stress sensitivity, and also reduce the rate of creep.

ACKNOWLEDGMENTS

The creep tests and the optical micro-examination were carried out by Mr. W. E. Carrington, and the specimens for examination with the electron microscope were prepared by Miss J. Batson. The paper is published by permission of the Director of the National Physical Laboratory.

REFERENCES

1. J. E. DORN: 'Creep and recovery,' 2255; 1957, Ohio, USA, ASM.
2. J. WEERTMAN: *J. Appl. Phys.*, 1957, **28**, 362.
3. W. KÖSTER: *Z. Metallk.*, 1948, **39**, 1.
4. S. N. ZHURKOV and T. P. SANFIROVA: *Soviet Phys.*, 1959, **3**, (8), 1586.
5. P. B. HIRSCH: 'Conference on internal stresses and fatigue,' Elsevier (Holland), 1959, 139.
6. J. FRIEDEL: *ibid.*, 220.
7. W. E. CARRINGTON *et al.*: *Proc. Roy. Soc.* (A) 1960, **259**, 203.
8. G. SAADA: *Acta Met.*, 1960, **8**, 200.
9. G. SAADA: Doctorate thesis, University of Paris, 1960.
10. J. D. BAIRD and B. GALE: unpublished work.
11. D. MCLEAN: *J. Inst. Metals*, 1952–3, **81**, 133–144.
12. I. S. SERVI and N. J. GRANT: *Trans. AIME*, 1951, **191**, 909.
13. P. FELTHAM and G. I. COPLEY: *Phil. Mag.*, 1960, 5, 649.

14. B. FAZAN et al.: *Acta Met.*, 1955, **3**, 470.
15. P. FELTHAM and J. D. MEAKIN: *ibid.*, 1959, **7**, 614.
16. P. FELTHAM: *Proc. Phys. Soc.* (B), **66**, 865.
17. J. WEERTMAN and P. SHAHINIAN: *Trans. AIME*, 1956, **206**, 1223.
18. P. FELTHAM: *Proc. Phys. Soc.* (*B*), 1956, **69**, 1173.
19. O. D. SHERRBY: *Trans. AIME*, 1958, **212**, 708.

An interpretation of the relationship between creep and fracture

P.W. Davies, B.Sc., Ph.D., and B. Wilshire, B.Sc.

The product of rupture life and minimum creep rate for nickel is found to be a constant E independent of stress and temperature (above 0·45 of the absolute melting point), in agreement with previous investigations on other metals. Experimental evidence is given that this product is also independent of small amounts of impurity. A comparison is then made of values of E for different face-centred-cubic metals.

It is considered that E is an approximation to the 'true creep elongation ε', defined as the maximum strain obtainable at the minimum creep rate (mcr) for the period (t_t) up to the onset of the tertiary stage of creep, since it is shown experimentally that $t_t \times$ mcr=constant (ε), independent of stress and temperature. A mechanism is then proposed which can account for the onset of tertiary creep after this limited extension at the minimum creep rate.

INTRODUCTION

AN EMPIRICAL RELATIONSHIP has been found to exist between rupture life and the minimum rate of deformation for a large number of pure metals and single-phase alloys tested under creep conditions.[1,2] In all cases the results could be represented by an equation of the form

$$\log t_r + m \log (\text{mcr}) = A \qquad . \qquad . \qquad . \qquad . \qquad . \qquad (1)$$

where m and A are constants, t_r is the time to fracture, and (mcr) is the minimum creep rate. The constant m was not found to vary appreciably from unity so that this relationship can be rewritten as

$$t_r \times (\text{mcr}) = \text{constant} (E) \qquad . \qquad . \qquad . \qquad . \qquad . \qquad (2)$$

It has been noted that the constant E is some measure of elongation. One interpretation of this relationship has been given by Feltham and Meakin[3] on the basis that creep fracture results from the linking up of grain boundary voids. Assuming that voids grow to a

The authors are with the Metallurgy Department, University College, Singleton Park, Swansea.

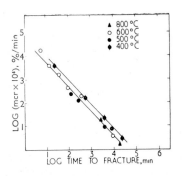

1 *Relation between log (mcr)
and log t_f for pure nickel
(99·99%+) tested at 400°, 500°, 600°,
and 800°C*

critical size for fracture by absorbing a constant fraction of the
vacancies created by the slip process, they consider that the time to
fracture should be very nearly inversely proportional to the creep
rate.

The present investigation was designed to examine this constant
E for various metals and testing conditions.

EXPERIMENTAL DATA

This investigation is confined to the limited number of face-centred-
cubic metals for which both creep and rupture data are available,
namely aluminium,[4] copper,[5] lead,[6] and silver.[7] However, even
when sufficient results are available, the materials have been tested
at different fractions of their absolute melting points and with
varying grain sizes and degrees of purity. Before a comparison of
the values of E for different metals can be made, it is therefore
necessary to investigate the effect of the above variables on this
constant.

Very few data are available on the effect of grain size on the creep
and fracture properties of pure metals. The results of Servi and
Grant[4] can be used to show that grain size has no effect on E, whilst
the data of McKeown[6] on lead and Dennison[8] on a single-phase
copper–aluminium alloy indicate that the elongation constant increases with decreasing grain size. Since no definite effect can be
established, the grain sizes of the pure metals compared in this
investigation were chosen as similar as possible. It has been shown
that for copper[5] E is independent of both stress and temperature in
the range 400–700°C.

To confirm this stress and temperature independence, tests were
carried out on pure (99·99%) nickel. The experimental procedure
used in this investigation has recently been described elsewhere.[9] The
results (Fig. 1) show no variation for tests at 800°, 600°, and 500°C, but

35

TABLE I Analysis of nickels, %

C	Si	Cu	Fe	S	Ni
0·04	0·41	0·04	0·07	0·008	99·43
0·006	...	0·003	0·02	0·002	99·97
0·006	...	...	...	0·001	99·99+

at 400°C there is a displacement in the relationship towards higher values of E. However, since 400°C is below the temperature range normally considered for high-temperature creep of nickel, i.e. below 0·45 of the absolute melting point, it can be concluded that E is independent of stress and temperature under high-temperature creep conditions.

To establish the effect of small amounts of impurities, three grades of nickel were investigated. The analyses are given in Table I. The results (Fig.2) show that E is independent of small amounts of impurities within the range tested.

It is therefore evident that values of E can be compared for various pure metals tested under high-temperature creep conditions, provided only that the grain sizes are similar. The comparative lines for copper, silver, lead, aluminium, and nickel are shown in Fig.3. Details of the grain sizes, purities, and values of E are given in Table II.

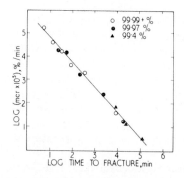

2 *Relation between log (mcr) and log (t_f) for three grades of nickel at 500°C*

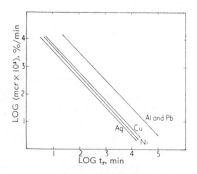

3 *Relation between log (mcr) and log t_f for various pure metals*

TABLE II Grain sizes, purities, and values of E

Metal	Purity, %	Grain size, grains/mm	Elongation constant, E	Reference
Silver	99·999	7–9	2	7
Aluminium	99·995+	5–20	32	4
Copper	99·99+	30	6	5
Nickel	99·99+	5–8	4·5	...
Nickel	99·97	5–8	4·5	...
Nickel	99·4	5–8	4·5	10
Lead	99·996	10	33	6

DISCUSSION

The significance of E

In relation to the normal creep curve it is clear from Fig.4 that E represents the maximum strain which can be obtained at the minimum creep rate if the material extended at this rate for the total rupture life. It therefore appears that under high-temperature creep conditions a metal is only capable of a limited extension at the minimum creep rate, before fracture.

The first indication of fracture is the increase in creep rate which occurs at the onset of the tertiary stage. This suggests that secondary creep ends when the effect of fracture processes become significant. It is therefore proposed to consider the elongation obtainable at the minimum creep rate until the onset of tertiary. The times to the onset of tertiary creep (t_t) are correlated with the minimum creep rates for pure nickel (99·99%) in Fig.5. The slope of this line is

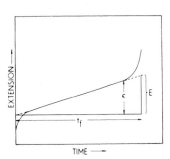

4 *Relation of ε and E to the creep curve*

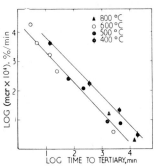

5 *Relation between minimum creep rate and time to the start of tertiary creep for pure nickel (99·99%+) tested at 400°, 500°, 600°, and 800°C*

37

unity, so that the results can again be represented by an equation of the form

$$(t_t) \times (\text{mcr}) = \text{Constant } (\epsilon) \qquad . \qquad . \qquad . \qquad . \qquad (3)$$

where the constant (ϵ) will be termed the 'true creep elongation'. This shows that under high-temperature creep conditions, the material goes into tertiary after a constant amount of deformation at the minimum creep rate independent of stress and temperature. The elongation constant E can be regarded as an approximation to the true creep elongation.

A recent review of the mechanisms of fracture under high temperature creep conditions[11] indicates that at low strain rates, fracture results from the formation of small voids on grain boundaries which are approximately transverse to the applied stress. It has been shown that grain boundary sliding is necessary for void nucleation[12] and a mechanism by which sliding can nucleate voids has been proposed by Gifkins,[13] and Chen and Machlin.[14] Gifkins suggests that where a slip band meets a grain boundary, accommodating slip in the adjacent grain results in the formation of a step or ledge, on the boundary. A ledge will impede sliding, resulting in stresses parallel to the boundary being set up in the region of the ledge. The magnitude of the shear stress developed on individual ledges depends on the shear relaxation length between ledges and the height of the ledge itself. When the stresses developed by the sliding are of the order of the theoretical cohesive stress of the metal, this mechanism will result in the formation of voids. Further growth of these voids can take place either by absorption of vacancies generated in the lattice[3] or by continued sliding.[14] Recent experimental evidence shows that during creep, no detectable increase occurs in the size of pre-existing voids (introduced by a process of sintering metal powder) even when these voids are situated on the grain boundaries.[9] It is also difficult to reconcile growth by vacancy absorption with the observed constant elongation at the minimum creep rate. Secondary creep ends when the voids grow to a size at which they can effect the creep rate. If the voids grow by vacancy absorption, then their size at any instant would depend on the number of vacancies generated by the slip within the grains. The total elongation up to the onset of tertiary creep would therefore govern the void size at this stage, as vacancies are generated equally well by the initial extension and during primary creep. The plot (Fig.6) shows that the total elongation to the onset of tertiary creep is stress dependent. Also, the contribution of crystal slip to the total elongation at the minimum creep rate increases with increasing stress.[15] Thus, on this basis, we should

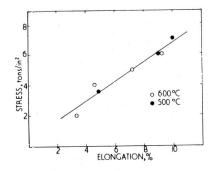

6 *Relation between stress and the total elongation up to the onset of the tertiary stage of creep*

expect the elongation constant to decrease markedly with increasing stress.

Chen and Machlin[14] have proposed that voids are not only nucleated but also grow by grain boundary sliding. With this mechanism, it is evident that the void size is governed by the extent of sliding which must then be the mode of deformation which is limited in the creep process. Using this concept, a mechanism is proposed in the following discussion which can account for the onset of tertiary creep after a constant amount of deformation at the minimum creep rate independent of stress and temperature.

From the preceeding discussion, it is considered that secondary creep ends when the effect of the voids becomes significant. It has been shown experimentally that voids are present early in the creep life[16] so that it would appear that these voids must grow to a certain size before they can affect the creep rate. One way in which they could cause an increase in the rate of deformation is by reducing the stress carrying area of the specimens. However, it has been shown that this effect is negligible and an alternative explanation has been proposed[9] which depends on the voids becoming stable under the prevailing vacancy concentration at the onset of tertiary creep.

We shall now consider a mechanism by which stable voids will be developed after a constant deformation at the minimum creep rate.

Elongation to produce a stable void

The mechanism of void formation suggested by Gifkins and Chen and Machlin would result in only one void being developed on each ledge. Balluffi and Seigle[17] have shown that the radius r of the smallest void which is stable is given as

$$r = \frac{2\gamma}{\sigma \cos^2 \Theta} \quad . \qquad . \qquad . \qquad . \qquad . \qquad (4)$$

where θ is the angle between the normal to the boundary and the

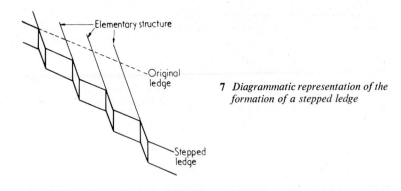

7 *Diagrammatic representation of the formation of a stepped ledge*

applied stress σ, and γ is the surface energy. If only one void were formed on each ledge, then the size of the stable void would be stress dependent. Therefore, if tertiary creep begins when the voids become stable, the true creep elongation would be stress dependent, contrary to the observed results.

However, it is considered that more than one void would be developed on each ledge. Even during rapid straining, some grain boundary sliding occurs.[18] Therefore, in the initial extension, grain boundary shear will result in a high stress concentration at the ledges. The stress at the ledges can rise to the order of the critical cohesive stress. However, before this stress is reached dislocation sources in the adjacent grain will become active on slip planes separated by approximately the distance observed in the 'elementary structure' of Wilsdorf and Kuhlmann-Wilsdorf.[19] This would give rise to a stepped ledge as shown diagrammatically in Fig.7. Such splitting up of ledges has been observed[19] for coarse slip bands on the surface of single crystals (Fig.8). Further sliding would result in decohesion, leading to the formation of a cavity on each step of the ledge. The cavities would tend to spheroidize in order to minimize the surface energy, so that a necklace of small voids, about 200–500Å apart would be formed on ledges 1–10 μin long. As creep continues, the sliding would cause the voids to grow until they eventually link up to form one large void on each ledge. The large void so formed is then considered to be stable for all stresses at which the material would fracture under creep conditions and the elongation to cause this link-up will be the true creep elongation.

The volume v of the void formed on each step of the ledge will then be given by

$$v = SHl \qquad \qquad \qquad (5)$$

where H is the ledge height, l is the length of each step, and S is the

8 *Stepped ledges formed by interaction of coarse slip bands at the surface of aluminium crystals*[19] × 7 500

amount of grain boundary sliding. Stable voids will then be developed when $l \simeq 2r$, where r is the radius of each small void. The stress and temperature dependence of the true creep elongation will then depend on how these factors affect the ledge height and the contribution of sliding to the creep deformation.

It is possible to derive the height of grain boundary ledges by a consideration of the dislocation structure of the deformed metal. Dislocations on the slip planes will pile up against the grain boundaries. An estimate of the stress concentration at the end of such a group of dislocations has been given by Cottrell.[20] The shear stress in the adjacent crystal at a distance x ahead of the leading dislocation is increased by a factor q given by

$$q = [1 + \left(\frac{L}{X}\right)^{\frac{1}{2}}] \qquad \qquad (6)$$

where L is the length of the slip band. When the stress concentration factor is large the dislocations produce the same concentrated stress, $\sigma \left(\frac{L}{X}\right)^{\frac{1}{2}}$, as does a freely slipping crack of the same length. If there is a dislocation source in the adjacent crystal at a distance x from the end of the pile-up, the stress tending to activate the source is directly proportional to the overall applied stress and the number of dislocations which will be generated by this source is therefore directly proportional to the applied stress. The accommodating slip controls the ledge height which may then be expressed as

$$H = K\sigma \left(\frac{L}{X}\right)^{\frac{1}{2}} \qquad \qquad (7)$$

where K is a constant.

41

This calculation suggests that the ledge height is directly proportional to the stress and is independent of temperature.

McLean [15] using a surface displacement technique, has shown that the contribution of sliding decreases with increasing stress. Although the results obtained in his investigation were plotted on a semi-log basis, they can be equally well represented by a direct plot of (e_s/e_t) against stress σ, where e_s is the elongation due to sliding and e_t is the total creep elongation. Thus, the results can be represented by an equation of the form

$$e_s/e_t = K^1/\sigma \qquad (8)$$

Dorn[21] has investigated the temperature dependence of the contribution of grain boundary sliding and has shown that for a given stress the ratio of e_s/e_t was constant over a range of temperatures. Thus it appears that the contribution of sliding to the total amount of the deformation at the minimum creep rate is inversely proportional to the applied stress and is independent of temperature under high-temperature creep conditions.

The volume of each small void at the onset of tertiary creep is given by

$$V = \frac{4}{3}\pi \left(\frac{l}{2}\right)^3$$

since $2r \simeq l$ when the voids link up. From equation (5) we have

$$S \times H \times l = \frac{4}{3}\pi \left(\frac{l}{2}\right)^3 \qquad (9)$$

Since S is proportional to e_s from equations (7) and (8) we obtain

$$e_t = k\left(\frac{X}{L}\right)^{\frac{1}{2}} \frac{l^2}{KK^1} \qquad (10)$$

where e_t is now the true creep elongation.

Since neither the ledge height nor the ratio of e_s/e_t is affected by changes in temperature, the true creep elongation calculated on the basis of the proposed mechanism is independent of both stress and temperature in accordance with experimental results. The values of the constants in this equation cannot easily be determined. However, the values of l have been shown by Wilsdorf and Kuhlmann-Wilsdorf[19] to vary for different metals. They give values for silver, copper, and aluminium of 250, 300, and 450Å respectively, which agree with the ascending order of the elongations for these metals shown in Table II.

SUMMARY OF PROPOSED MECHANISM

Most of the extension that takes place immediately on the application of the load occurs by slip within the grains, resulting in the formation of grain boundary ledges. The small amount of grain boundary sliding which also takes place in the initial extension causes a high stress concentration at these ledges. This stress can rise to the order of the theoretical cohesive stress when dislocation sources in the adjacent grain will become active. The separation of the active sources will be of the order of the distance between the fine slip lines observed by Wilsdorf and Kuhlmann-Wilsdorf.[19] This will give rise to a stepped ledge (Fig.6). Further sliding will result in fracture at the ledges leading to the formation of a cavity on each step. The cavities will tend to spheroidize forming a necklace of small voids on each ledge, which grow as creep continues until they eventually link up to form one large void which will be stable for all stresses which result in fracture. This linking up is considered to mark the onset of tertiary creep. On this basis the elongation ϵ that takes place at the minimum creep rate over the total time up to the start of tertiary creep can be shown to be independent of stress and temperature in accordance with observed results.

REFERENCES

1. F. C. MONKMAN and N. J. GRANT: *Proc. ASTM*, 1956, **56**, 593–605.
2. I. A. ODING and V. V. BURDUKSKY: 'Deformation and flow of solids', IUTAM Colloquium, Madrid 1955, 298–303; 1956, Berlin, Springer-Verlag.
3. P. FELTHAM and J. P. MEAKIN, in discussion: *J. Inst. Metals*, 1957–58, **86**, 539.
4. I. S. SERVI and N. J. GRANT: *J. Metals*, 1951, **3**, 909–916.
5. P. FELTHAM and J. D. MEAKIN: *Acta. Met.* 1959, **7**, 614–627.
6. J. McKEOWN: *J. Inst. Metals*, 1937, **60**, 201–222.
7. C. E. PRICE: Private communication.
8. J. P. DENNISON: *J. Inst. Metals*, 1957–58, **86**, 177–181.
9. P. W. DAVIES and J. P. DENNISON: *ibid.*, 1959–60, **88**, 471–476.
10. The International Nickel Co. (Mond) Ltd.: Private communication.
11. P. W. DAVIES and J. P. DENNISON: *J. Inst. Metals*, 1958–59, **87**, 119–125.
12. C. W. Chen, in discussion: *Trans. AIME*, 1956, **206**, 1416.
13. R. C. GIFKINS: *Acta Met.*, 1956, **4**, 98.
14. C. W. CHEN and E. S. MACHLIN: *ibid.*, 655.
15. D. McLEAN: *J. Inst. Metals*, 1952–53, **81**, 293–300.
16. C. W. CHEN and E. S. MACHLIN: *Trans. AIME*, 1957, **209**, 829–835.
17. R. W. BALLUFFI and L. L. SEIGLE: *Acta. Met.*, 1957, **5**, 449–454.
18. W. A. RACHINGER: *J. Inst. Metals*, 1952–53, **81**, 33–41.
19. D. KUHLMANN-WILSDORF and H. WILSDORF: *Acta. Met.*, 1953, **1**, 394–413.
20. A. H. COTTRELL: 'Dislocations and plastic flow in crystals'; 1953, Oxford, Clarendon Press.
21. J. E. DORN: 'Creep and fracture of metals at high temperatures' (NPL Symposium 1954) 89; 1956, London, HMSO.

Grain boundary serrations developed during creep

Arthur W. Mullendore and Nicholas J. Grant

During creep of a number of metals and alloys, grain bound-ary roughening occurs in conjunction with grain boundary sliding. The boundaries develop a rather regular saw-tooth appearance, the wavelength of the serration being a function of stress, temperature, and alloy composition. Observations of this phenomenon during creep of aluminium–magnesium solid-solution alloys and the relationship to grain boundary sliding, substructure adjacent to the grain boundary, and void formation are described. A mechanism for the develop-ment of the serrations is offered.

INTRODUCTION

DURING CREEP DEFORMATION of aluminium–magnesium solid-solution alloys under stress and temperature conditions which promote grain boundary sliding and migration, the grain boundaries become rough-ened and take on a saw-tooth appearance which is often striking in its regularity.

This serrated structure of the boundary was noted to be closely related to the formation of intercrystalline voids during creep; accordingly, some detailed observations of its character were made.

Previous observations of the serrated structure of grain boundaries have been made by Chang and Grant in aluminium,[1] by Brunner and Grant in aluminium and aluminium–magnesium alloys[2] and Grant in an aluminium–20%Zn alloy,[3] and by Cuff in an Fe–3%Si alloy.[4]

EXPERIMENTAL PROCEDURE

The observations of serrations in this study come from three types of tests:

(i) constant stress[5] and constant load[10] creep rupture tests of aluminium containing 0·94, 1·92, and 5·10%Mg, tested at 500°, 700°, and 900°F, and at stresses from 500 to 14 000 lb/in².

The authors are respectively Assistant Professor, and Professor of the Depart-ment of Metallurgy, Massachusetts Institute of Technology, Cambridge, Mass., USA.

(ii) a constant load test of a coarse-grained specimen of Al–1·92%Mg given successive elongations of 5, 5½, and 2% at a stress of 3 600 lb/in² at 500°F.

(iii) constant strain rate tests of Al–1·92%Mg at 510° and 715°F at a strain rate of 2% per hour, producing elongations from 0·3 to 5·3%.

The alloys kindly furnished by the Aluminium Company of America have the following composition, %:

Mg	Cu	Fe	Si	Al
0·94	0·002	0·007	0·004	bal.
1·92	0·002	0·003	0·002	bal.
5·10	0·002	0·002	0·004	bal.

The alloys were supplied in the form of swaged rods from which specimens for test groupings (i) and (ii) were machined and in the form of cold rolled plate for test group (iii). Specimens were machined from the stock and annealed at 1 000°F for times necessary to obtain the desired grain size, which was 0·9 mm for the constant stress specimens and 1·5 mm (average linear intercept) for the constant strain rate specimens. The constant load specimen was strained about 1% at room temperature after recrystallizing and then annealed at 900°F for 8 h to yield a 2·1 mm grain size. Electropolishing of specimens before and after testing was done in a solution of 30 cm³ of 60% perchloric acid and 100 cm³ glacial acetic acid.

A technique of electropolishing during microscopical examination of a surface was developed for determining the three-dimensional structure of the grain boundary. A polishing chamber with a window was used and the polishing solution was circulated through the chamber between the specimen surface and the viewing window. By periodically taking pictures of the grain boundary during polishing, its appearance in three dimensions could be determined. Depth of polishing was determined by reading the position of the micrometer focusing knob on the microscope.

RESULTS AND DISCUSSION

The appearance of grain boundary serrations which develop during creep was first investigated in a series of ruptured test specimens (group (i)) from the creep rupture investigation by Gemmell and Grant.[5] These specimens were sectioned longitudinally, mechanically polished, and then given an electrolytic polish. Figure 1 shows the stress/rupture data, the solid squares, triangles, and circles representing the specimens examined. The grain boundaries of specimens at the highest stress at which grain boundary sliding took place

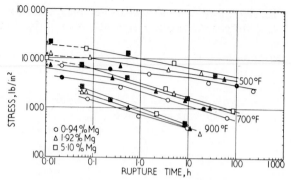

1 *Log stress/log rupture time for aluminium–magnesium alloys*[5]

(5·10 %Mg at 500°F) had very fine serrations as can be seen in Fig.2*a*. Numerous voids were observed on the grain boundaries. With decreasing stress the serrations became coarser and the voids were larger and less numerous (Fig.2*b*). At still lower stresses, the serrations became larger and more irregular in shape, this irregularity probably being associated with the long-range migration of the grain boundary.

The serration peaks appear to be associated with subgrain boundaries as indicated by Fig.2*c*, which is an electrolytically anodized

2a

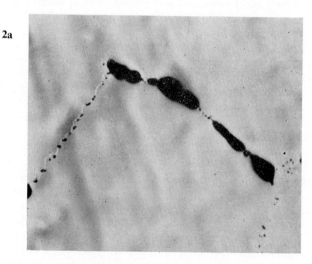

a 5·10%Mg, 500°F, 5 000 lb/in²
2 *a – c Grain boundary serrations and voids* × *100*

46

2b

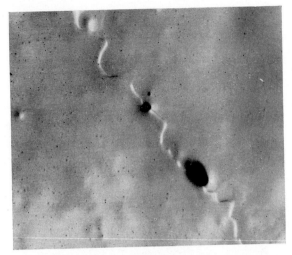

b   1·92%Mg, 700°F, 4 000 lb/in²

2c

c   Same as *b*, polarized light

specimen photographed with polarized light. It is not possible, however, to explain the formation of the serrations on the basis that the interfacial tension of the subgrain boundary causes localized migration of the boundary. The energy of the subgrain boundary is much too low to cause such a large deflection of the boundary.

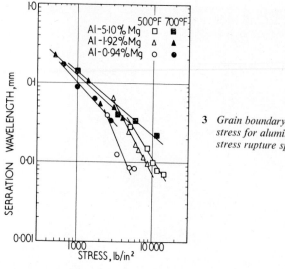

3 *Grain boundary serration size v. stress for aluminium–magnesium stress rupture specimens*

The serration wavelength was measured on the constant load specimens from the creep rupture investigation of Mullendore and Grant.[10] The values of the serration wavelength, λ, representing the average for ten randomly selected grain boundaries in each specimen, are plotted v. the stress, in Fig.3. It would seem that the serration wavelength is more strongly influenced by the stress than by the temperature or alloy composition, tests in the same stress range at 500° and 700°F giving similar values of λ. A temperature effect is indicated, however, by the difference of slope of the best straight lines through the data for each alloy at the two temperatures. The effect of composition on wavelength is greatest at high stresses and the lower temperature, increasing magnesium content resulting in a greater serration wavelength at a given stress.

The tests of the specimen in group (ii) gave an opportunity to observe the stages of development of serrations. This specimen, which was used for a study of orientation relationships in grain boundary sliding and void formation, was given three consecutive elongations of 5, $5\frac{1}{2}$, and 2% at 500°F at a stress of 3 600 lb/in², and examined both in the as-deformed and repolished states between elongations. Measurements were made of the serration wavelength, the included angle of the serration peak, and the fraction of grain boundary area (based on the surface observations) which was serrated. These measurements were made on eleven randomly orientated grain boundaries, each boundary being observed on two

TABLE I Development of serrations

| Total strain, % | Degree of serration | | | Grain boundary sliding, μm | Wavelength of serrated boundaries, μm | | Included angle of serration peak, ° | |
	smooth	slightly serrated	50–100% serrated		A*	B**	A*	B**
5	12	2	8	1·4–18·3	7–30 (av. 17)	...	107–140 (av. 121)	
10·5	2	5	15	2·2–21·3	8–40 (av. 22)	32–80 (av. 58)	110–150 (av. 124)	125–156 (av. 137)
12·5	1	6	15	2·6–22·4	...	...	...	...

A* Values for boundaries which serrated during first elongation.
B** Values for boundaries which serrated during second elongation.

perpendicular surfaces at a magnification of $\times 200$. After the first 5% elongation there was considerable variation in roughness of different boundaries and differences in the same grain boundary as viewed on two sides of the specimen. If one counts both observations for each grain boundary, the values listed under the heading 'Degree of serration' in Table I are obtained. Since the serrations appeared in patches with the remainder of the boundary smooth, it was possible to attach an approximate percentage figure to the degree of serration. The grain boundary displacements at this elongation varied from 1·4 to 18·3 μm. No relationship between amount of sliding and boundary roughness could be established except that the three boundaries with less than 4 μm displacement were smooth on both surfaces of observation. After $10\frac{1}{2}$% elongation, almost all the boundaries had some degree of serration and the final elongation of 2% produced little change. The wavelength of the serrations and the included angle of the serration peaks is given in Table I for the first two elongations. The boundaries (col. A) which were partly serrated after 5% elongation showed a small increase in wavelength and included angle at $10\frac{1}{2}$% elongation. This probably represents the tendency for the first formed serrations to be of somewhat shorter wavelength than those which form later on the same boundary. This tendency is again indicated by the wavelength values for the boundaries which first developed serrations during the second elongation (col. B).

It appears, then, that the serrations start to form rather early in the creep test and once formed do not change in wavelength or included angle very markedly.

Voids were observed on three of the serrated boundaries after 5% elongation and on four of the serrated boundaries after $10\frac{1}{2}$%

49

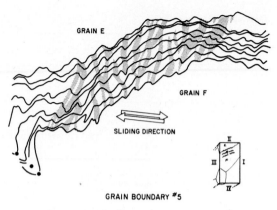

GRAIN E

GRAIN F

SLIDING DIRECTION

GRAIN BOUNDARY #5

4 *Projection on a plane perpendicular to the specimen axis* × *400*

elongation. They were on boundaries which had undergone a moderate to large amount of sliding (11·4 to 18·3 μm at 10½% elongation) and seemed to occur near the peaks of the serrations.

After the final elongation of this specimen, the nature of the three-dimensional structure of the grain boundary was examined to determine whether the serrations observed in two dimensions actually represented corrugations in volume and to see if the voids were elongated or equiaxed. The study of the topography of the grain boundaries was accomplished by sectioning the specimen at a small angle nearly parallel to the boundary, electropolishing under the microscope, and taking periodic pictures of the boundary during polishing. Then by copying the grain boundary traces in successive positions on to a single paper, the grain boundary features as projected on the plane of observation were obtained. Since the angle between the plane of observation and the grain boundary plane is small (usually 5–15°), dimensions in the projection are nearly equal to the corresponding ones in the grain boundary itself. Two of these projections are shown in Figs.4 and 5. These boundaries (numbered 5 and 11) were at angles of 77 and 73° to the tensile axis and the grain boundary displacements were 7 and 14 μm respectively. The serrations are shadowed to show their continuity in the direction of polishing.

The stages of development of grain boundary serrations can often be seen on the deformed surface of a specimen by the successive traces of the boundary caused by variation in the sliding and migration rates. Figures *6a* and *b*, from a constant strain rate (2% elongation per hour) specimen strained 4·0% at 700°F, show this

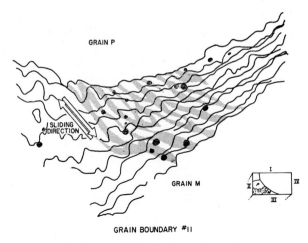

GRAIN P

SLIDING
&/DIRECTION

GRAIN M

GRAIN BOUNDARY #11

5 *Projection on a plane perpendicular to the specimen axis* × *400*

effect. One notes that the pattern of development of the serrations is not at all like that which would exist if they were caused by the uniform migration of the grain boundary being held up at periodic pinning points. If this were true, in Fig.6a the cusps of the serrations would be at the points closest to the original position of the boundary, not at the points of greatest migration. In Fig.6b, the rather steady migration progress of all parts of the boundary (with only a difference in rate of migration) would not be expected.

Studies of grain boundary sliding in polycrystals and bicrystals of Al–2%Mg have lead to the conclusion that the grain boundary displacements can be accounted for by slip crossing the grain boundary.[6] The sliding represents the unresolved component of shear when slip in one grain changes direction in crossing the grain boundary. An interesting feature of slip-induced sliding is its nature when the grain boundary is serrated. The contribution to grain boundary displacement by a unit of slip in grain *A* of Fig.7 is greater on the boundary forming one side of a serration peak than on the other. At the same time, the amount of slip in region *c* of grain *B* will be greater than in region *b*. Assuming the shear in grain *B* to be uniform further back from the boundary, a dislocation accumulation in region *b* results. In addition to this, it is quite likely, in view of the observation of Ogilvie[7] that the continuity of slip across a grain boundary depends on the boundary orientation as well as the relative grain orientations, that different slip systems may operate when the boundary changes direction. In particular, the sharp

51

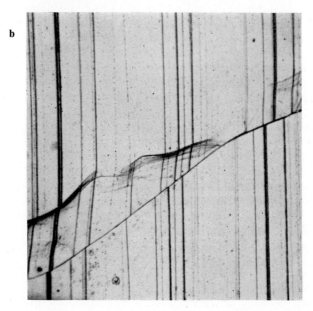

Grain boundary sliding and serration formation in Al–1·92%Mg, 715°F, 2%/h strain rate, 4·0% elongation. Vertical lines are reference scratches × 200

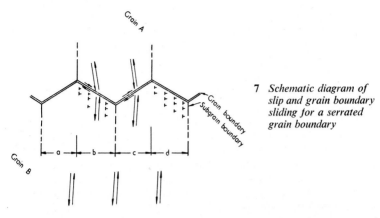

7 *Schematic diagram of slip and grain boundary sliding for a serrated grain boundary*

change of boundary direction at the serration peak and the associated discontinuity in the grain boundary sliding direction make the strain in this region complex. It would be surprising if these variations did not produce a difference in migration rate which would progressively develop the serrated structure of the boundary. Thus even a slightly irregular boundary such as might result from the intersection with subgrain walls represents an unstable condition in the presence of grain boundary sliding, and growth of the serrations should occur as long as appreciable sliding takes place.

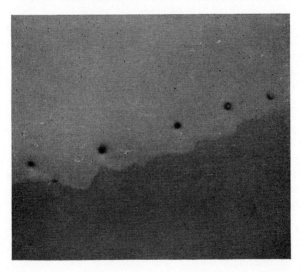

8 *Voids on one side of a grain boundary. Same grain boundary as in Fig.5* × *320*

53

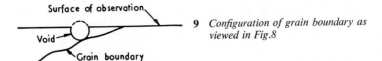

9 *Configuration of grain boundary as viewed in Fig.8*

A striking feature of the observations during polishing is that the voids always occur on one side of the grain boundary, near the peaks of the serrations. In fact, individual pictures of the grain boundary often show the voids completely separated from the boundary, as in Fig.8. This is the result of the plane of observation being almost parallel to the grain boundary plane and does not indicate that the voids do not touch the boundary just below the surface. Figure 9 indicates the configuration of the grain boundary and voids with respect to the surface of observation.

One must conclude that if the void nuclei are created after the serrations have developed, they probably originate on the subgrain boundary just to one side of the grain boundary. Their growth or propagation may subsequently be along the boundary.

The serration peak, representing the intersection of two segments of grain boundary and a subgrain boundary, is similar to a grain boundary triple point. It is therefore very likely that Zener's mechanism[8] for the origin of triple point cracks applies. The relaxation of shear stresses across the two segments of grain boundary forming a peak produces different amounts of sliding, and therefore tensile stresses exist across the subgrain boundaries intersecting the peaks. Cracks could then form on this subgrain boundary. The formation of this crack nucleus is a stress relief process, and if the temperature and stress conditions permit, the crack will have time to become rounded by surface diffusion.

One must still explain why voids are more numerous in the high stress tests where the serration wavelength is such that, other things being equal, the tensile stress across the subgrain boundary at the serration peak would be lower than for low stress specimens. The factor which is not equal, of course, is the ratio of migration rate to strain rate. This is low for the high stress specimens. Thus, in agreement with Nield and Quarrell,[9] the role of migration as a stress relief mechanism is thought to have a very important effect in the prevention of intercrystalline cracking.

CONCLUSIONS

Grain boundary serrations are found to occur only in conjunction with grain boundary sliding and migration. They form after an elongation sufficient to develop the substructure adjacent to the boundary which is characteristic of these creep conditions. The peaks of the serrations represent intersections of subgrains with the boundary and, in view of the stress and composition dependence of serration wavelength, this subgrain size is a function of stress and alloy content.

Serrations form prior to void formation and voids are not always associated with serrated boundaries. The voids are found to originate on one side of the boundary near the peaks of the serrations but it is not known at present whether this is the side in the direction of migration or away from it. The voids are thought to result from high stress concentrations at the peak produced by sliding. Grain boundary migration rate is found to have an important role in determining whether the stresses reach the level at which the void nucleus will form.

ACKNOWLEDGMENTS
The authors wish to express their appreciation to Materials Central, Wright Air Development Division, Dayton, Ohio, USA. for their sponsorship of this programme under Contract AF 33(616)–5926.

REFERENCES
1. H. C. CHANG and N. J. GRANT: *Trans. AIME*, 1952, **194**, 619–625.
2. H. BRUNNER and N. J. GRANT: *ibid.*, 1960, **218**, 122.
3. N. J. GRANT: 'Fracture' (*ed.* B. L. AVERBACH *et al.*); 1959, MIT Technology Press and John Wiley, New York.
4. F. B. CUFF, Jr.: Private communication.
5. G. D. GEMMELL and N. J. GRANT: *J. Metals*, 1957, **9**, 417.
6. A. W. MULLENDORE and N. J. GRANT: 'Grain boundary sliding during creep of an Al–2% Mg. Alloy,' paper submitted to AIME.
7. G. J. OGILVIE: *J. Inst. Metals*, 1952–53, **81**, 491–495.
8. C. ZENER: 'Fracturing of Metals', 3: 1948, Cleveland, Ohio, USA, ASM.
9. B. J. NIELD and A. S. QUARRELL: *J. Inst. Metals*, 1956–57, **85**, 480–488.
10. A. W. MULLENDORE and N. J. GRANT: *J. Metals*, 1954, **6**, 973–979.

The shear properties of grain boundaries in copper

S. Harper, Ph.D., B.Sc.

The rate of grain boundary sliding in copper bicrystals has been studied for both high and low-angle boundaries. The stresses used have been so limited that no detectable grain deformation occurred, the displacement due to grain boundary sliding being of the order of 1 μm or less. It is concluded that the model of a viscous grain boundary restrained by geometric irregularities is inadequate to explain all the observed features.

INTRODUCTION

EXPERIMENTAL STUDIES of grain boundary sliding have been in general of two types. The first type has consisted of measurements of anelastic phenomena in polycrystalline specimens. Kê,[1] following the work of Zener and his associates,[2,3] showed that, for aluminium, magnesium, iron, copper, and copper alloys at stress amplitudes well below the elastic limit, there exists a 'peak' in the internal friction spectrum associated with the presence of grain boundaries in the material. Kê concluded that this energy loss was due to a viscous sliding at the grain boundaries which was limited only by elastic restraints at grain corners and by assuming the internal friction peak to be associated with a single relaxation time he derived the constants in the equation of viscous movement

$$v = A\sigma e^{-Q/RT}$$

where v is the velocity of grain boundary sliding under the applied shear stress σ at absolute temperature T. R is the gas constant while A and Q are constants for a given material.

Similar work has since been done on aluminium and aluminium alloys,[4] copper and copper alloys,[5,6] silver,[5] titanium,[7] zirconium,[8] gold,[9] and tin.[10]

This explanation of the internal friction peak met with considerable success. Assuming a reasonable value of grain boundary thickness of 3 atom diameters the value of grain boundary viscosity can be determined from anelastic measurements and when extrapolated

The author is Head of General Metallurgy Section, The British Non-Ferrous Metals Research Association, London.

to the melting point gave fair agreement with the known viscosities of the liquid metals. Again, if the only restraint to grain boundary sliding is the elastic stresses set up at the triple points, then the value of the relaxation time of the phenomenon is proportional to grain size and Kê found this to be approximately true. Other workers[4] have pointed out, however, that the relaxation time is more critically dependent on grain size than the linear relationship.

Kê[11] has proposed that the atomistic mechanism of grain boundary sliding is similar to one suggested for creep[12] where the controlling action is the squeezing past each other of neighbouring atoms. According to this argument the activation energy for grain boundary sliding should equal that for self diffusion and Kê found such agreement for aluminium but this equality does not apparently hold for copper[5] or tin.[10] In Kê's analysis, however, it is assumed that the sliding process can be described by a single relaxation time, in other words that all the grain boundaries within a polycrystalline specimen slide at the same rate with the same activation energy. The experimentally determined internal friction peaks occur over too wide a range of frequencies for this to be true however, and it is probable that a wide range of relaxation times is involved.

Mott[13] has proposed a more sophisticated model in which the boundary is considered as a network of regions of good and bad fit between the two adjoining crystals. The elementary sliding process is then considered to be a localized melting of a number of atoms around a region of good fit. Predicted rates of sliding from this mechanism are, however, much higher than those found experimentally.[14]

In more recent years there has been more emphasis on the second type of experimental approach in which the rate of sliding at a single plane grain boundary in a bicrystal specimen has been studied as a function of orientation, stress, temperature etc. Such work has been done on tin,[15,16] aluminium,[17-19] and copper.[20]

The main difference between the two types of experiments lies in the magnitude of the sliding displacement. The anelastic measurements involve movements along a given boundary of between 1 and 10Å while the bicrystal experiments involve movements of between $5 \cdot 10^4$Å and 10^6Å. With this large difference it is perhaps not surprising that very great differences in behaviour of the grain boundary are observed in the two types of experiments.

Table I shows the values of A and Q of the viscous flow law for three metals determined by both internal friction and bicrystal sliding experiments. Although the temperature dependence of the two processes is very similar the absolute rates of sliding observed

57

TABLE I Values of A and Q for three metals

Material	Experiment	A, cm³dyn⁻¹s⁻¹	Q, Kcal/mol	Ref.
Aluminium	Internal friction	18	34	1
	Bicrystal	∼3·10⁻⁸*	40	21
Tin	Internal friction	54	19	10
	Bicrystal	2·3 × 10⁻⁴	19·2	16
Copper	Internal friction	15	33	5
	Bicrystal	∼1 × 10⁻⁷*	40	20

* The values of A cannot be deduced exactly as the investigators reported that the rate of sliding was not independent of time, but for comparison it has been assumed that in the early stages the rate of sliding obeys a viscous law as found by other workers.[16,17]

in bicrystals are many orders of magnitude smaller than those deduced from anelastic experiments.

There are many other major differences between the behaviour observed on single grain boundaries in bicrystals and the 'averaged' behaviour predicted from anelastic experiments.

Effect of time

All investigators on bicrystals have found that the rate of sliding decreases with time but there is no agreement as to the precise form of the variation. With aluminium it has been claimed that in the early stages of a test the grain boundary sliding displacement is linear with time followed by a rate of sliding which decreases with further increases in time,[17] a second investigator claimed that the amount of sliding is proportional to $t^{\frac{1}{2}}$,[18] while another shows that there is an instantaneous initial shear followed by a shear rate which diminishes with time without an initial linear portion.[19] With tin[16] some sliding displacement/time curves had a linear region for short times followed by a sliding rate which decreased with time, while other curves had an early decreasing rate followed by regions where the rate remained constant, which was in turn followed by a further decreasing rate. With copper the sliding displacement varied as $t^{\frac{1}{3}}$.

The sliding displacement varied in a cyclic manner (jerky flow) in all three metals but was not invariably so. An induction period before sliding begins has been found in some (though not all) cases in aluminium, but has not been observed in copper or tin.

Effect of stress

In aluminium one investigator[18] found a threshold stress below which grain boundary sliding does not occur but this has not been substantiated by later workers.[17,19] The rate of sliding has been found to be exponentially dependent on stress[17] though this does not appear to hold at low stress levels[18] but in any case the rate of grain boundary sliding in aluminium is much more sensitive to stress than the linear relationship of viscous flow. On the other hand the initial rate of sliding appears to be linearly proportional to stress in both copper[20] and tin.[16]

Metallographic appearance

A common feature of all the work on bicrystals has been that extensive deformation has occurred in the crystalline material around the grain boundaries, sometimes causing sideways migration of the grain boundary into relatively strain free regions. Rationalizations of the phenomena have been on the lines that rapid stress relaxation at the grain boundaries by means of Kê-type shear has led to stress concentrations at locking points which then relax by crystalline shear or possibly vacancy diffusion. Differences exist, however, in the opinions held as to the structure and mode of formation of the obstructions on the grain boundary which restrict the Kê-type slip.

At the risk of adding to the confusion it was felt worthwhile to attempt experiments on grain boundary sliding which fell between the relatively coarse movements involved in reported bicrystal experiments and the extremely small oscillatory movements required to satisfy the observed anelastic effects. Accordingly some experiments have been made on grain boundary sliding in copper bicrystals measuring the displacement of one grain relative to the other by means of an optical interference method so that displacements as small as 50Å could be detected compared with the 1–10Å of the anelastic measurements and the 10^4–10^6Å involved in earlier bicrystal experiments. The technique is tedious and no attempt has been made to derive phenomenological relationships between the usual creep parameters and only qualitative comparisons with the 1–10Å and 10^4–10^6Å movements have been made.

EXPERIMENTAL METHODS

The copper used was high purity electrode copper vacuum melted and cast. When in the form of bicrystals it had the following impurity levels:

P	< 100 ppm if any
As, Fe, Mn, Si, Ag, Sn, Te, Zn	< 10 ppm each if any
Pb	< 3 ppm if any
Sb	< 2 ppm if any
Bi, Co, Ni, O_2	< 1 ppm each if any

Bicrystals were grown in graphite moulds in a vacuum furnace by unidirectional solidification on to two single crystal 'seeds'. Both monocrystals and bicrystals appeared free from the lineage sub-structures that have been reported.[22] If the bicrystals which were about 1 cm × 1 cm in cross-section were more than 1–1½ cm long it was found that many of them had curved boundaries with the boundary sometimes curving off to the side and terminating one of the crystals. On examining some hundreds of bicrystals it was not found that this curving of the boundary was not a function of orientation[23] but that the migration of the boundary occurred after solidification. This was shown by so arranging the mould that the last copper to solidify had a V notch on the boundary position. This device anchored the boundary at the base of the notch but it still curved out in the centre of the bicrystal. One case was found where the grain boundary had migrated to the side of the bicrystal and then moved along the free surface leaving two totally unconnected crystals of identical orientation separated by a crystal of the second orientation of the bicrystal pair.

A two circle optical goniometer[24] was used for orientation determination and also for orienting seed crystals within the mould. Bicrystals could be grown to a preselected orientation with an accuracy of ±1°.

The bicrystals were shaped by mounting in dental wax and cutting with a miniature mechanical saw using a fine piercing saw blade. This produced a flat surface with plastic deformation, as shown by X-ray asterism, localized to a region 0·003in thick from the cut face. This distorted region was then removed by etching and electropolishing.

The test pieces finally produced had an octagonal cross-section as indicated in Fig.1 with a plane grain boundary parallel to the prism axis and passing through two opposite prism faces. A shear stress was applied to the boundary by applying a compressive stress

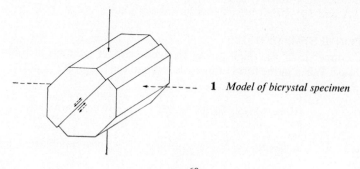

1 *Model of bicrystal specimen*

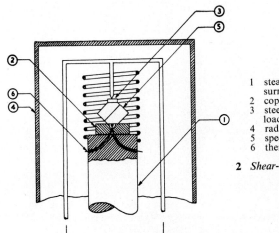

1 steatite column surmounted by heater coil
2 copper anvil
3 steel pressure plate with loading stirrup
4 radiation shield
5 specimen
6 thermocouple

2 *Shear-testing apparatus*

as shown. The tests were carried out in vacuum (10^{-5} mmHg) in an apparatus shown diagrammatically in Fig.2, the temperature of the specimen being controlled to $\pm\frac{1}{2}$°C. The amount of grain boundary sliding was measured by cooling to room temperature, removing the specimen from test and taking multiple beam interferograms[25] of the step produced at the junction of the grain boundary and the free surfaces. Figure 3 shows a typical interferogram of a step caused by sliding at a grain boundary.

Some experiments have been carried out on simple low-angle boundaries. The tilt boundaries used were twins in that the grain boundaries were the mirror planes of the family (hkk). This series of boundaries may be generated by rotating each crystal through an angle θ in opposite directions about a common <110> in the grain boundary plane. As θ is increased the density of edge dislocations

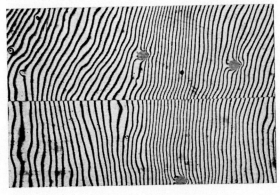

3 *Interferogram of grain boundary sliding displacement of about 1000Å*

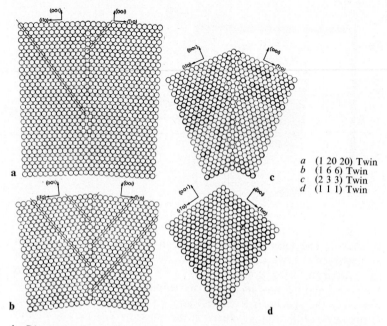

a (1 20 20) Twin
b (1 6 6) Twin
c (2 3 3) Twin
d (1 1 1) Twin

4 *Diagrammatic representations of type (hkk) twins. The plane of the paper is in all cases the (110) plane. The lines represent the intersection of extra half planes of a (111) type, which are perpendicular to the plane of the paper.*

forming the tilt boundary is also increased. Maximum disorder occurs at around 20–25°, as the angle is further increased the misfit at the boundary decreases again until the commonly occurring growth twin (111) is reached at $\theta = 35°$ 16′. This progression is illustrated in Fig.4 which shows models of (1 20 20), (1 6 6), (2 3 3) and (111) twins. With these bicrystals the direction of shear was in the common <110> (at right-angles to the paper in Fig.4). This configuration was chosen because the edge dislocations forming the grain boundary cannot contribute to a shear deformation in this direction. Other tests have been carried out on bicrystals of random orientation.

The applied stresses varied between 5 and 10 g/mm² at temperatures of from 450–600°C.

EXPERIMENTAL RESULTS

The sliding displacement at a grain boundary was not uniform across the boundary but exhibited variations which appeared as undulations in the height of the step produced on the free surface.

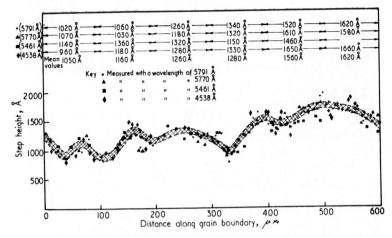

5 *Grain boundary glide-distribution curve measured with four different wavelengths and interference patterns*

The measurement of step height at a given point on the surface by interference fringes assumes that the slope of the surface is uniform between two adjacent fringes, and if this is not so errors will occur. To ensure that any undulations on the surface are real it is necessary to vary the fringe spacing by altering the wavelength of the monochromatic light used or by altering the wedge angle between the specimen and the plane reference surface. Figure 5 shows the results of such measurements on a (1 6 6) tilt boundary after testing for 20 h at 500°C under a shear stress of 5 g/mm². The step height at the junction of the grain boundary and the free surface is plotted as a function of distance along the boundary for a total distance of 0·6 mm. There is some scatter of individual results but they do all follow the same general trend of contour along the grain boundary step so that the variations in the amount of grain boundary sliding are real.

From many such measurements it was found that by taking the arithmetical mean of step height measurements over a region from 0·5–1·0 mm a mean value of grain boundary sliding displacement could be obtained which was reproducible to within ±10Å. This is an excessively tedious operation and some mean values are averaged over a length of 0·1 mm (about 10 interference fringes) only. Such average figures are tabulated in Fig.5. By this method variations in reproducibility of about 100Å occur. The cross-hatched band in the figure represents an uncertainty in the step height of 100Å.

63

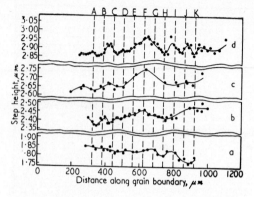

6 *Grain boundary glide-distribution curves measured after periods of a 22·5 h, b 44·5 h, c 66·5 h, d 88·75 h, under a shear stress of 7·1 g/mm², at 500°C*

Figure 6 shows the sliding displacement along a region of a grain boundary at various stages in the sliding-displacement-time curve, while Fig.7 shows the difference between the displacement at positions *A–K*, shown in Fig.6, and the mean displacement over the whole region. These results are taken from a random orientation boundary stressed at 7·1 g/mm² at 500°C. Regions on the grain boundary were tagged by means of characteristic patterns of micro-hardness indentations placed some distance from the grain boundary. By this means sliding displacements could be measured at the same points along the grain boundary at various stages of the test, the error in successive positioning being about 1 μm.

This experiment was repeated several times with essentially similar results. In all cases in some regions of the grain boundary (cf. regions *A-D* and *E-H*, Figs.6–7) the sliding rate is high so that neighbouring regions are left behind; this will persist until the region has moved more than the surrounding area by a distance of a few

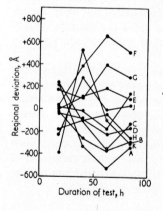

7 *Variation of regional grain boundary glide from the mean value as a function of time*

64

hundred angstrom units; it will then slow down while the neighbouring regions accelerate and finally pass it. Some prominent maxima or minima in the displacement, such as F, Fig.6, persist for long periods of time but the others disappear more rapidly, changing from a 'hill' to a 'valley' at the free surface in 20 h or less. It was thought that this phenomenon might be purely a surface effect caused by regions of local strain on the surface. To test this possibility mechanical scratches and microhardness indentations were placed across some boundaries before and during the progress of a test, but they had no detectable effect on the sliding displacement in their immediate vicinity. Furthermore, specimens whose surfaces had been deeply electropolished after cutting to remove deformed surface layers showed similar variations in sliding displacement across the boundary as specimens which had been ground flat on emery paper before light electropolishing although the latter surface showed an appreciable degree of X-ray asterism.

To summarize the information on these microvariations in sliding displacement:

  (i) they are real, being often 5–10 times the experimental uncertainty

  (ii) they are variable in amplitude but are in general a few hundred angstrom units high and occur over a region of about 50–100 μm wide

 (iii) they appear in the very early stages of grain boundary sliding, thus local variations of 500Å to zero have been found in short-time tests

 (iv) they do not grow in proportion to the mean value of sliding displacement, the difference from the mean movement remaining roughly the same though the latter may be varied from 500–30000Å.

  (v) they appear and disappear in a cyclic manner

 (vi) they are not detectably sensitive to strain on the free surface

 (vii) they occur in both random irrational boundaries and simple low-angle tilt boundaries.

Mean values of sliding displacement

The mean values of sliding displacement averaged over distances of approximately 0·1 mm along the grain boundary showed considerable variation from one specimen to another and also between various regions of the same specimen. Figure 8 shows the sliding displacement/ time curves for five regions of a random orientation boundary up to a sliding displacement of 3 μm (30000Å) after testing at 500°C under a shear stress of 7·5 g/mm².

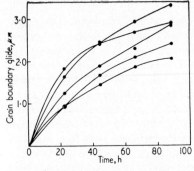

8 *Grain boundary glide as a function of time for random boundary under a stress of 7·5 g/mm², at 500°C*

Figure 9 shows similar curves averaged in these cases over 0·5 mm length of boundary with displacements up to 2000Å for a random boundary (7·5 g/mm², 450°C), a (1 6 6), and a (2 3 3) tilt boundary (both 7·5 g/mm², 500°C). In all cases studied the rate of grain boundary sliding decreased with time. With the intermittent type of measurements used it is not possible to define the sliding displacement/time curve with any precision but there is no reason to assume a linear portion even below displacement of a few hundred angstrom units. With random-type grain boundaries all the curves could be fitted within reasonable error to a power law of the form

$$\text{displacement} \propto (\text{time})^n$$

but n varied between 0·6 and 0·7 from specimen to specimen and from one region of a specimen to another and insufficient results are available to see whether these variations of n are real or not.

For purposes of rough comparison the 'initial rate of sliding' has been defined as the mean rate of sliding in the first 20 h of a creep test. Table II gives experimentally determined values of this initial rate of sliding for various grain boundaries and temperatures all at a shear stress of 7·5 g/mm² and extrapolated rates of sliding at the same temperatures and stress from internal friction experiments.

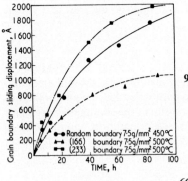

9 *Displacement/ time curves for boundaries as indicated*

66

TABLE II Mean initial rates of grain boundary sliding, in units of 10^{-10} cm/s

	Temperature, °C 300	450		500	550
Internal friction*(ref.5)	5.9×10^2	2.9×10^5		1.3×10^6	5.2×10^6
(ref.6)	2.8×10^2	2.6×10^5		1.5×10^6	4.4×10^6
Bicrystals 'random'		0·71	0·80	29·5 13·9 12·3	
				39·2 18·7	
		0·96	2·1	22·4	
		1·03			
(1 6 6) tilt				1·22 1·19 0·89	3·47 3·85†
				0·89	2·58 3·64
				0·7	
				0·74	
(2 3 3) tilt				1·25	
Twist boundary				1·17	

* Extrapolated assuming a Newtonian viscous law.

† Determined on a grain boundary which had been previously tested at 500°C. The results given in each 'box' are from one grain boundary, single results being averaged over 0·5–1 mm length of boundary. Where several results are given for one grain boundary they refer to different regions of the same boundary averaged over 0·1 mm lengths of grain boundary.

The mean initial rates of grain boundary sliding are thus smaller than those required to explain the anelastic experiments by a factor of 10^5–10^6 although the total grain boundary sliding displacements measured here are only of the order of 500–1000Å.

Insufficient results are available over a sufficiently wide temperature range to derive an activation energy for the sliding process. The activation energy determined from such data will also depend on the value of the time exponent n which is not precisely known.

Effect of orientation

As can be seen from Table II the mean initial rates of sliding are much smaller in rational low-angle boundaries than in 'random' boundaries under similar conditions. Figure 10 shows the effect of reversing the applied stress on *A* a (1 6 6) tilt boundary and *B* a twist boundary on a common (110) plane of the same angular misorientation, under a shear stress of 7·5 g/mm² at 503°C. The rate of grain boundary sliding decreases more rapidly at longer times than a simple power law, the total grain boundary displacement approaching a constant value. On reversing the stress between $\frac{1}{2}$ and $\frac{1}{3}$ of

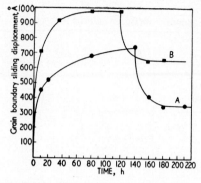

10 *Effect of stress reversal on* (A) *a tilt and* (B) *a twist boundary (7·5 g/mm², 503°C)*

the total displacement is recovered before sliding again appears to cease entirely. This 'prestraining' produces much work-hardening of the grain boundary and it was thus found necessary finally to increase the stress to 12·5 g/mm² or alternatively raise the temperature to above 650°C before any further detectable sliding occurred. Figure 11 shows a more complicated series of variations in test on a (1 6 6) tilt boundary with an applied stress of 7·5 g/mm². The first full lines indicate the duration of testing at 503°C, the broken lines at 551°C.

After 65 h at the lower temperature the rate of grain boundary sliding has fallen to a very low value. The temperature was then raised to 551°C for two 4-h periods leading to a considerable increase in the rate of sliding. A further 40 h at 503°C produced no detectable movement whatsoever. When the temperature was again raised to 551°C some further movement occurred in 4 h.

The temperature was then lowered to 503°C and the stress reversed when the grain boundary sliding in the reverse direction was found to be almost constant after 40 h. A further 10 h at 551°C gave a large displacement though this had apparently almost reached a constant value after a further 30 h. The stress was again reversed so that it was applied in the original direction at 551°C for 40 h. A very small movement only was detected (not plotted in Fig.11).

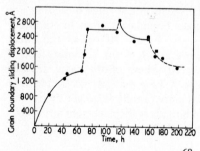

11 *Sliding displacement at a (1 6 6) tilt boundary. Full lines represent testing at 503°C, broken lines at 551°C. Both under a stress of 7·5 g/mm²*

68

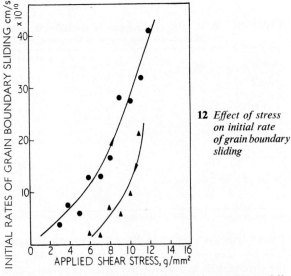

12 *Effect of stress on initial rate of grain boundary sliding*

To summarize, the rate of grain boundary sliding falls rapidly after movements of about 1500Å. Raising the temperature by 50°C causes a further rapid rate of sliding but this decreases rapidly so that at a displacement of around 2500Å the grain boundary appears 'locked'. On reversing, the stress rates of movement comparable with the initial forward rate of sliding are obtained which decay very rapidly, the rate of movement being nearly zero after about half the displacement has been recovered. Reversing the stress to the original direction gives only a very slight movement as if the boundary were almost completely locked.

It is notable that these stoppages in sliding occur at such low values of displacement whereas random boundaries under the same stress and temperature were still sliding rapidly after movements of 10–15 times this value.

Effect of stress

A random grain boundary was tested at 500°C with the stress increased in unit increments from 3–12 g/mm², the grain boundary sliding movements being measured after 4 h at the lower stresses and 1 h at the higher stresses. The stress was then reduced by the same increments, the movement being measured after 1 h at each stress except for the 7 and 6 g/mm² stresses where periods of 10 h had to be used. Figure 12 shows the mean rate of sliding plotted against stress for the descending and ascending stress series, the displacement being measured at each stage over the same 1 mm length of grain boundary. It is apparent that the initial rate of grain boundary

TABLE III **Mean rates of movement of six different regions on random grain boundaries in copper bicrystals containing traces of lead (7·5 g/mm²)**

Sequence	Temp., °C	Duration of test, h	Direction of stress application	Mean rate of movement, cm/s × 10⁻¹⁰					
10 ppm lead									
1	450	20	Forward	8·4	9·1	9·6	8·3	8·6	7·0
2	400	20	„	ND					
3	400	10	Reverse	8·3	9·6	9·5	5·5	8·6	7·3
4	400	10	Forward	ND					
Annealed 2 h at 900°C followed by:									
5	400	10	„	2·2	3·5	4·4	2·2	3·7	1·6
6	450	10	„	6·5	9·4	4·4	8·4	7·6	11·7
50 ppm lead									
1	450	5	Forward	17·8	19·0	20·8	22·1	24·3	26·2
2	400	10	Reverse	6·2	4·6	2·8	5·6	5·4	4·5
Annealed 2 h 900°C followed by:									
3	450	10	Forward	8·3	10·0	11·0	10·2	12·9	14·4
4	400	15	Reverse	8·2	8·7	8·6	8·6	8·9	9·8

ND, not detected = $<0·1 \times 10^{-10}$ cm/s

sliding increases very rapidly with increase in applied shear stress. It is also clear that the rate of boundary sliding is very sensitive to the mechanical history of the grain boundary and that the strain produced at a high stress level exhausts the boundary for subsequent strain at a lower stress level.

Effect of alloying

As has been emphasized the reproducibility of the results is poor and this may be due in part to variations in composition of the copper. With the bicrystal specimens a complete monoatomic layer of a foreign species at the grain boundary only represents a change in the mean composition of the specimen of the order of 0·05 ppm.

To examine this point further and to see if segregation at the grain boundaries is an important factor, a series of tests under an applied stress of 7·5 g/mm² have been performed on two random grain boundaries in copper containing 50 ppm and 10 ppm of lead respectively. Both these concentrations are probably above the solubility limit which appears to be ~1 ppm at 500°C,[26] but evidence of precipitation at the grain boundary was only observed in the 50 ppm lead material. Table III gives the mean rates of sliding movement of six different regions of each of the two grain boundaries.

Much higher rates of grain boundary sliding are obtained with these small amounts of lead present, extrapolating from the results obtained at 500° and 450°C the initial rates of sliding for a random boundary in pure copper would be about 1×10^{-10} cm/s at 450°C and $0·05 \times 10^{-10}$ cm/s at 400°C. Straining at a high temperature 'exhausts' the grain boundary and on lowering the temperature the movement stops, but this high-temperature prestraining has little or no effect on low-temperature movement in the opposite direction.

Annealing a work-hardened grain boundary only partially restores the original rate of grain boundary sliding. The rate of sliding in the bicrystal containing 10 ppm of lead appears fairly insensitive to temperature between 400° and 450°C. There is, however, a complicating factor here in that as the temperature is increased some re-solution of precipitated lead or redistribution of lead in equilibrium segregation will occur, so possibly tending to lower the rate of grain boundary sliding.

Metallographic appearance of grain boundary

All the grain boundaries studied had microscopically flat surfaces. In all specimens studied no evidence of plastic deformation could be found around the grain boundary. The optical interferometric method used for measuring grain boundary sliding is a sensitive means of detecting slip bands or regions of local surface tilt but no disturbance of any kind could be detected around the grain boundaries either by this method or by electron microscopy using replicas even when large amounts of grain boundary sliding ∼10 μm had occurred. Subsequent experiments have shown, however, that slip bands can be detected in isolated instances where large displacements ∼100 μm have occurred at temperatures of around 750°C.

In general also no detectable sideways migration of the grain boundary occurred during grain boundary sliding. The position of the grain boundary has been defined on a free surface to $\pm\frac{1}{20}$ μm by means of microhardness indentations close to the boundary and by measuring carbon replicas of the region at stages during the test. An exception to this occurred with the bicrystal containing 50 ppm of lead. Precipitate particles could be detected at the grain boundary in this specimen and considerable sideways migration of the boundary occurred during the test. In some cases what appeared to be a sideways migration of the boundary occurred on the free surface at right-angles to the stress direction where a step is produced by the grain boundary sliding. This, however, proved to be purely a surface effect due to the sharp step being filled in by surface diffusion, and the grain boundary inside the specimen did not migrate. Check experiments showed that this surface movement had no effect on the rate of grain boundary sliding.

DISCUSSION

To summarize briefly the experimental findings:

1. The rates of grain boundary sliding at small displacements of less than 1000Å are much smaller than those predicted from

internal friction experiments and are not constant but decrease with time.

2. Sliding movements at a grain boundary do not occur uniformly but in small pulses though the movement over a large area of grain boundary is smoothly continuous with time. The size of the pulses and the area over which they occur appears to be independent of the total amount of grain boundary sliding.

3. The rate of movement is sensitive to the disorder of the grain boundary, a rational symmetric boundary sliding much more slowly than a more highly disordered one. The displacement at a symmetric boundary appears to reach a limiting value at a given temperature and stress.

4. The rate of movement increases more rapidly with stress than a linear relationship and is also sensitive to the previous strain history of the grain boundary.

5. Work hardening of the grain boundary is to some extent determined by the direction of shear; reversing the stress permits movement in the opposite direction, which starts off at a rate similar to that of an 'unhardened' grain boundary but tails off much more rapidly. Grain boundary sliding in one direction can be stopped by prestraining at a higher temperature in the same direction but is relatively unaffected by prestraining in the opposite direction.

6. Small additions of lead have a large effect in increasing the rate of grain boundary sliding.

7. Large shear movements can occur at a grain boundary without any sideways migration of the grain boundary or detectable plastic deformation in the surrounding regions.

The large differences in behaviour observed between the small-displacement anelastic behaviour and the large-displacement bicrystal experiments have generally been explained by postulating that the rate-controlling process is the plastic shearing of irregularities or locking points on the grain boundary, new locking points being continuously generated by plastic deformation in the neighbouring grain material. This is supported by the fact that bicrystal shear experiments have invariably involved considerable plastic distortion in the neighbouring crystalline regions. Kê-type viscous sliding is thus relegated to the role of causing stress relaxation between locking points with a consequent concentration of stress at these locking points. This viscous sliding occurs very rapidly so that a completely relaxed state is obtained in times which are very short compared with the times involved here. The total sliding movement involved in this type of relaxation is also very small. For example if it is assumed that the free distance between neighbouring locking points is of the same order of the specimen size (1 cm) then we may consider the totally relaxed grain boundary as a flat, infinitely thin crack with the shear stress in the plane of the crack. With the stresses used here the maximum elastic movement of such a configuration will only be of the order of a few hundred angstrom units.[27]

This explanation is difficult to believe when plastic deformation cannot be detected around the grain boundary plane. It is also difficult to reconcile this picture with the effect of the orientation of the grain boundary. To modify the rate of grain boundary sliding by altering the rate of Kê-type sliding would involve decreasing the rate of Kê-type sliding by a factor of 10^4–10^5 to make the stress relaxation the controlling process, and if the orientation effect is to alter the creep characteristics of the crystalline material then the rate of sliding should vary with the orientation of the surrounding crystalline material and not specifically with the misorientation of the boundary. The crystals of the (1 6 6) boundary each have a slip and twinning plane inclined at about 30° to the grain boundary plane with a slip direction parallel to the direction of shear, while none of the irrational boundaries which slipped more rapidly had their nearest slip or twinning mechanism appreciably closer than this. Again the bicrystals containing lead gave rates of grain boundary sliding up to twenty times faster than similar lead-free boundaries. It must be noted, however, that the rate of sliding was smaller than the extrapolated rate of a layer of liquid lead a few atoms thick by a factor of 10^9. This increase in sliding rate cannot be due to an acceleration of Kê-type sliding, which is too rapid to be the rate-controlling process even when no lead is present, and it is unlikely that the rate of formation or shearing of grain boundary locking points is so markedly affected by the 1 ppm of lead in solution in the copper.

It would thus appear that the grain boundary sliding observed here is a function of the grain boundary interface itself and that Kê-type sliding is not operative at displacements greater than a few atom distances. The pulse type movements observed may thus be due to loop-like movements of mobile discontinuities in the grain boundary plane.

It is possible that the smaller initial rate of sliding movement leading to almost complete cessation of sliding observed in the rational boundaries is because the boundaries studied deviated from the ideal orientations given by about 1 degree of arc. The structure of an ideal (1 6 6) or (2 3 3) boundary may be regarded as a wall of parallel edge dislocations and the shear stress was applied along the dislocation axis and perpendicular to their Burgers vector. The movement of such dislocations can only occur if they break away and move into the adjoining crystal and such movement cannot contribute to the sliding displacement observed.

It is thus possible that a perfect (1 6 6) or (2 3 3) boundary would have a very large resistance to grain boundary sliding and the small amount of sliding observed is due to a further widely spaced network of discontinuities, corresponding to the small angular displacement from the ideal boundary, which are constrained to move in the grain boundary plane.

ACKNOWLEDGMENTS

This work forms part of a research programme carried out in the laboratories of The British Non-Ferrous Metals Research Association. Grateful acknowledgments are due to the Director and Council of the Association for permission to publish this paper, and to Mr R. Eborall for many helpful discussions.

REFERENCES

1. T. S. Kê: *Phys. Rev.*, 1947, **71**, 533–546; *ibid*, 1947, **72**, 41–46.
2. A. Barnes and C. Zener: *ibid.*, 1940, **58**, 87.
3. C. Zener *et al.*: *Trans. AIME*, 1942, **147**, 98–103.
4. C. D. Starr *et al.*: *Trans. ASM*, 1953, **45**, 275–285.
5. S. Pearson and L. Rotherham: *Trans AIME*, 1956, **206**, 881, 894–901.
6. K. J. Marsh: *Acta Met.*, 1954, **2**, 530–545.
7. J. N. Pratt, *et al.*: *Acta Met.*, 1954, **2**, 203.
8. W. J. Bratina and W. C. Winegard: *J. Metals*, 1956, **8**, 186–189.
9. D. R. Marsh and L. D. Hall: *ibid*, 1953, **5**, 937–942.
10. L. Rotherham, *et al.*: *J. Inst. Metals*, 1951, **79**, 439–454.
11. T. S. Kê: *J. App. Phys.*, 1949, **20**, 274–280.
12. E. Orowan: *J. West Scotland ISI*, 1947, **54**, 45–96.
13. N. F. Mott: *Proc. Phys. Soc.*, 1948, **60**, 391–394.
14. D. McLean: 'Grain boundaries in metals', 278; 1957, Oxford, Clarendon Press.
15. R. King *et al.*: *Nature*, 1948, **161**, 682.
16. K. E. Puttick and R. King: *J. Inst. Metals*, 1951–2, **80**, 537–544.
17. S. K. Tung and R. Maddin: *J. Metals*, 1957, **9**, 905–910.
18. F. N. Rhines *et al.*: *Trans. ASM*, 1956, **48**, 919–951.
19. F. Weinberg: *Trans. AIME*, 1958, **212**, 808–817.
20. J. Intrater and E. S. Machlin: *J. Inst. Metals*, 1959–60, **88**, 305–310.
21. B. Fazan *et al.*: *J. Metals*, 1954, **6**, 919–922. (*Note:* Value of Q derived from Rhines *et al.*, *op. cit.*)
22. E. Teghtsoonian and B. Chalmers: *Canad. J. Physics*, 1951, **29**, 370–381.
23. B. Chalmers: *ibid.*, 1953, **31**, (1), 132–146.
24. C. S. Barrett and L. H. Levenson: *Trans. AIME*, 1940, **137**, 76–84.
25. S. Tolansky: 'Multiple bean interferometry of surfaces and films'; 1948, Oxford, OUP.
26. *See* J. S. Smart in 'Discussion of non-ferrous rolling practice' 144; 1948, New York, AIME.
27. A. T. Starr: *Proc. Camb. Phil. Soc.*, 1928, **24**, 489–500.

Discussion 1

The five preceding papers were presented and discussed at this session.

Mr R. Eborall (BNFMRA): These five papers represent pretty fairly the pre-occupations of the metallurgist who has to think about what goes on in a metal during creep, but there is much more emphasis on fracture processes than on the control of creep rate. This is possibly because we now know a lot more about how to make a creep-resistant alloy than we do about how to control creep ductility. Creep ductility is an important limitation in some alloys since it often sets a limit to the amount by which a metal can be stiffened against creep by alloying. It is not always so: sometimes the limit is set by the ductility at room temperature either before or after the creep takes place. Titanium alloys are a case in point.

Professor Cottrell's paper on creep fractures will obviously be used as a source of ideas for a long time. It seems we have gone quite a long way towards understanding creep fractures, particularly the high-stress type of cracking. At low stresses the mechanism of cavity growth looks on the way to solution, but the mechanism of nucleation of the cavities is almost anybody's guess. It is interesting, however, to see how the Zener concept of stress concentration through grain boundary sliding has now been extended to account for the nucleation of these small cavities as well as the cracks formed at higher stresses.

Professor Cottrell is rather tentative about the nucleation of cavities at low stresses but tends, I think, to discount the nucleation at a jog in the boundary rather than the nucleation at a foreign particle, on the grounds that it is not easy to build up a sufficiently high stress because the Griffith criterion cannot easily be met. Nucleation at a foreign particle is easy to accept, but I rather wonder whether dismissal of jogs is quite justified, because the situation is not quite the one envisaged by Griffith (or by Starr or Stroh).

Suppose you have a free-sliding interface such as a grain boundary and consider the stress concentration at the end. The stresses which tend to make this interface move are balanced by a stress system involving the whole region beyond the end of the free-sliding interface. Where you have a small ledge in the grain boundary the situation does not seem the same. The whole of the force acting on the two sides of the free-sliding interface has then to be held by this small obstruction, and it is hard to avoid the conclusion that the average stress on the ledge is concentrated by a factor L/h, where L is the free-sliding length (e.g. length between ledges) and h is the height of the ledge. For a small ledge (e.g. 10Å) a very high stress could be obtained. I think it is harder to see why such stresses should not be dissipated by shearing of the jog in the boundary, if indeed one exists.

On the other hand, a metal which really seems to be immune to low creep elongation (at say 350°C upwards) is titanium. This is a metal which has the characteristic of dissolving oxide impurities and other similar compounds, so that it should be a 'clean' metal; and this perhaps is a bit of experimental evidence in favour of the oxide or nucleation hypothesis.

How could creep ductility be improved? One point is clearly that all these mechanisms of failure depend on stress concentration through some kind of sliding for initiation of the crack or cavity. Now in all cases the stress causing failure goes up as the free-sliding distance goes up and therefore, as indicated by Professor Cottrell, you can hope to get a better result by reducing the free sliding distance. It may be possible to reduce the grain size, at the cost of lower creep strength, and where good creep ductility is essential this does seem to be a solution, provided the fine grain size is always retained. Another way of reducing the free-sliding distance is to put in precipitates which will lock the grain boundary sliding, but they must be the right ones and have a strong interface with the parent metal, or they will themselves act as cavity nuclei.

Another approach is to consider the energy of the new fracture surface, since this always appears in expressions for the fracture strength. It is obvious that additions to the metal can lower this energy because things which concentrate at a free surface must lower the surface energy, by Gibb's equation. On the other hand, it should be possible to choose an addition element which will segregate at the grain boundaries *before* fracture, and which would remain lying in the new fracture surface momentarily although not in equilibrium there; such an element could in principle be so chosen as to raise the energy of the new surface and so increase the resistance to fracture.

Another point here is that Dr McLean, in a paper quoted by Professor Cottrell, did indicate that in some alloys the interfacial energy involved in fracture was lower than the ideal one for the matrix metal. Again, one could do something about this, perhaps by finding what elements were present which caused that lowering and then making alloy additions which would take care of them.

McLean and Hale's paper is a fascinating piece of metallography, and provides a very nice example of the direct checking which it is now possible to carry out on dislocation calculations. I note that dislocation climb is still considered to be the rate controlling mechanism and presumably, therefore, the general ideas about what to put in an alloy to stop it creeping are not much altered, but the calculation of the optimum distribution of precipitate particles seems quite new and should be fruitful. Could Dr McLean and his colleagues say how far the structures described are typical of those formed during the creep of other metals?

Dr E. D. Hyam (UKAEA): In connexion with Professor Cottrell's paper, it is perhaps appropriate to mention that much useful and interesting information about intergranular creep voids can be obtained from electron microscope studies of fracture surfaces.

Where the fracture examined is the actual path of rupture during test, the surface detail can reveal much about the stages by which rupture occurs (e.g. void growth, followed by shear) but may be complicated by corrosion effects. You can either look at the surface of the actual rupture, i.e. the part that broke during tensile or creep test, or you can take half the broken test and hit it with a hammer and replicate it. You can see what that tells you further along the grain length.

In some materials, in which grain surface voids promote intergranular brittle fracture, it is more convenient to form the creep voids and then to break the specimen deliberately by impact at low temperatures; the form and distribution of the voids are revealed in great detail on the exposed intergranular surfaces and it is often possible to select areas showing various stages in the growth and link-up of voids to form fissures.

A lot of work has been done at the Windscale laboratories on these types of voids developed in certain circumstances. Work by W. H. Chatwin has revealed that they can develop in certain circumstances in irradiated uranium. An account of their development in beryllium under conditions of relatively fast tensile strain (12%/h) at 700°C will be published shortly.[1]

I should now like to illustrate these remarks briefly by reference to voids which we observe in irradiated Magnox (Mg – 1%Al) fuel element cans. Figure *A*

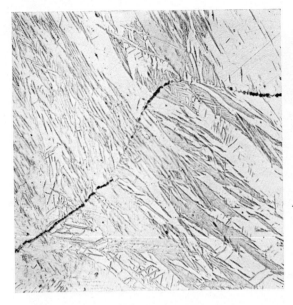

A *Typical example of grain boundary voids in Magnox*
× 120

shows a typical example of grain boundary voids in Magnox. Under conditions described by Eldred *et al.*[2] intergranular creep voids sometimes develop at grain boundaries; chains of voids several micrometres in diameter can be observed

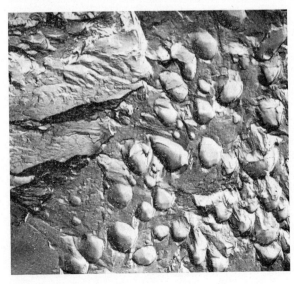

B *Exposed surface of an impact fracture in Magnox containing grain boundary voids*
× 1 300

C *Same region
as Fig.B,
showing
inclusions in
some voids
× 6500*

there. Corrosion effects make high-resolution electron microscopy of metallographic sections of this material rather difficult. However, if this material is notched at a suitable place, as in Fig.B, and then fractured by impact at liquid nitrogen temperatures, brittle fracture can often be induced along or near the boundaries which contain voids; in their absence, the fracture produced is of the transgranular shear type. The exposed voids are shown here. It is seen that in the plane of the boundary the voids at $1-8\mu$m across, are often closely clustered and possess a rudimentary but definite polyhedral shape. On some grain faces voids are elongated in a particular direction; grain boundary sliding to the extent of a few micrometres is known to have occurred in this material and might conceivably account for this.

Figure C illustrates the presence of small inclusions ($0\cdot2-1$ μm dia.) which were observed in about 40% of the voids; voids <2 μm dia. do not, however, appear to contain them. In this material, such inclusions are always replicated as raised features. If we assume that each void nucleated at an inclusion interface, then these observations imply that 50% of the replicated voids will contain inclusions and that, in the other 50% the surface diffusion which develops the polyhedral low surface energy shape of the voids will obliterate any surface trace of such features.

Some striking examples of this type of void can be observed in beryllium. The specimens which will be described have all been pulled in tension to fracture at 12%/h at 600°C. In irradiated beryllium the voids form preferentially at grain corners and spread along grain edges.

Figure D shows the structure at about 1 cm from the region of test rupture revealed by subsequent impact fracture at room temperature. These are the triangular fissures seen at 'triple points' on a metallographic section, and they illustrate very well the shape of these voids as viewed parallel to the axis of tension.

In beryllium irradiated to $\sim2\times10^{19}$nvt at $<300°$C, similar fracture after the

78

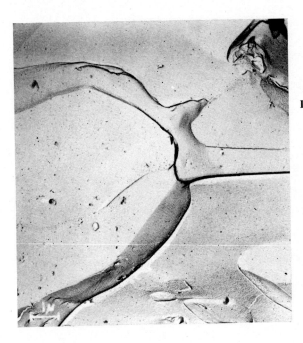

D *Unirradiated beryllium, tensile tested to failure at 12%/h at 600°C, showing fissures along grain edges exposed by impact fracture ~1 cm from the region of test failure*

× 7 500

tensile test showed that the voids in the gauge length form on grain surfaces rather than at grain edges. Figure E(i) shows an area where these voids are discrete and polyhedral, while Fig.E(ii) shows an adjacent area where the voids are linking up and spreading sideways.

These structures provide some indication of the possible mechanism of nucleation of the grain-surface voids in irradiated beryllium; about half the truly polyhedral voids (i.e. those $>1\mu$m) contain small angular inclusions: these are sometimes extracted on the replicas but have not so far been identified. The problem is further complicated, however, by the presence of radiation-induced gas in the material (0·05 cm³ He at NTP/cm³ beryllium). In other specimens it has been observed that grain surfaces in unstressed parts contain gas bubbles 0·01–0·1 μm in size but grain surfaces in the gauge length contain spherical voids 0·1–1 μm in size. It is therefore inferred that some gas bubbles act as nucleation sites for large grain-surface cavities and fissures.

One further point about these discrete voids is that it is difficult to reconcile their random location over grain surfaces with the more regular arrangement of void sites which might be expected from nucleation on slip steps. In irradiated beryllium there is not so far any clear evidence that inclusions are necessary at the points where grain edge voids nucleate.

The growth of grain-surface voids and grain-edge fissures can be very rapid: about 1 h for the specimens in question, but about 10 min is sufficient at 700°C in some cases. The applied stress for the specimens (~9000 lb/in²) is, in fact, sufficiently large to counterbalance the surface tension forces of small voids (e.g. 0·1 μm dia.) but the presence of any helium gas in such voids would assist growth.

E (i)

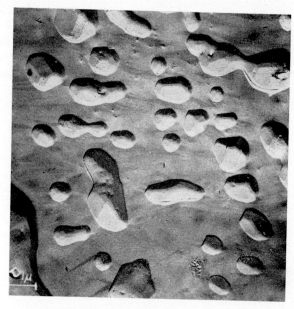

(i) discrete voids
× 7500

E (ii)

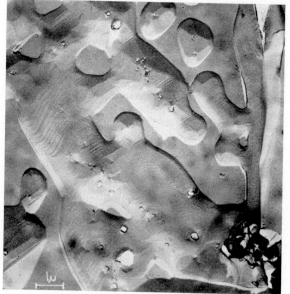

(ii) linked voids,
on grain
surfaces
exposed by
impact fracture
∼1 cm from
the region of
test failure
× 7500

80

E (iii)

(iii) closely-spaced
polyhedral
voids on the
hot-tensile
rupture
surface
× 2 000

E *Beryllium irradiated to* ∼2×10^{19} *nvt at* ≯300°C *and tested as for material of Fig.D*

The polyhedral voids on the grain surfaces are roughly equiaxed up to a few μm dia. and are seldom more than 1–2 μm deep. They then appear to grow by spreading sideways, without further increase in depth. The pronounced development of terrace contours inside the voids (and also in grain-edge fissures) is evidence that rapid surface migration is occurring. The observations thus seem entirely consistent with a growth mechanism involving rapid diffusion of atoms to the grain boundary. I think it is very interesting that the structures do seem so much in accord with the suggestions Professor Cottrell made in his paper.

There is one further point to be made, namely, that the total elongation of the specimen depends to some degree on what is happening in the region of actual rupture. It is a common observation that the incidence of fissuring or cavitation is more marked in this region.

In irradiated beryllium the grain-edge fissures are broader near the final rupture and spread more extensively over grain surfaces. An interesting structure was observed on the actual rupture surface of some specimens. Figure E(iii) shows a specimen irradiated and tested under the same conditions as before: the rupture surface shows very many closely spaced polyhedral voids having a wide range of size. It would be difficult to say at this stage that this indicates rapid nucleation of grain-surface voids in the final stages of failure of the specimen in this region, but it does serve to draw attention to the non-uniform nature of void development along the gauge-length of a tensile specimen.

Dr P. **Feltham** (Department of Metallurgy, The University, Leeds): In the formula for the time to rupture t_r derived by Hull and Rimmer, which Professor Cottrell discusses in his paper, one has

$$1/t_r \propto (\sigma/T) D$$

where σ is the applied stress, T the temperature, and D the coefficient of grain boundary self-diffusion. Now, extensive evidence shows that in pure metals, and often in alloys,

$$1/t_r \propto \dot{\epsilon},$$

where $\dot{\epsilon}$ is the steady creep rate. Several examples of this relation are cited by Davies and Wilshire in their paper in this symposium. If the theory of Hull and Rimmer were of general validity one should therefore expect to have:

$$\dot{\epsilon} \propto (\sigma/T)D$$

which gives a wrong dependence of the creep rate both on stress and on temperature. In pure metals the temperature dependence of the creep rate is generally determined by an activation energy equal to that of self-diffusion which, in silver, referred to by Hull and Rimmer, is about 46 kcal/g-atom, while that for grain boundary self-diffusion is only 20 kcal/g-atom. Their interpretation of the mechanism of void formation in creep is therefore unsatisfactory. While grain boundary diffusion may be an essential stage in void formation, e.g. facilitating vacancy transport in the boundary, the rate controlling mechanism is probably the flow of vacancies, formed by integranular slip, to heterogeneously nucleated pores. That nucleation should occur preferentially at grain boundaries is not surprising, because it will there be favoured by severe lattice distortions and relatively high concentrations of vacancies and impurities. The fact that cracks form mainly on boundaries which are nearly normal to the tensile axis of the creep specimen also suggests that owing to inhibition of stress relaxation by shearing a tensile stress criterion akin to that of Griffith may determine the strain, equal to $\dot{\epsilon}t_r$, at which fracture takes place.

Concerning the various mechanisms of void generation involving the formation of ledges, it appears that the theoretical cohesive strength would have to be overcome at the instant at which the ledges slide apart to open a hole, i.e. a small slit would have to form before the two surfaces could separate. In the light of present day knowledge of dislocation distributions in metals it seems unlikely that sufficiently high stresses could build up in grains during creep to allow this to take place. Thus, again, while separation of ledges may enlarge existing voids, and could thus play a part in the processes leading to creep fracture, it could neither give rise to holes nor determine the rate of development of fracture.

In connexion with the paper by McLean and Hale I want to raise two points, the first relating to the steady creep rate as expressed by their equations

$$\dot{\epsilon} = A(\sigma/G)^n \exp(-Q/RT) \quad . \quad . \quad . \quad . \quad . \quad (1)$$

and

$$\dot{\epsilon} = B \exp\left\{-[Q-(\beta\sigma/G)]/RT\right\} \quad . \quad . \quad . \quad (2)$$

I think it is quite clear from Fig.1 of their paper that equation (1) does not represent the creep data for metals, although they believe that it does, at least at lower stresses. Further, remembering that the curves are plotted in the rather insensitive double logarithmic representation, one can certainly not regard them as being reasonably superimposed. In fact if one looks at the curves for the face-centred cubic metals only one finds that the lowest one refers to aluminium, followed higher up by lead, γ-iron, nickel, copper, and 70–30 α-brass in the order given, i.e. the lower the stacking fault energy of the metal the higher does its curve lie in the diagram. I do not propose to discuss this very interesting feature at present, but I want to emphasize that this systematic arrangement of the curves provides further support for our belief that a facile superposition of creep curves in the manner attempted in Fig.1 of the paper is not possible.

The authors then discuss equation (2), and show that creep data refute its validity at low stresses, but that at high stresses the creep rate does appear to increase exponentially with stress. Now, it is clear *a priori* that equation (2) must fail at low stresses, for it predicts a finite strain rate at zero stress. It is well known, however, that equation (2) is an approximation, convenient for use at high stresses, to the rate-process equation

$$\dot{\epsilon} = 2B \exp(-Q/RT) \sinh(\beta\sigma/GRT) \qquad . \qquad . \qquad . \qquad (3)$$

in which β may depend upon the temperature. Already 18 years ago McVetty[3] showed that in a number of steels he studied, the effect of stress on the creep rate was represented much better by the 'sinh' law than by σ^n. Also, at low stresses the 'sinh' term can be approximated by power laws over comparatively wide ranges of the stress. The compilation of creep data shown in Figs.1 and 2 of the paper does not therefore provide support in favour of equation (1) and against equation (2), but rather the other way around. The work of Dorn, mentioned by McLean and Hale, may have lent some plausibility to the concept of a stress-independent activation energy in creep; later analyses of his experimental method[5, 6] have, however, led to the conclusion that his results do in fact support the view that the activation energy is stress-dependent.

Secondly, I want to say a few words about the creep mechanism proposed by McLean and Hale. I agree that in the steady stage of creep the mean dimensions of the substructure, e.g. the size of the network, remain almost constant as a result of a dynamic equilibrium in which the rates of disintegration and reconstitution of the network are approximately equal. However, I am not clear about the rate determining mechanism; it must either be the rate of climb or the rate of formation of breaks in the dislocation network. As in the model proposed by the authors, these two processes are interdependent the more difficult (slower) one must necessarily determine the creep rate. Now since, as mentioned, the activation energy of creep is frequently close to that of self-diffusion, it seems preferable to choose the climb mechanism, which could be associated with such an activation energy, rather than the formation of breaks; there appear to be no good reasons for assuming that the tearing of the dislocation mesh should be controlled by the activation energy of self-diffusion.

We are then faced with the question how the stress influences the climb of dislocations. The authors say that 'the stress will exert the usual directing effect on climb, which for normal stresses gives a term in σ outside the exponential equation (1)'. While it is not particularly difficult to devise dislocation models of creep leading to power laws of the type of equation (1), it is not clear to me how such a power law can be obtained with the model proposed by the authors. However, even if a plausible derivation were proposed, it would not be obvious how it could be reconciled with the non-linearity of the creep curves compiled in Fig.1 of their paper.

Mr T. A. Myers (Metallurgy Department, University of Leeds): I have performed creep experiments on face-centred cubic cobalt in the temperature range 450–600°C. Figure F shows (on the right hand side) a plot of log $\dot{\epsilon}$ against stress, which gives a straight line at any given temperature with a break in the isotherms at a characteristic stress σ_c'. This type of curve has been observed before,[7] and appears to be an inherent feature in the creep of face-centred cubic metals. The break is not due to the manner of representing the data.[7]

On the left of Fig.F, log $\dot{\epsilon}$ is plotted against log σ. It can be seen that cusp-shaped curves are obtained with the nodal points at the same stresses σ_c' as in

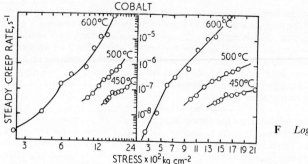

F *Log ė v. stress*

the previous representation. Similar curves have been obtained at Leeds, for example with 90–10 α–brass.[8] Thus it appears that a power law representation of the creep data is here inappropriate; in fact the data show an exponential dependence of the steady strain rate on the stress.

I should also like to comment on the suggestion by McLean and Hale concerning the observation that fine-grained metals creep faster than coarse-grained ones. Recent work at Leeds on a number of well annealed metals has shown that if creep occurs at stresses exceeding σ_c', then the steady strain rate increases with the square of the grain size,[7] while at stresses below σ_c' there is no observable grain-size effect. It appears that a fine-grained metal may creep faster or slower than a coarse-grained one; clearly it is necessary to examine grain-size effects in conjunction with changes in the intragranular structure.

Mr **F. J. Beer** (English Electric Co. Mechanical Working Laboratory): When ductile metal is subjected to cyclic straining beyond the elastic range, the relation between strain-range and number of cycles to failure is represented by the graph shown in Fig.*G*. The data on which this graph is based are the result of a number of experimental investigations carried out in the recent past in various research centres, and it is worth mentioning that the findings turned out to be very consistent and were remarkably little influenced by differences in mechanical properties, temperature, and speed of cycling.[9–13]

It can also be shown from the graph that plastic deformation is a near reversible process. At a strain range of, say, 1% it takes about 5000 cycles to failure. That means that the material can absorb, in cyclic deformation, a total of 5000% strain in tension as well as in compression, whilst in one-sided deformation it takes no more than about 25% to produce rupture. An inescapable conclusion is that, whatever it may be that happens inside the metal during plastic deformation, it must be a process reversible to a large degree. The change taking place during one stroke is nearly undone during the opposite stroke and only a small permanent change remains, which gradually builds up into damage.

With regard to plastic-strain fatigue data as a design basis for thermal stresses, when these data became known in the past few years, it looked as if, for many practical purposes, thermal stresses could be regarded as perfectly harmless. Even allowing for local concentrations, it is difficult to imagine thermal distortions of more than $\frac{1}{2}$%. As can be seen from Fig.*G*, this requires about 20 000 cycles to failure and there are many cases in practice where power, or other hot plant equipment, cannot possibly get hot and cold more than 1 000 times during its whole life.

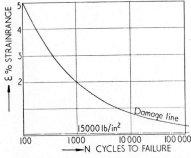

G *Strain range v. cycles to failure*

Practical designers had often complained that stress analysts tended to be over-cautious with regard to thermal stresses, and had claimed that theory was liable to show severe over-stress in arrangements which, in fact, had proved perfectly satisfactory in operation.[14] When comparing the damage line in the graph with the strain due to 15 000 lb/in², which is about the limit allowed for thermal stresses in many design standards, these complaints appeared more than justified.

It was a surprise when reports were recently published of practical experience with large steam turbines operating at high temperatures.[15] It was stated that the thermal strains imposed during start were up to 0·3%. According to Fig.G this should require over 100 000 cycles to failure. In fact, severe cracking was found after about 50 starts.

It was stated that the cracks were mostly intergranular and looked like creep failures, and also that practically all the damage had occurred at well over 600°F. Similar trends can be seen from recently published results of thermal shock tests carried out at the NGTE Farnborough.[16] Rapid destruction seemed to be associated with intergranular cracking and high temperature.

It seems, therefore, that under certain conditions, the reversible process in plastic deformation breaks down and is replaced by rapid destruction. High temperature, creep and intergranular cracking seem to play an important part in this phenomenon.[17]

In conclusion, this is then how we stand at present. There seem to be two kinds of mechanism occurring in plastic strain cycling, one leading slowly to destruction and one rapidly, and we cannot tell yet which to expect in a particular case.

At this stage, the mechanical engineer must appeal for help to metal physicists and metallurgists. When faced with the necessity of finding the right compromise between the opposite demands of safety and economy, one could hardly think of a more disconcerting situation than not to know whether a job is sound for 50 cycles or for 100 000.

Dr **A. F. Brown** (Solid State Physics Laboratory, Natural Philosophy Department, University of Edinburgh): Several of the papers we are discussing deal with the nucleation and growth of grain boundary voids. The conclusions in them are based on experiments mainly on polycrystals. For results on bicrystals we have to rely entirely on the elegant experiments of Intrater and Machlin.[18] Now Intrater and Machlin used grain boundaries having a very small area[19]; only 2–4 mm in the direction of sliding and about 3 mm deep. They did not section their specimens to see the interior but polished in from the surface. Even so, their published pictures[18] suggest that the voids appear first in the regions near the free surface.

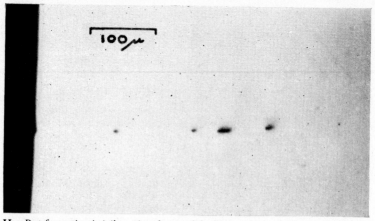

H *Dot formation in 'A' section, larger slide distance*

D. A. Blackburn in our laboratory has been carrying out grain boundary sliding experiments on perfect bicrystals of copper at temperatures of 500–800°C. The total slides of 25–70 μm are obtained in times of 1–3 weeks.[3] His bicrystals are more massive than were used in Intrater and Machlin's experiments, the boundary is >1 cm long in the direction of sliding and 3 mm thick. After sliding we section the specimen by means of a slitting wheel, either in a plane normal to the direction of sliding ('A'section') or on a plane which contains the direction of sliding ('B' section). The surfaces are then polished using diamond dust.

The observations we make are that when the slide distance is less than 20 μm we see no evidence of damage. With larger slide distances, the 'A' sections which expose a 3-mm length of grain boundary usually have their middle millimetre free of evidence of damage whilst the outer millimetres show small dots (Fig.*H*). These, we may for the moment, identify as 'voids'; another interpretation of their nature will be mentioned later. In the 'B' sections likewise, the voids are not usually found far from the steps which mark the surface. Figure *I* is a typical section of the 'B' type and shows a surface step corresponding to 70 μm of sliding. The damage along the boundary is heavy but extends inwards for only the distance shown, that is 500 μm.

Now on the analysis given by Professor Cottrell we must assume that nuclei for void damage are formed all along the boundary but that *in bicrystals at least* the presence of voids is determined by a process which involves diffusion from the free surface.

To prove this, it would be necessary to show that the depth of the chain of voids below the surface is proportional to the diffusion depth δ and not to the amount of slide. Now the grain boundary diffusion depth δ is not the quantity $\sqrt{Dt}$ which occurs in bulk diffusion, but may be conveniently identified with the quantity

$$\delta = \left(\frac{W}{2}\frac{D'}{D}\right)^{\frac{1}{2}}(\pi Dt)^{\frac{1}{4}}$$

where W=assumed width of grain boundary=2 atoms; D'=grain boundary diffusivity, which occurs in Fisher's theory and which plays the same part in grain boundary diffusion as $\sqrt{Dt}$ plays in bulk diffusion.

86

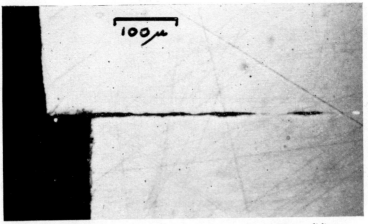

I   *Typical 'B' section showing surface step corresponding to 70 μm sliding*

Unfortunately, in our experiments which were carried out for a purpose[20] other than to observe voids we varied δ only between 100 and 200 μm and we did not slide many specimens to the extent required to produce voids. So at the risk of generalizing from three specimens (each examined in a large number of sections however) it appears that

    (i) the depth below the surface to which damage occurs, is several times δ and is greater in the specimens where δ is greater

    (ii) the amount of damage within this depth depends on the amount of deformation, varying from no visible damage when the slide is less than 20 μm to total disintegration of the boundary in one specimen where the slide reached 500 μm.

Thus in Fig.*I* the damage is severe but does not go deep whilst in Fig.*H* which corresponds to a larger value of δ (higher temperature and longer time of anneal) but less deformation, the damage goes in deeper but is less severe. These results should be treated with reserve since they are based on so few specimens. They seem worth reporting, however, since as Dr Harper says, experiments on bicrystal sliding are laborious and it may be some time before sufficient evidence accumulates to test them. Moreover, conclusions similar to the above seem to be consistent with the pictures of grain boundary damage published by Intrater and Machlin.[18]

I have two further admissions to make: first, in the experiments which produced Figs.*H* and *I* we were diffusing silver in at the same time as the grain boundary was sliding. The concentration of silver, however, nowhere exceeded 0·1% and it cannot have affected the results since we found similar voids in specimens deformed without silver diffusion. Secondly, it is possible that the damage shown in the figures is not voids at all but oxide particles. This suggestion is supported by the observation made by Intrater and Machlin that the appearance of the damage varied as between bicrystals deformed in vacuum and those deformed in a reducing atmosphere (hydrogen). If anything then, this suggestion supports our claim that the cause of the visible damage comes from the free surface.

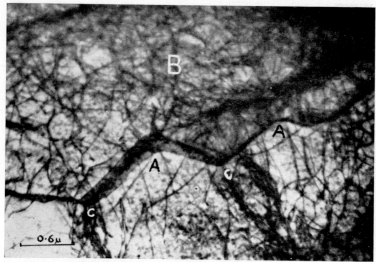

J   *Specimen deformed 15%; The large-angle grain boundary is migrating into the high dislocation density areas of grain B. Migration is held up where the cell walls intersect the grain boundary at C*

To conclude, our results refer only to bicrystals. In grain boundaries far from a free surface in a polycrystalline aggregate, the source of the voids, if they are voids, might be the vacant spaces which arise at grain corners during creep.

Dr J. Glen (Colvilles Ltd): Regarding the practical problem of intercrystalline failure, there is no cause for concern provided the material fails with a high elongation. Professor Cottrell has given us an important and timely survey of the subject but does he not think that more emphasis should be given to low elongation failures? Personally I believe that such failures are fundamentally different because they result from some factor other than the four listed in the conclusions of Professor Cottrell's paper.

I am very much intrigued by Fig.14 in the paper by McLean and Hale. Is there any evidence that a dislocation can push a tiny particle ahead of itself? The right-hand side of the diagram is of more practical importance. This suggests that with increased particle spacing the creep rate also increases. If a Mo–V type steel is tempered for times varying from 5 to 1000 h at 690°C it can be assumed that particle spacing increases with increased time of tempering. If creep tests are carried out at say 6 tons/in² and 600°C the results would agree with the diagram. However, as was shown both by the late Dr R. W. Bailey and myself, the opposite effect is obtained on testing at a lower stress namely, the creep rate decreased with increasing time of tempering. This example serves to emphasize how difficult it is to choose a simple criterion of creep resistance which can be used to elucidate the more theoretical aspects of this subject.

WRITTEN CONTRIBUTION

Dr J. E. Harris and **Dr P. G. Partridge** (CEGB, Berkeley Nuclear Laboratories) wrote: In 1950 Beck and Sperry[21] observed a non-uniform form of grain-boundary migration during the annealing of cold-worked aluminium. This 'strain-induced

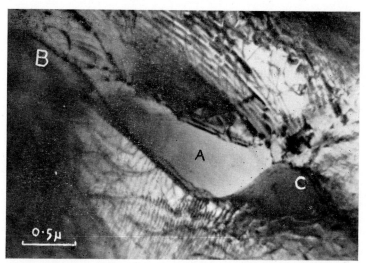

K *Specimen deformed 20%; a low dislocation density region A beside the migrating grain boundary B–C*

boundary migration' is unlike normal secondary recrystallization since it results in an increase in grain-boundary area. The driving force in this case must be the difference in stored energy between the neighbouring grains. In his model for the process Beck[22] suggested that where a grain with a large cell size is adjacent to another grain having a smaller cell size, the common grain boundary would migrate into the latter grain. The migration would be irregular due to parts of the grain boundary being 'pinned' at its intersection with the walls of the larger cells.

The purpose of this note is to demonstrate that the irregular grain boundaries developed during the creep-deformation of polycrystalline magnesium[23] is a result of this strain-induced grain boundary migration. Annealed sheet specimens of a Mg–0·7%Al–0·005%Be alloy (Magnox) have been deformed to varying extents at a tensile strain-rate of 2%/h in an oil bath maintained at 230°C. The specimens were 0·01 in. thick and the average grain diameter was 0·006 in. In the as-annealed condition the grains were equiaxed and the grain boundaries were smooth and regular.

An electron transmission photograph of a deformed specimen is shown in Fig.*J*. The large-angle grain boundary separates regions of high and low dislocation density, for example at the positions marked 'A'. In these regions the grain boundary is migrating into the high dislocation density areas of grain 'B'. However, where the cell walls meet the boundary at the positions marked 'C', migration is either slower, non-existent or in an opposite sense.

In Fig.*K* is shown a very low dislocation density region (A) beside the original migrating grain boundary B–C. The enlarging of such low dislocation density areas due to further grain boundary migraiion could eventually result in the formation of new grains in the manner recently suggested by Bailey.[24] It is in fact found that at later stages in the creep process a network of new grains form along the original grain boundaries and similar structures have been reported by Stacey.[25]

The irregular grain boundaries cannot slide past each other in any simple manner during subsequent creep deformation. It is known that the irregularities are associated with a localized cell structure,[15] and it is probable that the shearing forces in the region of the grain boundary are accommodated by increasing the degree of misorientation across the cell walls. Thus, in this case, it is possible that both irregular grain boundary migration and preferred growth of heavily tilted cells are operative during the early stages of recrystallization.

AUTHORS' WRITTEN REPLIES

Professor Cottrell wrote: I am grateful to Mr Eborall for his valuable remarks. He is of course quite right to emphasize that the stress state at a jog in a sliding interface is not exactly the same as that envisaged by Griffith, Starr, and Stroh. I think the point is, as Mr Eborall has recognized, that unless there is some special weakness in the boundary, such as a non-wetting substance, the stresses concentrated at a jog or anywhere else are likely to be dispersed by shear processes before they become strong enough to break the boundary. I agree that much still remains to be understood about the nucleation of cavities but am encouraged by Dr Hyam's beautiful photographs to think that we may now have an experimental technique capable of solving this problem.

In reply to Dr Feltham's discussion, Hull and Rimmer stated quite clearly in their paper that the inverse dependence of the rupture time on stress is valid only for the hydrostatic component of a combined stress state; and that for the deviatoric component the relation is quite different. Dr Feltham's criticism is therefore, I believe, based on a misconception.

In reply to Dr Glen's remarks it is not clear to me that the factors mentioned in my paper cannot explain the low-elongation fractures. For example, if the spacing of cavities on a grain boundary is, say, one-hundredth of the grain diameter, then the rupture elongation could be as small as 1%. It would be very interesting to know of experimental evidence which Dr Glen may have to show that other factors are at work in brittle creep fractures.

Dr McLean and **Dr Hale** wrote: We cannot reply to Mr Eborall from experimental evidence as we have not yet examined the structure after creep in metals other than iron. It is perhaps worth mentioning, however, that an experimental plot for silver[26] like Fig.11 of our paper (stress v. $\sqrt{\rho}$, where ρ is the dislocation density), determined for room temperature deformation, gives much the same slope as in Fig.11, as do two determinations for room-temperature deformation using iron of different purities.[27, 28] These results tend to generalize the relation expressed by Fig.11 and suggest that similar three-dimensional dislocation networks to those described in the paper will be found in other simple metals.

Dr Feltham raised several points. Our replies are as follows:

(1) we still think that Fig.1 demonstrates that eqn (1) expresses creep data quite well, provided the stress is fairly small, as the plot in Fig.1 gives straight lines in its left hand half and this is what eqn (1) requires;

(2) we fully agree that our eqn (2) is an approximation to a sinh law but think it is a good enough approximation. However, before explaining this we should point out an error in eqn (2) and Fig.2 of our paper. In both these it does not correspond to the assumed situation to 'normalize' the stress by dividing by the elastic modulus. The stress appears in eqn (2) because it is assumed to do work during the thermal activation represented by Q. This work is a direct function of the stress, not of stress $\div$ modulus, and it is more sensible to write instead of eqn (2)

$$\dot{\epsilon} = Be^{\frac{Q - \beta\sigma}{kT}} \qquad . \qquad . \qquad . \qquad . \qquad . \qquad (2a)$$

90

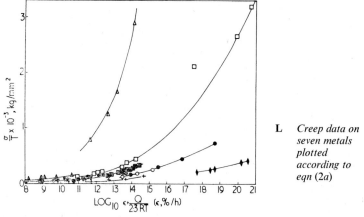

L *Creep data on seven metals plotted according to eqn (2a)*

The plot corresponding to eqn (2a) is reproduced in Fig.L, and of course bears out the points made in connexion with Fig.2 in the paper.

Returning now to Dr Feltham's discussion, the key question is the size of the factor β. The full sinh expression is only necessary if $\beta\sigma \sim kT$. When $\beta\sigma/kT \gg 1$, the sinh law is well approximated by eqn (2a); when $\beta\sigma/kT \ll 1$, sinh $\beta\sigma/kT = \beta\sigma/kT$. These two conditions seem to be the only ones the experimental observations allow one to entertain, and even the first of these is not compatible with all the experimental observations. Thus, the second condition applies if the applied tensile or compressive stress assists climb of an edge dislocation directly. β is then equivalent to b^3, where b is the atomic spacing (assumed equal to the Burgers vector), and $\beta\sigma/kT \sim 10^{-2}$ (assuming $b = 2\cdot5 \times 10^{-8}$ cm, $\sigma = 10$ dyn/cm^2, $T = 800°K$). We believe that this is the kind of situation that obtains in practice hence the passage on p.30 which Dr Feltham quotes. To get away from this condition β must include a stress concentration factor and difficulties arise when feasible stress concentrations are considered. One source of stress concentration considered by Mott[29] and Weertman[30] is a pile-up of dislocations. Mott rejected this source on the grounds that experimental observation of slip bands formed during creep could not be reconciled with the idea; our electron microscope examination supports his view since it has not revealed any piled up groups. Another source of stress concentration, and it seems to be the only source compatible with the three dimensional network observed in our work, is that the stress acting on a long length of dislocation assists climb of a short length. This makes $\beta\sigma \gg kT$. For, given the dislocation pattern observed there seems no alternative except to believe that this long length equals x, the mean spacing of the network, because there is no smaller natural length to be seen. β then becomes xb^2. As $x \sim 10^3b$ or greater, $\sigma xb^2/kT \sim 10$ or more, and eqn (2a) is then a good approximation to the sinh law. However, there is a strong reason for also rejecting this source of stress concentration as an important factor. Since $x = 0\cdot4$ Gb/τ (from eqn (4) of the paper; τ is the shear stress), $\sigma xb^2/kT \sim Gb^3/kT$. This expression is independent of stress, so that the activation energy is reduced in the presence of a stress by a constant amount, and one cannot explain the influence of stress on creep rate through an influence on activation energy. The difficulty about accepting Dr Feltham's argument concerning the sinh law will now be clear. It required that β should incorporate a stress concentration factor and this cannot easily be reconciled with experimental observation. Even if it could, β has to lie in a particular range which it is difficult to account for.

91

(3) In our model, breaks in the network are made by climb, which therefore is the rate controlling process.

Mr Myers' remarks about the effect of grain size are interesting. Grain size seems to be as complex a quantity as hardness.

In reply to Professor Nutting, the way a dislocation is supposed to push a particle through the metal is closely analogous to the way a wire drawn through treacle would move ball bearings contained therein. It might clarify matters to explain briefly how the calculation of the speed of this process was made. In a metal under stress, dislocations exert a pressure on any particle they encounter. As a consequence, there is a deficiency of vacancies in the vicinity of the forward side of the particle and an excess in the vicinity of the rearward side. It is assumed that there is no atomic interchange between the particle and matrix, which amounts to assuming relatively strong atomic bond in the particle. Vacancies therefore flow round the particle from the rearward side to the forward side and the particle moves forward to close up the gap.

REFERENCES

1. 'Symposium on the metallurgy of beryllium', 1961, Oct., Institute of Metals and Chapman and Hall, to be published.
2. V. W. ELDRED et al.: Proc. 2nd UN Int. Conf. on peaceful uses of atomic energy, Geneva 1958, 5, 510.
3. P. G. McVETTY: Trans. ASME., 1943, 65, 761.
4. P. FELTHAM: Brit. J. Appl. Phys., 1955, 6, 26.
5. Z. S. BASINSKI: Acta. Met., 1957, 5, 684.
6. P. FELTHAM and J. D. MEAKIN: ibid., 1959, 7, 614.
7. P. FELTHAM and G. J. COPLEY: Phil. Mag., 1960, 5, 649.
8. G. J. COPLEY: Ph.D. Thesis. Leeds University, 1959.
9. P. P. BENHAM: Met. Rev., 1958, 3, 203–237.
10. L. F. COFFIN: Trans. ASME, 1954, 76, 931–950.
11. J. F. TAVERNELLI and L. F. COFFIN: Trans. ASM, 1959, 51, 438.
12. A. JOHANNSON: Proc. Colloquium on fatigue, Int. Union theoretical and applied mech., Stockholm, Sweden, 1955, May, 112–122.
13. A. C. LOW: Proc. Int. Conf. fatigue in metals, 1956, London, 206.
14. F. J. BEER in discussion: Proc. Inst. Mech. Eng., 1952–53, 18, (10).
15. S. B. COULTER and R. L. JACKSON: Trans. ASME 1960, 82A, 227–238.
16. E. GLENNY et al.: J. Inst. Metals, 1959–60, 88, 449–461, 2010.
17. F. J. BEER, in discussion, ibid., 1960–61, 89, 436.
18. J. INTRATER and E. S. MACHLIN: Acta Met., 1959, 7, 140.
19. J. INTRATER and E. S. MACHLIN: J. Inst. Metals, 1959–60, 88, 305–310.
20. D. A. BLACKBURN and A. F. BROWN: 'The use of radioisotopes in the physical sciences and industry', The International Atomic Energy Agency, Vienna, 1961.
21. P. A. BECK and P. R. SPERRY: J. Appl. Phys., 1950, 21, 150.
22. P. A. BECK: Advances in Physics, 1954, 3, 245.
23. J. W. SUITER and W. A. WOOD: J. Inst. Metals, 1952–53, 81, 181–184.
24. J. E. BAILEY: Phil. Mag., 1960, 5, 833.
25. R. D. STACEY: Metallurgia, 1958, 58, 125.
26. J. E. BAILEY and P. B. HIRSCH: Phil. Mag., 1960, 5, 485.
27. W. CARRINGTON et al.: Proc. Roy. Soc., 1960, A 259, 203.
28. A. S. KEH: Private communication.
29. N. F. MOTT: 'Creep and fracture of metals', 21; 1955, London, HMSO.
30. J. WEERTMAN: Appl. Phys., 1957, 28, 362.

A study of the alloying behaviour of an austenitic base containing 20%Ni, 20%Cr, and 20%Co

H. C. Child

The alloying behaviour of an austenitic base containing 20%Ni, 20%Co, 20%Cr, *with the remainder iron, has been studied in both the solution treated and the aged conditions. Alloy additions have included* Mo, W, Nb, Ti, V, Al, Be, Cu, C, B, *and* N. *Where an element is known to form a carbide its alloying effect has also been determined in the same base but with* 0·45% *carbon also present. The lattice parameter, the proof stress at* 650°C, *and the rupture strength at various temperatures have been evaluated in both heat treated conditions.*

INTRODUCTION

MUCH OF the impressive research and development of high temperature austenitic alloys that has been carried out in recent years has been concerned with a detailed study of a single alloy or close chemical variations of it. A notable exception to this is the work of Nisbet and Hibbard[1] who studied the properties of several Ni–Co–Cr–Fe bases with additions of the commonly used alloying elements. These workers studied cast alloys and interpreted their creep results using the Larson and Miller[2] techniques. They found that where an 'incongruous' element such as Mo was in excess of the solubility limit a range of values for the Larson and Miller parameter was obtained and they deduced the solubility limit from the change from single value of the parameter to a range of values. As a result of their studies they were able to rationalize many features of the alloying behaviour of cast austenitic (face-centred cubic) alloys.

Earlier work by the authors[3] had studied the alloying behaviour of a wrought austenitic base containing 20%Ni, 20%Co, 20%Cr, and 0·5%C, with particular reference to creep/rupture strength. It was apparent from this work that the alloying behaviour of the various strengthening elements studied would be very different in

The author is research manager of Jessop-Saville Ltd.

the absence of carbon and the aim of the present study was, therefore, to investigate the effect of various alloying additions to the same base, both with and without carbon, and to determine various physical and mechanical properties.

In the earlier work, the study had been confined to the creep and rupture properties over the relatively narrow temperature range 750–800°C. The properties studied in this instance included rupture strength over the temperature range 650–950°C, the proof strength at 650°C, and the lattice parameter. All these properties have been studied both in the aged and unaged conditions so that as far as possible the mechanism of the alloying effect could be explained.

SCOPE OF THE INVESTIGATION

The base selected for study, 20%Ni, 20%Co, 20%Cr, remainder iron, represents a typical high alloy austenite, which has been the basis of much research by earlier workers, such as Cross and Simmons.[4] For convenience, the investigation has been divided into two parts.

PART 1

The first part is a study of the alloying behaviour of the following elements, Mo, W, Nb, Ti, V, Al, Be, Cu, C, B, and N, when added to the above base.

The bulk of the alloys were air melted and the base contained 0.8%Mn and 0.3%Si as well as the elements noted. Some of the alloys studied at a later date were vacuum-melted and have nitrogen contents between 0.001 and 0.005% compared with an average value of 0.05% for those air melted. The vacuum melts include the series containing Al, Be, Cu, B, and one specific titanium-containing alloy.

A solution treatment temperature of 1280°C was chosen, as experience indicated that this temperature results in effective solution of most of the excess phases without causing burning. A 10-min soak was used and the alloys were then oil quenched.

All the alloys were tested in this condition and also after ageing at 750°C. At this temperature it was found that the ageing reaction was often virtually completed in 100 h and many of the alloys were tested with this ageing treatment. It was apparent from some of the lattice parameter measurements that equilibrium was certainly not attained in this time. Indeed the value of the lattice parameter measurements is twofold; first, they indicate the degree of lattice strain which can be achieved by quenching the alloys to a super-saturated state, and second they show to what extent precipitation occurs in moderate times at 750°C. In some instances the solubility limit and the degree of equilibrium attained can be assessed.

In many cases the precipitation reaction at 750°C was also studied by means of electrical resistivity measurements. An electrolytic extract from most of the alloys was examined by X-ray analysis, and the phases present in the solution-treated and the aged condition determined. The proof strength at 650°C and the rupture strengths at 650° and 750°C were evaluated both in the aged and unaged condition. At 950°C, where ageing effects were unlikely to be of major importance, the rupture strength was evaluated in the solution-treated condition only.

PART 2

Where the alloying additions investigated in Part 1 were known to be capable of forming carbides, i.e., Mo, W, Nb, V, Ti, and B the work of Part 1 was also carried out on a base containing 0·45%C. Also included in this section of the paper is a comparison of the alloying behaviour of these various elements with and without carbon.

EXPERIMENTAL TECHNIQUES
Material preparation
The alloys were melted in either a 20-lb spark gap furnace or a 20-lb vacuum induction furnace. In both cases $2\frac{1}{2}$in ingots were cast and hammer cogged to $\frac{1}{2}$in square bar.

Lattice parameters
The specimens for lattice parameter determination were lightly ground to remove the scale and then the cold worked layer removed by electrolytic etching in 50% HCl for 20 min using a current density of 3A/cm². A back reflection technique similar to that used by Sachs and Weerts[5] was used.

Electrolytic extraction
Electrolytic extractions were carried out using 5% (by weight) aqueous HCl electrolyte, a platinum cathode, and a current density of 0·05 A/cm². The extract was identified by the X-ray powder technique.

Electric resistivity
The change in electrical resistivity with time at various ageing temperatures was determined potentiometrically with the specimen lagged in asbestos in a tubular furnace, and kept at the ageing temperature by means of a Prosser-type controller.

95

Rupture testing

The creep/rupture tests were carried out in 15-cwt tensile units. As far as possible one test at a fixed stress and temperature was carried out to compare the creep strength of the alloys with a minimum of testing time. This proved practical for all the alloys at 10 tons/in², at 750°C and for most of the alloys at 15 tons/in², at 650°C. Certain of the very strong alloys, however, had to be tested at 20 tons/in² or 25 tons/in², at 650°C and the rupture duration at 15 tons/in², estimated. In the case of the tests at 950°C, it proved easier to determine the 100-h rupture strength by carrying out several tests at different stresses as the alloys covered a wide range of strengths.

Proof strength and creep tests

These tests were carried out in cantilever creep units.[6] The 1% proof strength was evaluated at 650°C for all the alloys and for many of the series this varied so greatly with composition that creep tests at one stress and temperature were impractical. Where such tests were feasible, they have been carried out at 18 tons/in², at 650°C.

PART 1 LOW-CARBON ALLOYS

For brevity, the experimental results are given in detail only for the Mo series and summarized in the other cases unless the results are considered to be of particular interest.

EXPERIMENTAL RESULTS
Molybdenum alloys

The effect of 0–15% Mo on the standard base containing 20%Ni, 20%Co, 20%Cr, 0·04%C, 1%Mn, 0·3%Si has been studied. Those alloys containing up to 12%Mo forged successfully, but the alloy containing 15%Mo proved unforgeable.

The change of electrical resistivity at 750°C with time was studied for most of the alloys of the series. A typical curve for the 9%Mo

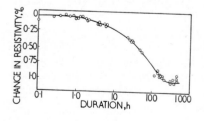

1 *Typical graph showing change of electrical resistivity with time at 750°C for a 9·1%Mo alloy*

alloy is shown in Fig.1, and the estimated time to reach minimum electrical resistance for the series is noted below:

Mo,%	Time, h
0	100
1·7	100
4·1	160
6·1	300
7·7	300
9·1	300

The progressive drop in resistance is due to the depletion of the matrix in alloying elements and the time taken to reach minimum resistance is a measure of the time taken to fully age the alloy. It has been shown by the authors that the time taken to reach hardness maxima on ageing is comparable to that required to reach minimum resistivity for austenitic alloys[3] of this type.

The lattice parameter (Fig.2) of the solution-treated material increased progressively with Mo content, but there was evidence of an excess molybdenum phase in the microstructure of the alloys containing more than 8%Mo. Ageing the alloys resulted in a reduction in lattice parameter at all molybdenum levels. In the alloy containing no molybdenum, this may be attributed to the removal of carbon from solution by the precipitation of $M_{23}C_6$ type carbide.

The solubility of Mo at 750°C would appear to be about 5% from the lattice parameter measurements but it is interesting to note that the 6%Mo alloy did not change its parameter appreciably on ageing. This effect has been observed on several of the series studied in that while heavily supersaturated alloys age markedly those which are only slightly supersaturated are very sluggish in their behaviour.

It is quite likely that the solubility of Mo is considerably less than 6% and that the picture presented by Fig.2 is due to failure to attain equilibrium at the comparatively low temperature of 750°C.

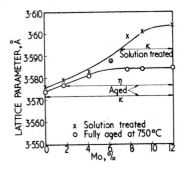

2 *Effect of molybdenum on the lattice parameter*

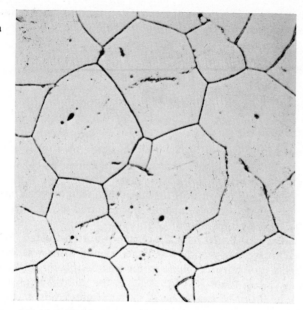

a
a Base alloy, OQ 1 280°C, aged 100 h at 750°C; DPN 169   ×500

3 (*a – k*) *Some typical alloys*

Even the $1 \cdot 7 \%$ Mo alloy in the aged condition shows marked grain boundary precipitation (Fig.3*b*) compared with the base alloy (Fig.3*a*). This grain boundary phase has not been positively identified and could be carbide. Electrolytic extraction and X-ray analysis revealed the presence of Fe_4Mo_2C in all the aged samples but no other phase could be identified, yet the presence of an intermetallic phase cannot be ruled out. At these very low carbon contents a molybdenum intermetallic phase would be expected at the higher Mo levels and the microstructure of the higher $\%$ Mo alloys in the aged condition contains large amounts of second phase in finely dispersed form. The microstructure of the 12% Mo alloy is shown in Fig.3*c*. The work of Guard and Prater[7] suggests that this is similar to their epsilon phase $(Fe,Co)_7(Mo,W)_6$. Some massive particles of this phase can also be seen in Fig.3*c* and, as said earlier, these are present in the solution-treated condition in alloys containing more than 8% Mo.

In the quenched condition, Mo causes only slight improvement in the 1% proof strength at 650°C (Fig.4*a*) but after ageing at 750°C, marked improvement occurs particularly above 6% Mo. The 12%

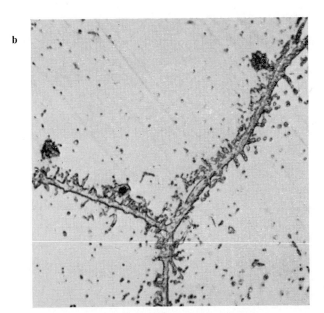

b   1·7%Mo, OQ 1 280°C, aged 100 h at 750°C; DPN 147   × *1 000*

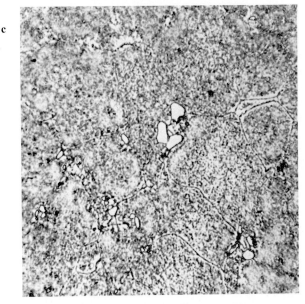

c   12%Mo, OQ 1 280°C, aged 100 h at 750°C; DPN 262–315   ×*500*

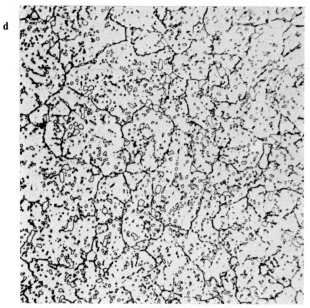

d 20%W, OQ 1280°C, aged 100 h at 750°C; DPN 291   *× 500*

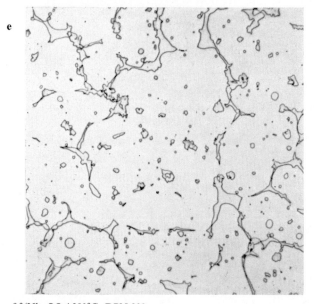

e 8%Nb, OQ 1280°C; DPN 232   *× 500*

f

8 %Nb, OQ 1280°C, aged 100 h at 750°C; DPN 285   × *500*

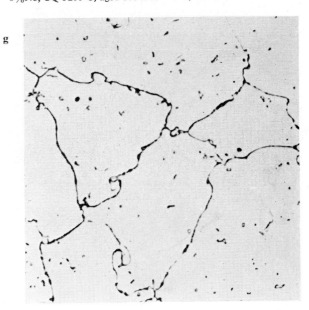

g

g 3 %Ti, OQ 1280°C, aged 100 h at 750°C; DPN 337–368   × *500*

h

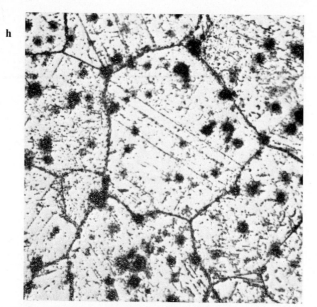

h 9%V, OQ 1280°C, aged 100 h at 750°C; DPN 218   ×*500*

i

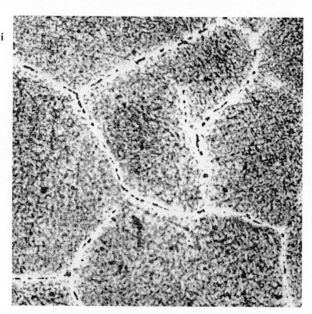

i 4%Al, OQ 1280°C, aged 100 h at 750°C; DPN 320   ×*500*

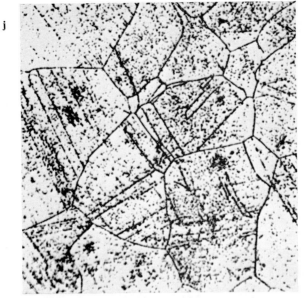

j

0·5 %Be, OQ 1280°C, aged 100 h at 750°C; DPN 229–263   ×500

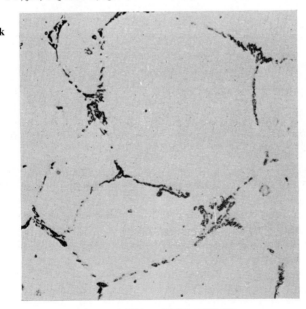

k

k 0·2 %B, OQ 1280°C, aged 100 h at 750°C; DPN 187   ×500

103

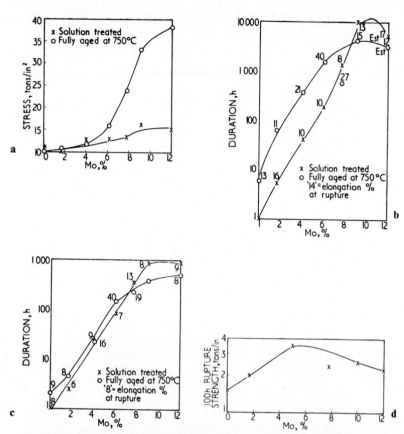

4 *Effect of molybdenum on (a) 1% proof strength at 650°C   (b) rupture life and ductility when tested at 15 tons/in² at 650°C   (c) rupture life and ductility when tested at 10 tons/in² at 750°C   (d) 100 h rupture strength at 950°C*

alloy has a proof strength of 38 tons/in², aged compared with 15 tons/in², unaged, indicating the magnitude of the precipitation hardening effect.

The rupture strength at 650°C (Fig.4*b*) in both heat-treated conditions is at a maximum at about 10%Mo and below this content of Mo, ageing has a beneficial effect. All the alloys are ductile. At 750°C (Fig.4*c*) the rupture strength maximum is at about 12%Mo and ageing has very little effect.

At 950°C (Fig.4*d*) the rupture strength of solution treated material is at a maximum at about 5%Mo. This content was estimated to be the effective solubility limit from the lattice parameter

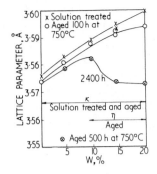

5 *Effect of tungsten on the lattice parameter*

measurements and it is interesting to note that the rupture strength maximum occurs at this Mo content at the very high test temperature of 950°C when ageing effects might be expected to be at a minimum.

Tungsten alloys

Alloys containing up to 20%W were successfully forged. The electrical resistivity studies at 750°C showed that up to 9·1%W, the precipitation reaction was completed in 100 h, but the 14·4%W alloy took approximately 2 000 h to reach minimum resistivity.

The lattice parameter measurements (Fig.5) indicated that all the alloys could be readily supersaturated by oil quenching from 1 280°C. Precipitation in 100 h at 750°C was slight at all W levels but particularly so below 9%. The higher W alloys did show evidence of marked precipitation with ageing times of 500 h and more and the value of lattice parameter found for these high W alloys after these long ageing times suggested a very low true solubility of W.

No intermetallic phase could be identified in any of the alloys aged at 750°C although $(FeW)_6C$ was found in the higher W alloys. After ageing for 100 h at 950°C, the phase Fe_3W was found in the electrolytic extracts.

The microstructure of the 20%W alloys in the aged condition (Fig.3d) shows a considerable amount of relatively massive excess phase, probably Fe_4W_2C present even after solution treatment and little evidence of finely dispersed precipitant. The proof strength at 650°C is raised progressively to 25 tons/in² by W additions up to 20%, but ageing for 100 h causes only a slight improvement, (3 tons/in²) at the higher W levels. The 14·4%W alloy has also been aged for 2 400 h and there is a marked improvement in proof strength, from 17 tons/in² solution-treated to 32 tons/in². The extreme sluggishness of the precipitation-hardening reaction is again in evidence.

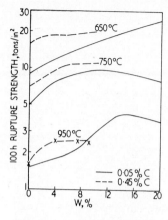

6 *Comparison of the effect o, tungsten on the rupture strength of solution-treated alloys with or without carbon addition*

The rupture strength (Fig.6) at 650°C increases progressively up to 20%W and at all W levels ageing for 100 h results in a moderate increase in rupture strength. At 750°C the alloys behave in a similar fashion.

The 100-h rupture strength of solution-treated material at 950°C reaches a maximum of 4·2 tons/in² at about 16%W. The excellent strength of this alloy compared with the best Mo alloy (3·5 tons/in²) may be attributed to marked reluctance of supersaturated W alloys to precipitate.

Niobium alloys

Additions up to 10%Nb have been studied and up to 8%Nb the alloys were forgeable.

Resistivity studies at 750°C indicated that ageing was substantially completed after 100 h, and all the alloys were aged accordingly. Lattice parameter measurements (Fig.7) show that whilst this ageing time is sufficient to produce equilibrium at 750°C in the 6% and 8%Nb alloy, the 3·2% alloy remains supersaturated after this treatment. A phase with a similar structure to eta carbide but believed

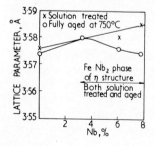

7 *Effect of niobium on the lattice parameter*

to be a form of Fe_2Nb_3 was found in electrolytic extracts of all the series, including the 3·2%Nb alloy, in both the solution-treated and the aged condition. The solubility limit must, therefore, be less than 3·2%. Quenching from 1 280°C again results in a supersaturated lattice but the maximum observed lattice strain is less than for the Mo and W series.

The microstructure of the 8%No alloy in both the solution-treated and the aged condition is shown in Fig.3e and f respectively. There is a considerable quantity of the excess phase Fe_2Nb_3 at the grain boundaries and dispersed through the grains in massive form in the solution-treated sample. After ageing the matrix contains much finely dispersed precipitate.

The 650°C proof strength is at a maximum of 25 tons/in at 7% niobium but ageing results in only a small improvement. The rupture strength (Fig.8) at 650°C is at an optimum at 6% Nb in the solution-treated condition, and ageing causes slight improvement up to 4%Nb and then has a disadvantageous effect. At 750°C the optimum strength occurs at approximately 4%Nb and ageing is disadvantageous at all levels. The high ductility (10–40%) of all the alloys is noteworthy. At 950°C niobium improves the rupture strength but there is little change in strength between 3% and 8%Nb.

Ageing is comparatively rapid compared with the Mo and W systems and ageing before testing has only a moderate strengthening effect on the proof strength at 650°C and the rupture strength at 650°C of the lower Nb alloys. For the other conditions studied, prior ageing is disadvantageous and at 950°C the effect above 3% is negligible, indicative of rapid overageing, at this temperature.

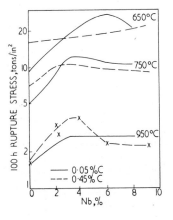

8 *Comparison of the effect of niobium on the rupture strength of solution-treated alloys with and without carbon addition*

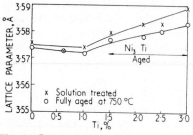

9 *Effect of titanium on the lattice parameter*

Titanium alloys

Alloys containing up to 3% Ti have been successfully forged. In the case of the 3%Ti alloy a duplicate vacuum melt has been tested.

Resistivity measurements indicated that 100 h at 750°C was adequate to fully age the alloys, and this was confirmed by lattice parameter measurements (Fig.9) which were the same after 500 h as at 100 h for the 1·5% and the 2·5%Ti alloy. Below 1%Ti had little effect on the lattice parameter in the solution treated and aged condition. Above this content there was a progressive increase in the parameter for both conditions. This is attributed, at least partly, to the scavenging effect of Ti, and the formation of titanium dioxide, and titanium cyanonitrides, nullifying solid-solution hardening by small additions.

The lattice parameter decreased on ageing to some extent at all

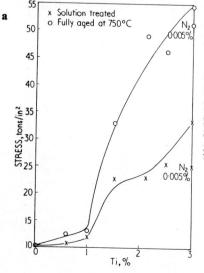

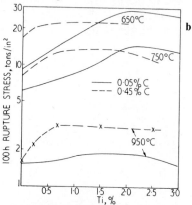

10 *(a) Effect of titanium on the 1% proof stress at 650°C (b) Comparison of the effect of titanium on the rupture strength of solution-treated alloys with or without carbon addition*

titanium levels. At the lower levels this may be attributed to the precipitation of $Cr_{23}C_6$ type carbide but an intermetallic phase, Ni_3Ti, was found in the extracts of the aged alloys containing more than $1.5\%Ti$. The progressive increase of the parameter in the aged condition is indicative of sluggish precipitation as equilibrium is not attained. Extracts of the $3\%Ti$ alloy contained the Ni_3Ti type phase even in the solution treated condition although the microstructure of this alloy, even in the aged condition (Fig.3g) showed only slight evidence of this phase. Titanium carbide was identified in all the alloys in small amounts.

The 650°C proof strength (Fig.10a) is raised progressively by Ti in both heat-treated conditions, but ageing causes a pronounced increase above $1\%Ti$.

The very high proof stress (33 tons/in²) of the solution-treated $3\%Ti$ alloy is indicative of pronounced solid-solution hardening, and the solution-treated proof strength can be increased to 55 tons/in² by ageing, illustrating the potency of this process also. The vacuum-melted alloy behaved similarly to the air-melted alloy.

The rupture strength at 650°C (Fig.10b) increases with Ti content up to about 2.2% in the solution-treated condition. Ageing the alloys is detrimental at all Ti levels. A noteworthy feature is the low ductility ($1-2\%$) at rupture of the higher Ti alloys particularly in the aged condition. At 750°C the rupture strength of solution-treated material is again at an optimum at about 2.2% and ageing is detrimental. The vacuum-melted alloy was very similar to the air-melted equivalent. At 950°C the rupture strength is only very slightly improved by Ti, there being a peak at $2\%Ti$.

Vanadium alloys

Vanadium additions of up to 10% have been investigated and all the alloys forged successfully.

Vanadium is known to have a catastrophic effect on the high-temperature scale resistance of alloys of this type and for this reason electrical resistivity studies at 750°C in air proved impractical. The ageing process was studied, therefore, by determining the change of lattice parameters with time at 750°C and ageing was found to be substantially completed after 30 h.

Vanadium causes pronounced expansion of the lattice (Fig.11) but none of the alloys showed much change on ageing. Apart from kappa carbide, $Cr_{23}C_6$, no phases were identified in the electrolytic extracts. The microstructure of the 9% V alloy in the aged condition (Fig.3h) shows evidence, however, of more marked precipitation than could be due to kappa carbide. The proof strength at 650°C

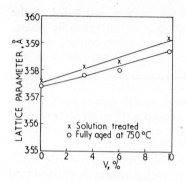

11 *Effect of vanadium on the lattice parameter*

increases moderately to 17½ tons/in² with V content, and there is a further slight increase on ageing.

The rupture strength (Fig.12) at both 650°C and 750°C is at an optimum at about 3%V, and ageing has a slightly detrimental effect. The occurrence of this maximum in creep strength indicates an effective solubility of about 3%. As there was no evidence of such a solubility limit from the lattice parameter or proof strength measurements, it is questionable whether the ageing period of 30 h was indeed adequate.

No tests were carried out at 950°C, owing to the severe scaling which occurs with alloys of this type at such a high temperature.

Aluminium alloys

Alloys containing up to 6%Al were vacuum melted, but only those with up to 4%Al forged successfully. Lattice parameters measurement in the solution-treated condition and after ageing for 100 and 500 h at 750°C (Fig.13) indicate that the alloys are fully aged after 100 h and the solubility of Al is less than 1%. Supersaturation is

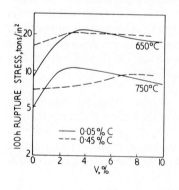

12 *Comparison of the effect of vanadium on the rupture strength of solution-treated alloys with or without carbon additions*

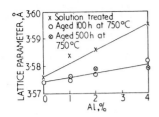

13 *Effect of aluminium on the lattice parameter*

readily achieved as illustrated by the substantial increase in lattice parameter in the solution treated condition.

Electrolytic extraction of the 4%Al alloy revealed a phase which is believed to be Ni$_3$Al. The microstructure of this alloy in the aged condition (Fig.3i) shows evidence of heavy precipitation of the phase in finely dispersed form within the grains and in somewhat more massive form round the grain boundaries.

Aluminium above 2% has a pronounced solid solution hardening effect and the 4%Al alloy has a proof stress of 30 tons/in^2 at 650°C. The ageing reaction is moderate at all levels, and causes an improvement.

The creep rupture strength at 650°C and 950°C is not improved by Al additions (Table I), a result in line with the observed propensity for overageing.

Beryllium alloys

Alloys containing up to 0·6%Be have been vacuum melted and successfully forged. Lattice parameter measurements (Fig.14) decrease with increasing Be as might be anticipated from the small atomic diameter, 2·22 Å, of beryllium. Ageing the alloys causes a further decrease which can be attributed to the precipitation of kappa carbide Cr$_{23}$C$_6$. However, the 0·6%Be alloys shows a slight increase in parameter on ageing, presumably due to precipitation of a beryllium-containing intermetallic phase. Comparison of the lattice parameter after 100 and 500 h shows that ageing is substantially completed after 100 h at 750°C. A trace of an unknown phase was found in the aged 0·5% and 0·6%Be alloys after electrolytic

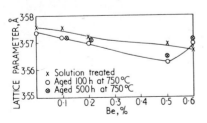

14 *Effect of beryllium on the lattice parameter*

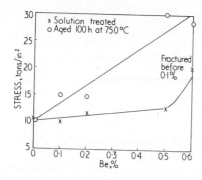

15 *Effect of beryllium on the 1%
proof strength at 650°C*

extraction, but otherwise only kappa carbide was found. The microstructure of the aged 0·5%Be alloy (Fig.3*j*) indicates that considerable precipitation of a finely dispersed phase has occurred. The solubility limit of Be is therefore, apparently between 0·2% and 0·5%.

In the solution treated condition Be has little effect in the 650°C proof strength (Fig.15) up to 0·5%. The 0·6% alloy was, however, very brittle and fractured at 20 tons/in² before the 1·0% proof stress was reached. Ageing has a pronounced beneficial effect in the 0·5% and 0·6%Be alloys.

The rupture strength at 650°C is not affected appreciably by Be but there is a progressive embrittling effect, as shown by the low elongation at rupture. Ageing has no significant effect.

Beryllium in very small amounts has a moderately beneficial effect on the 950°C rupture strength as shown by the following results:

Be, %	100-hour rupture strength at 950°C, tons/in²
0	1·65
0·1	2·1
0·2	1·6
0·5	1·7
0·6	1·65

Copper alloys

Alloys containing up to 8%Cu have been vacuum melted but the 8% alloy could not be forged satisfactorily. The addition of up to 4%Cu was found to have no significant effect on any of the properties studied.

Carbon alloys

The effect of carbon additions has been studied up to 0·65%C, as it was known from previous experience that higher carbon contents

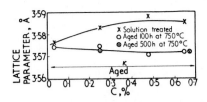

16 *Effect of carbon on the lattice parameter*

would not be readily forgeable. Carbon causes a progressive increase in the lattice parameter (Fig.16) of solution-treated material and ageing, which is completed in 100 h at 750°C, is pronounced in all instances and indicates the solubility of carbon to be very low. The lambda phase Cr_7C_3 has been identified in the higher carbon alloys in the solution-treated condition but on ageing was only found in the 0·65%C alloy. Throughout the series kappa carbide $Cr_{23}C_6$ was found in the aged material. The microstructure of the 0·05%C alloy, consisting of simple austenitic grains, is shown in Fig.3a.

Carbon progressively improves the 650°C proof strength (Fig.17) in both the solution-treated and the aged condition. Ageing causes a marked improvement at all carbon levels. Kappa carbide is obviously a potent age hardening precipitant under these conditions and some of the minor effects observed in the other alloy systems are undoubtedly due to its presence in small amounts owing to the residual carbon content of 0·04% present in all the alloys.

Carbon similarly improves the rupture strength at 650°C and 750°C (Table I) the optimum being at 0·65%C or greater. Ageing before testing is detrimental, indicative of the ease of overageing with

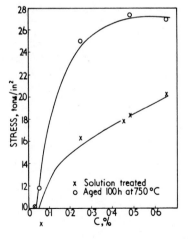

17 *Effect of carbon on the 1% proof strength at 650°C*

113

TABLE I Detailed comparison of 0·05 %C alloys

Alloy system	Maximum lattice parameter, Å		Maximum 1% proof stress at 650°C tons/in²		Maximum 100-h rupture strength, tons/in²					
	Solution-treated	Aged 100 h at 750°C	Solution-treated	Aged 100 h at 750°C	650°C Solution-treated	Aged	750°C Solution-Aged treated		950°C Solution-treated
Base alloy	3·576	3·573	10	10	13·4	11·5	(5)	(5)	1·5–1·65
Mo	3·604	3·585	16	38	25·5	23	13·8	12·8	3·5
W	3·600	3·594	25	29	22·5	24·5	11·2	13·2	4·2
Nb	3·585	3·579	25	29	27	23	12·1	11·6	2·7
Ti	3·589	3·583	33	54	>27	23·6	14·4	13·2	1·85
V	3·592	3·587	17·5	19	21·8	20·3	10·8	10·1	...
Al	3·595	3·582	30	40	13·4	13·0	...	...	1·8
Be	3·567 (minimum)	3·563 (minimum)	20	30	13·8	13·4	...	...	2·1
C	3·588	3·574	20	27	18·6	17·6	9·4	7·8	2·5
B	3·576	3·574	12	13	13·4	13·0	...	...	1·8
N	3·582	3·574	10·5	12·5	15·0	16·0	...	...	1·75

$Cr_{23}C_6$ type carbide. Carbon has a very detrimental effect on the ductility at rupture, which is less than 2% when the carbon is above 0·3%.

At 950°C the 100 h rupture strength is definitely improved by carbon but the trend is obscure as the results illustrate:

C,%	100-h rupture strength at 950°C, tons/in²
0·05	1·5
0·25	2·5
0·45	1·8
0·65	2·2

Boron alloys

Alloys containing up to 0·2%B have been vacuum melted and successfully forged. The nitrogen contents of all the alloys lie between 0·002–0·005%. The lattice parameter is not affected appreciably by boron contents in this range as will be seen from the following results:

B,%	Lattice parameters, Å, after the following ageing times at 750°C		
	0	100 h	500 h
0	3·575	3·573	3·572
0·035	3·575	3·574	3·575
0·2	3·576	5·572	3·575

No boron phase could be identified in the electrolytic extracts, which did, however, contain kappa carbide.

The microstructure of the 0·2%B alloy in the aged condition (Fig.3k) shows evidence of an intergranular eutectic which by comparison with Fig.3a, can be attributed to boron.

Boron increases the 1% proof at 650°C. slightly (Table I) and this is further increased to a very slight extent by ageing due to kappa precipitation. Boron does not, however, improve the rupture strength at 650°C and the effect at 950°C is also negligible (Fig. 33).

Nitrogen alloys

Nitrogen additions up to 0·15% have been studied by vacuum melting the alloys to remove nitrogen and adding the desired content by means of high-nitrogen ferrochrome immediately before tapping.

These nitrogen additions caused a slight increase in lattice parameter of the solution-treated material, as can be seen from the following results. Ageing the alloys resulted in a decrease, the magnitude of which indicated a very low solubility of nitrogen. Ageing was completed in 100 h.

N,%	Lattice parameter, Å, after ageing at 750°C for		
	0	100 h	500 h
0·004	3·575	3·573	3·572
0·05	3·576	3·574	. . .
0·15	3·582	3·573	3·576

Nitrogen had no significant effect on the proof strength at 650°C, and caused a minor improvement in rupture strength at 650° and 950°C, the increase being about 10% and 5% in terms of stress at these temperatures.

GENERAL DISCUSSION OF RESULTS OF PART 1

Before comparing the effect of the various alloying elements it must be stressed that the conclusions hold only for an austenitic alloy containing 20%Co, 20%Ni, 20%Cr, and an iron base with a small residual quantity of carbon, i.e. 0·05%. The optimum physical and mechanical properties obtainable with each alloy system are summarized in Table I.

Additions of Mo, W, Nb, Ti, V, Al, Be, C, B, and N have been made to this base and the properties studied in the solution-treated condition, i.e. oil quenched from 1 280°C. This treatment was effective in retaining a supersaturated solution of all the elements studied, as judged by lattice parameter measurements. All the elements caused an increase in parameter except Be which caused a decrease and B which had no effect. Mo, W, and Al additions caused the

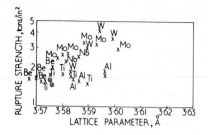

Note: Combined cross and circle symbol refers to base alloys

18 Comparison of the 100-h rupture strength at 950°C on the lattice parameter for solution-treated alloys

largest increase. The lattice parameter may be taken as a measure of the solid-solution hardening effect due to the various elements.

It was found, however, that there is no correlation between the lattice strain of this supersaturated solution and the 650°C proof strength or the creep rupture strength. As an example the 100-h rupture strength at 950°C is compared in Fig.18 with the lattice parameter for a selection of the solution-treated alloys.

Solid-solution hardening does, however, play a large part in determining the mechanical properties of the alloys, but, as most of the alloys are in a state of non-equilibrium in the solution-treated condition, the ability of the alloy to resist decomposition of the supersaturated solution and consequent precipitation of an excess phase is of major importance. Ageing the alloys at 750°C for 100 h caused a decrease in parameter in all cases (except Be) but it is noteworthy that a high degree of lattice strain due to solid-solution hardening was retained in several systems. Tungsten was outstanding in this respect but Mo and V also showed a marked effect.

The 650°C proof strength in the solution-treated condition was increased by all the addition elements studied except B and N, but the effect was most pronounced with Ti and Al. After ageing for 100 h at 750°C, all the alloys showed an increased in proof strength. The optimum alloy of the Mo and Ti series showed a much greater increase than any of the other alloys and the Ti alloy in the aged condition had a 1% proof strength at 650°C of 54 tons/in², a much higher value than any other alloy.

Considering rupture strength at 650°C, in the solution-treated condition, all the additions studied had a beneficial effect except Al, Be, and B. The outstanding strengthening elements were Nb, Ti, and Mo. It is noteworthy, however, that after ageing, the only alloys which showed an improved 650°C rupture strength were those containing W. The 750°C rupture strength was very similarly effected by both alloying additions and the ageing treatment.

Considering rupture strength at 950°C, very few of the addition

116

elements caused any significant improvements in strength, W and Mo being outstandingly effective and Nb and C moderately so.

PART 2   0·45% CARBON ALLOYS

EXPERIMENTAL RESULTS

Molybdenum alloys

Alloys containing up to 10%Mo were melted but difficulty was experienced in forging alloys containing more than 9%. A limited amount of material was obtained, however, from a 9·5%Mo heat.

The change of electrical resistivity at 750°C with time for these alloys indicated that minimum resistivity was substantially achieved in the following times:

Mo,%	Time, h
0	100
2	100
3	100
4·6	100
6·2	100
7·7	4
9·5	3

The very short time for complete ageing at the highest Mo levels is believed to be due to the presence of excess phase even after solution treatment (OQ 1280°C, 10 min).

A study of the effect of ageing time at 750°C on the lattice parameter (Fig.19) showed that a minimum was reached in about 100 h with the base alloy, but the 3%Mo alloy was still showing appreciable drop in parameter after 2 000 h. It is apparent, therefore, that the ageing process in these alloys is very sluggish and that the attainment of minimum resistivity is no indication of equilibrium.

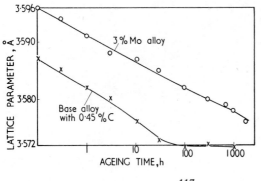

19 *Effect of ageing time at 750°C on the lattice parameter of two alloys*

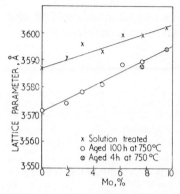

20 *Effect of molybdenum on the lattice parameter of 0·45%C alloys*

This is accounted for at least in part by the difficulty of measuring the very small resistivity changes, particularly when they occur over a period of time.

The lattice parameter (Fig.20) of the solution-treated material increases progressively with Mo content, but there is metallographic evidence of excess phase at Mo contents above 4%. The microstructure of this phase in a 5%Mo alloy is shown in Fig.21a, and is a

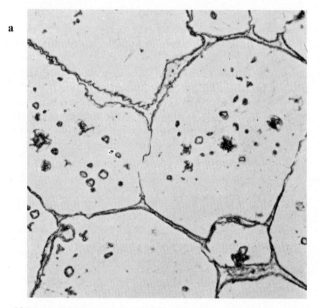

a 5%Mo–0·45%C alloy, OQ 1280°C; DPN 216   ×500

21 (*a* – *e*) *Some typical alloys*

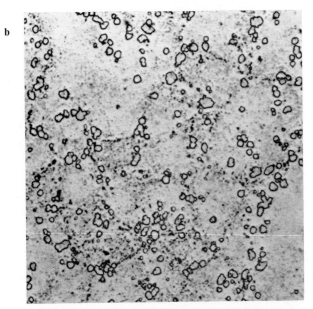

b 10%W–0·45%C alloy, OQ 1 280°C; DPN 287   ×*500*

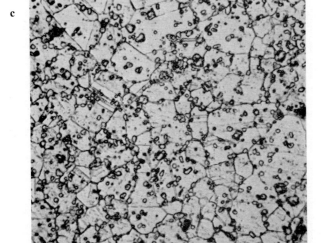

c 6%Nb–0·45%C alloy, OQ 1 280°C; DPN 199   ×*500*

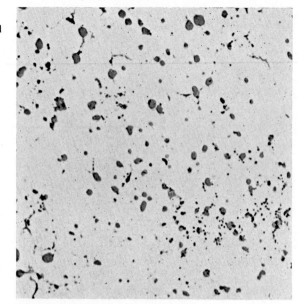

d 9%V–0·5%C alloy, OQ 1280°C; DPN 213   ×500

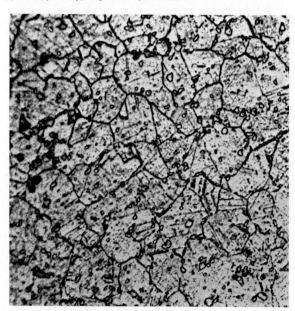

e 2·5%Ti–0·45%C alloy, OQ 1280°C; DPN 211   ×500

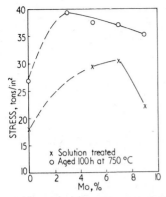

22 *Effect of molybdenum on the 1% proof stress at 650°C of 0·45%C alloys*

finely dispersed grain boundary eutectic. Ageing the alloys for 100 h at 750°C caused a drop in the lattice parameter at all Mo levels.

Eta carbide Fe_4Mo_2C was found in solution-treated alloys containing 3%Mo and over, and in all the aged Mo alloys. The solution-treated alloys with no Fe_4Mo_2C, contained lambda carbide Cr_7C_3, while those with Fe_4Mo_2C also contained kappa carbide $Cr_{23}C_6$. All the aged alloys also contained $Cr_{23}C_6$.

The addition of Mo caused a substantial increase in the 650°C proof strength of solution-treated material and ageing the alloys results in a further substantial improvement (Fig.22). In both heat-treated conditions an optimum content of 3–6%Mo was indicated.

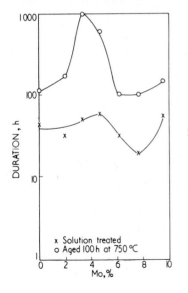

23 *Effect of molybdenum on time to 1% total plastic strain at 18 tons/in² at 650°C, 0·45%C alloys*

When creep tests were carried out at 650°C (Fig.23) Mo proved to have little effect on the creep strength of solution-treated alloys, but in the aged condition there was a pronounced maximum at about 3%Mo.

It would appear that the precipitation of Fe_4Mo_2C is most effective in promoting creep resistance when the Mo content is between 2% and 5%. Above this level, the alloys apparently over-age too rapidly for the most effective strengthening. The upper trend of the curves in Fig.23 at higher Mo contents is attributed to the formation of the intergranular carbide network (*see* Fig.21a) which has a strengthening effect. The precipitation of Fe_4Mo_2C, under creep conditions at 650°C is apparently so slow that there is no pronounced effect of Mo on solution treated material.

When rupture strength (Fig.24) at 650°C is considered there is a pronounced optimum in strength at 4·5%Mo for both heat-treated conditions. Presumably the higher strain rate under these conditions is sufficient to induce more pronounced precipitation of Fe_4Mo_2C in the solution-treated material, with a resulting strengthening effect. The trend to a second maximum mentioned earlier is much more pronounced for rupture conditions. The aged alloys are stronger at all molybdenum contents.

Under rupture conditions at 750°C, the alloys show somewhat similar behaviour (Fig.24). The minimum in rupture strength at about 7–8%Mo is, however, suppressed somewhat and alloys containing from 3–9·5%Mo have essentially similar rupture strength. Again the aged alloys are superior.

At 950°C suppression of the minimum between the 'precipitation optimum' and the 'grain boundary carbide optimum' is complete

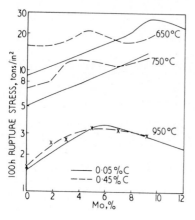

24 *Comparison of the effect of molybdenum on the rupture strength of solution-treated alloys with or without carbon addition*

122

and the rupture strength of solution-treated materials shows one optimum at 5–7%Mo (Fig.24).

In Fig.24, the rupture strength at 650–950°C is compared for Mo alloys with 0·05% and 0·45%C. It is interesting to note that the strengths of the two series are surprisingly similar. In the case of the higher carbon series, however, there is a pronounced superiority at lower Mo contents attributable to the precipitation of Fe_4Mo_2C. This effect is not found at the higher temperatures.

The usefulness of a 0·45%C addition would seem to lie mainly in the achievement of comparable mechanical properties at lower molybdenum contents than with a low carbon content of 0·05%.

A more detailed comparison of the effect of carbon is given in Table II. The maximum lattice parameter achieved with solution-treated material is comparable for both carbon series but the 0·45%C series retained a higher parameter on ageing. While solution-treated 0·45%C alloys had better 1% proof strength at 650°C than their low carbon counterparts, the aged alloys were very similar in strength.

Tungsten alloys

Alloys containing up to 10%W were melted and successfully forged. Resistivity measurements at 750°C showed that the alloys all fully aged in 100 h.

The lattice parameters (Fig.25) of solution-treated alloys increased progressively with tungsten content indicating the ease of super-saturating by oil quenching from 1 280°C. The aged material had a significantly lower parameter due to the precipitation of $Cr_{23}C_6$ and Fe_4W_2C. The latter phase was, however, only positively identified by electrolytic extraction and X-ray analysis in the 10%W alloy. $Cr_{23}C_6$ was found in all the other alloys in both the solution-treated and the aged condition.

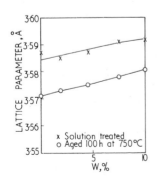

25 *Effect of tungsten on the lattice parameter of 0·45%C alloys*

TABLE II Detailed comparison of 0·05% and 0·45%C alloys

Alloy system	Maximum lattice parameter, Å		Maximum 1% proof stress at 650°C, tons/in²		Maximum 100-h rupture strength, tons/in²				
	Solution-treated	Aged at 750°C	Solution-treated	Aged at 750°C	650°C Solution-treated	Aged	750°C Solution-treated	Aged	950°C Solution-treated
Base alloy 0·05%C	3·576	3·573	10	10	13·4	11·5	(5)	(5)	1·5–1·65
0·45%C	3·587	3·571	18	27	16·0	15·2	(7)	(7·6)	1·8
Mo 0·05%C	3·604	3·585	16	38	25·5	23·0	13·8	12·8	3·5
0·45%C	3·602	3·594	30	39	21·2	26·0	13·0	13·6	3·3
W 0·05%C	3·600	3·594	25	29	22·5	24·5	11·2	13·2	4·2
0·45%C	3·592	3·581	24	37	20·0	20·4	11·0	10·0	2·4
Nb 0·05%C	3·585	3·579	25	29	27	23	12·1	11·6	2·7
0·45%C*	3·587*	3·578	20	27	20	20	10·5	10·5	3·8
V 0·05%C	3·592	3·587	17·5	19	21·8	20·3	10·8	10·1	...
0·45%C	3·591	3·583	23	28**	21·0	17·8	9·5	9·0	...
Ti 0·05%C	3·589	3·583	33	54	27	23·6	14·4	13·7	1·85
0·45%C*	3·587*	3·576	19	27	22½	21·4	13·5	13·2	3·2
B 0·05%C	3·576	3·574	12	13	13·4	13·0	...	...	1·8
0·45%C*	3·588*	3·572*	18	35	20·0	20·0	...	...	2·65

* Alloy containing 0% addition, i.e. base alloy
** Only studied up to 5%V

The highest W alloy, 10%, (Fig.21b) showed no evidence of the intergranular eutectic found in the alloys containing the highest Mo contents. The absence of a maximum lattice parameter in the aged condition is again indicative of failure to attain equilibrium in 100 h at 750°C.

Tungsten caused a moderate increase in the 650°C proof strength in the solution-treated condition and there was a pronounced increase on ageing all the alloys. The ageing effect was most pronounced at 4%W (Table II). Under creep conditions at 650°C W had little effect and indeed at the higher levels was detrimental in aged alloys, presumably owing to an over-ageing effect. This may be contrasted with the Mo alloys where ageing was beneficial at all levels. It could be explained by the predominance of $Cr_{23}C_6$ instead of Fe_4M_2C in the W series, as the former carbide is known to be prone to over-ageing effects.

Under rupture conditions (Fig.6) at 650°C W had a progressive beneficial effect, but ageing before testing caused no improvement as was the case with the Mo series. At 750°C there was an effect, but ageing in this case was detrimental at all W levels. At 950°C the rupture strength was again improved by W but was effectively constant between 4% and 10% addition.

Considering Fig.6, which illustrates the effect of C on W-containing alloys, as with the Mo alloys there is an improvement with carbon owing to carbide precipitation but the general effect is to give optimum properties at lower W contents. Unfortunately, alloys containing more than 10%W were not tested (owing to known difficulties in forging) but it would appear from the graphs that above 10%W, carbon would have but little effect.

The maximum lattice parameter of the 0·45%C alloys is less than that of the low carbon series, indicative of less solid solution strengthening, and unlike the Mo series there is no suggestion that the presence of carbon is making the ageing process more sluggish. The 1% proof stress at 650°C in the aged condition is the only property which is significantly higher for the 0·45% carbon series (Table II).

A general comparison of the 0·45%C, Mo, and W series suggests that the W alloys overage more readily than the Mo. It was somewhat surprising, therefore, to find that at 950°C (Fig.6) the rupture strength of alloys with the same W content but a higher carbon content were superior, unlike alloys of the Mo series (Fig.24). It would have been expected that the higher carbon W alloys would have readily overaged at 950°C. This suggests that the precipitation at 950°C in the W series with 0·45%C is of a different phase than at lower temperatures but no evidence was found of this. It is interesting to

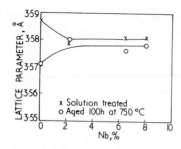

26 *Effect of niobium on the lattice parameter of 0·45%C alloys*

contrast too, the fact that in the low carbon alloys (Part 1) W alloys proved more resistant to overageing than did Mo.

Niobium alloys

Alloys containing up to 9%Nb were melted and successfully forged. Resistivity measurements on a selection of these showed that a minimum resistance was reached in about 200 h at 750°C.

Lattice parameter measurements (Fig.26) showed that the addition of Nb resulted in a decrease in parameter for solution-treated material. This was interpreted as a removal of carbon from the matrix by Nb, and the existence of substantial quantities of niobium carbide in the solution-treated materials confirms this hypothesis. The microstructure of the 6%Nb alloy in the solution treated condition (Fig. 21c) shows this undissolved niobium carbide in globular form. This was the first case in this investigation where substantial solution of carbide could not be achieved at 1 280°C.

After ageing, there was a decrease in the lattice parameter due to further precipitation of niobium carbide NbC, and kappa carbide $Cr_{23}C_6$. These two phases were identified after carbide extractions in alloys containing up to $6\frac{1}{2}$%Nb in both heat-treated conditions. The higher Nb alloys contained only niobium carbide (NbC) in the solution-treated condition. In the aged condition they also contained a phase similar in structure to eta carbide, but believed to be a form of $FeNb_2$. This phase was also found in the low carbon alloy series.

Niobium was found to have little effect on the 650°C proof strength in either the solution treated or the aged condition. The improved strength in the latter condition must be attributed mainly to the precipitation of kappa carbide ($Cr_{23}C_6$) as the effect is present even without niobium. The creep strength at 650°C (Fig.27) was very substantially reduced by the addition of niobium and this is again attributed to the removal of carbon from solid solution as niobium carbide. The aged alloys showed some improvement over their solution-treated counterparts but niobium again caused a reduction in strength.

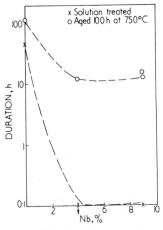

27 *Effect of niobium on the time to 1% plastic strain at 18 tons/in² at 650°C*

Considering rupture strength (Fig.8) at 650°C niobium caused a progressive improvement up to 9%, the limit of forgeable alloys. Ageing had little effect. At 750°C the rupture strength was at an optimum at about 4–6% with ageing again having no appreciable effect. At 950°C the rupture strength shows a maximum at 3% or 4%Nb. This maximum is much more pronounced than that at 750°C and is considered indicative of a high-temperature ageing process.

Comparing the rupture strengths of 0·05% and 0·45% carbon alloys (Fig.8) very similar strengths are found at 650° and 750°C. At 950°C, however, the alloys containing 3–4%Nb with 0·45%C do show a significant improvement over their low carbon counterparts. This is the first case found in this investigation where the presence of 0·45%C has produced a significantly higher optimum strength than that found in the low carbon series.

A study of Table II, however, shows that this is an isolated effect and that in general the level of mechanical properties and lattice strains found in the two carbon series is similar with the low carbon series stronger at the lower temperatures.

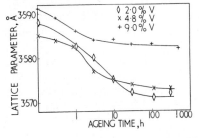

28 *Effect of ageing time at 750°C on the lattice parameter of vanadium alloys*

127

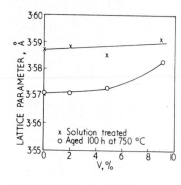

29 *Effect of vanadium on the lattice parameter of 0·45% C alloys*

Vanadium alloys

Alloys containing up to 9%V were melted and successfully forged. Due to the high rate of oxidation found at 750°C with these alloys, resistivity measurements were not carried out but lattice parameter changes with time (Fig.28) indicated that ageing was substantially completed in 100 h for all the alloys. It will be seen from Fig.29 that vanadium additions have a very limited effect on the lattice parameter of both solution treated and aged material. There is, however, a marked increase in parameter in the aged condition for high (9%V) vanadium alloys. These results are somewhat difficult to interpret and presumably arise from the summation of several effects. The limited increase of parameter with the addition of V to solution-treated material may be explained by the difficulty of achieving complete solution of vanadium carbide (V_4C_3). The rise in parameter above 5%V in the aged condition is due to the solution of vanadium which is present in excess of that required to precipitate vanadium carbide V_4C_3.

Lambda carbide (Cr_7C_3) was found in the 2%V alloys as solution treated and all the aged samples contained V_4C_3 and $Cr_{23}C_6$. The microstructure of the 9%V alloy is shown in Fig.21*d*.

Vanadium produces a moderate increase in 650°C proof stress and this is further increased by ageing, although less so than with the base alloy (Table II). The creep strength at 650°C (Fig.30) is increased slightly by small additions of V, there being an optimum at 2% for solution treated material. Aged material is, however, substantially weakened at all vanadium contents.

The rupture strength (Fig.12) at 650°C is increased by vanadium, there being an optimum at 2% for solution treated alloys. Aged alloys are progressively improved by vanadium but are weaker than their solution-treated equivalents. At 750°C the effect is more complex. Solution-treated alloys have an optimum strength at 6–9%V

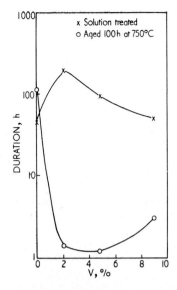

30 *Effect of vanadium on the time to 1% plastic strain at 18 tons/in³ at 650°C*

while aged alloys are strongest at 5%V. Ageing improves low-V alloys up to about 5% but above this level weakens them.

Comparing 0·05% and 0·45% alloys (Fig.12) it will be seen that both series have a very similar level of rupture strength. Unlike the other carbide-forming systems studied, there is no evidence of improved strength over a range of alloy content due to precipitation of a vanadium carbide phase. The optimum proof strength at 650°C of the 0·45%C alloys is much higher than that of the 0·45%C alloys is much higher than that of the 0·05%C alloys (Table II).

Effect of titanium

Alloys containing up to 2·5%Ti were melted and successfully forged. Resistivity studies at 750°C indicated that minimum resistivity was achieved in about 100 h for all the alloys.

With solution-treated material (Fig.31) titanium additions caused no increase in lattice parameter but resulted in a small reduction due to removal of carbon from solution. Aged material had a lower parameter owing to precipitation of TiC but the lattic parameter was the same at all titanium levels.

The microstructure of the 2·5%Ti solution-treated alloy is shown in Fig.21*e* and consists of particles of TiC in an austenite matrix. The alloys with less than 1%Ti also contained Cr_7C_3 in the solution-treated state as well as TiC. Aged alloys all contained $Cr_{23}C_6$ as well as TiC.

129

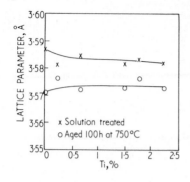

31 *Effect of titanium on the lattice parameter of 0·45%C alloys*

The addition Ti first reduces the proof stress at 650°C (Fig.32) as carbon is removed from solution and then causes a gradual increase due to solid-solution hardening. Ageing improves the proof strength at all levels of Ti and the effect is, therefore, attributable mainly to $Cr_{23}C_6$ precipitation.

The rupture strength (Fig.10*b*) at 650°C increases progressively to a maximum of 2·5%Ti but ageing the alloys results in reduced strength except at very low Ti contents (< 1%). At 750°C there is a similar trend but the optimum rupture strength is at 1·0–2·0%Ti and ageing is again only effective below 1·0%Ti. At 950°C the rupture strength is increased, there being a flat maximum between 0·7% and 2·5%Ti.

Comparing the 0·05% and the 0·45%C alloy series, it will be seen (Fig.10*b*) that at 650° and 750°C similar optimum strengths are achieved by titanium additions but there is evidence of marked carbide strengthening at levels of Ti less than 1·5%. At 950°C this effect is very marked and the higher carbon alloys are markedly stronger at all titanium levels. This is the second instance of a higher optimum strength in the 0·45% carbon series. The 650°C proof strength is much less for 0·45%C alloys (Table II).

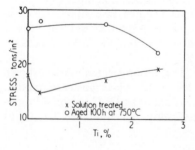

32 *Effect of titanium on the 1% proof stress at 650°C, 0·45%C*

Effect of boron

Alloys containing up to 0·035%B were vacuum melted and successfully forged. It should be noted that the various trace elements, particularly oxygen and nitrogen, will be different in this series and hence the base alloy is not the same as that used for the other series. It is interesting to note that it is significantly stronger.

The change of lattice parameter with time is given below:

| | | Lattice parameter, Å | |
B content	Unaged	Aged 100 h at 750°C	Aged 500 h at 750°C
0	3·588	3·572	3·570
0·01	3·585	3·570	3·570
0·35	3·584	3·569	3·570

It will be seen that boron causes a slight lattice contraction and that the alloys are fully aged after 100 h at 750°C, boron having no effect on the change of lattice parameter due to ageing. No boron phase could be detected in extracts, nor did boron affect the microstructure.

Boron has no effect on the 1% proof stress at 650°C for solution-treated material but the highest boron addition (0·035%) caused a substantial improvement on ageing (Table II). The rupture strength was very slightly improved by boron at 650°C and this effect was more evident at 950°C (Fig.33).

Comparison of low carbon and 0·45%C alloys (Fig.33) shows that boron has a better effect in the higher carbon alloys although this is very slight. The improvement in the strength of the 0·45%C series is mainly due to the carbon itself and to the vacuum melting process used for this series.

It is interesting to note that boron additions cause a lattice contraction with 0·45%C alloys and have no effect on the parameter

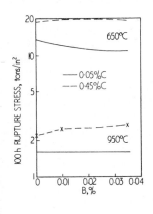

33 *Comparison of the effect of boron on the rupture strength of solution-treated alloys with or without carbon addition*

of 0·05%C alloys. There is obviously some connection between boron and carbon although this may not necessarily be the existence of a boron carbide phase.

GENERAL DISCUSSION OF RESULTS OF PART 2

Before comparing the effect of the various alloying elements, it must be stressed that these conclusions hold only for an austenite base containing 20%Co, 20%Ni, 20%Cr, with an iron base and a carbon addition of 0·45%.

Various carbide-forming elements, Mo, W, Nb, V, Ti, and B have been added to this base and the alloys have been studied in the solution-treated condition, i.e. oil quenched from 1 280°C. It was found possible, judging by lattice parameter measurements, to achieve substantial solution of the carbides by this treatment except in the case of the Nb and Ti series. It is interesting to note that in no case did the addition of alloying elements to the 0·45%C base result in a higher maximum value of lattice parameter, than that found in 0·05%C alloys in the solution-treated condition. It may be assumed, therefore, that there will be no enhanced solid-solution hardening effect in the 0·45%C series compared with the 0·05%C series.

Ageing the alloys caused a decrease in parameter in all cases due to precipitation of carbon and after ageing for comparable durations at 750°C to the 0·05%C alloys, the highest values of lattice parameter found in each of the series was comparable with that found in the low carbon investigation. An exception occurred with the molybdenum series where the 0·45%C series had a higher maximum lattice parameter than the 0·05%C series. It may be inferred that in general the presence of carbon and the precipitation of carbide phases instead of intermetallic phases, causes no significant change of ageing rates for the systems studied.

Of the alloying elements studied, only Mo caused a large increase in the 650°C proof strength in the solution-treated condition, while W and V caused a moderate increase (Table II). In the aged condition Mo, W and V caused considerable increases in the 650°C proof strength whilst the other elements studied had little or no effect. Considering creep strength at 650°C only Mo-containing alloys in the aged condition showed any appreciable improvement in strength.

In the solution-treated condition, the optimum alloy in each series had a 650°C rupture strength about 25% greater than the base alloy. Only in the case of the Mo series was the rupture strength significantly improved by prior ageing at 750°C.

It will be seen, therefore, that Mo is the most effective addition to the 0·45%C alloys for optimum proof strength, creep, and rupture strength at relatively low temperatures, i.e. 650°C.

All the alloying additions studied caused very substantial improvements (50–100%) to the rupture strength at 750°C, in the solution treated condition. Ageing before testing had little or no effect in any case. The most effective elements were Mo and Ti for this criterion.

Similarly, at 950°C the rupture strength was improved by 50–100% by all the alloy additions studied, with Nb being the outstanding element and Mo and Ti nearly as effective.

As might be expected from the lattice parameter data, there was little difference in the optimum properties which could be achieved in the 0·05%C and the 0·45%C investigations. The main trend was that the required alloy addition for optimum strength tended to be less for the 0·45%C materials.

Outstanding exceptions to this generalization are:

(i) low-carbon titanium alloys have an outstanding proof strength of 650°C in the aged condition. This level of strength, 54 tons/in² is specific to this system and is due to Ni_3Ti precipitation and none of the other intermetallic or carbide precipitation reactions can equal it.

(ii) The 950°C rupture strength of the low-carbon tungsten alloys is also outstanding and is not approached by the 0·45%C tungsten series or equalled by any other system.

(iii) The 950°C rupture strength of the optimum alloy of both the Nb and the Ti–0·45%C series is much greater than the strength of the equivalent 0·05%C series. It is apparent that the strengthening effect of TiC and NbC precipitation is only effective at 950°C in this investigation. It is likely that longer time tests at lower temperatures might also have shown up this effect.

CONCLUSIONS

(a) General

1. All the additions studied caused solid-solution hardening in the solution-treated condition except the very strong carbide-forming elements, niobium and titanium, where there was little effect in the presence of carbon. There was no correlation, however, between the lattice strain and the mechanical properties obtained.

2. Most of the alloy systems have an optimum rupture strength at an additive content beyond the solubility limit. The existence of this optimum is associated with the increasing tendency to overage as the degree of supersaturation of the matrix is increased.

3. A prior ageing treatment increased the proof strength at 650°C but in general there was no corresponding improvement in the rupture strength at either 650° or 750°C. The alloys were tested in the 'fully aged' condition, and it is possible that a shorter ageing time or a lower temperature would have resulted in improved rupture strength.

4. For low-temperature properties, the low-carbon alloys developed the optimum properties. At higher temperatures, however, e.g. rupture strength at 950°C, niobium and titanium carbide were shown to be effective precipitants.

5. Attempts to correlate the strengthening effect of all the alloying elements studied in terms of solid-solution hardening or stability of the supersaturated solid solution have been unsuccessful.

(b) Low-carbon alloys

1. For relatively low temperature applications, e.g. 650°C, Ti is the best addition element, but Nb, Mo and W are also very effective.

2. At higher temperatures, e.g. 950°C, W is the outstanding addition with Mo the only other element giving substantial improvement.

3. These conclusions as regards rupture strength may be correlated with the ability of the alloy to resist precipitation under stress. It is noteworthy that only the W alloys are improved with regard to rupture strength by an ageing treatment before testing.

(c) 0·45%C alloys

1. In general, the presence of carbon causes the optimum alloy of a given series to contain less alloy addition, but does not improve the optimum properties. Outstanding exceptions are the optimum Nb and Ti alloys at 950°C. These have a much higher rupture strength than their low carbon counterparts.

2. There are no outstanding improvements in rupture strength at 650°C, except with an optimum molybdenum addition. This alloy proved significantly stronger when aged before testing and is unique in this respect.

3. At 750°C, Mo and Ti proved the most effective addition.

4. At 950°C, Nb is the most effective alloying element, but Mo and Ti are also outstanding.

ACKNOWLEDGMENT

The author acknowledges the assistance given by Mr T. K. Jones with the X-ray techniques, and various other colleagues who have helped with the experimental work.

REFERENCES

1. J. D. NISBET and W. R. HIBBARD: *Trans. AIME*, 1953, **197,** 1149–1165.
2. F. R. LARSON and J. MILLER: *Trans. ASME*, 1952, **74,** 765–771.
3. G. T. HARRIS and H. C. CHILD: 'Symposium on high-temperature steels and alloys for gas turbines', *ISI Spec. Rep.* no. 43, 1951, 67–80.
4. H. C. CROSS and W. F. SIMMONS: ASTM Symposium on material for gas turbines, 1946, 3–51.
5. G. SACHS and J. WEERTS: *Z. Physik*, 1930, **60,** 481.
6. G. T. HARRIS and H. C. CHILD: *JISI*, 1950, **165,** 139–144.
7. R. W. GUARD and T. A. PRATER: *Trans. ASM*, 1957, **49,** 842–856.
8. H. SCOTT and R. B. GORDON: *Trans. ASME*, 1947, **69,** 583–599.
9. W. F. SIMMONS *et al.*: ASTM Spec. Tech. Pub. no. 170, 1953.

Interrelation of structure and stress—rupture properties of nickel—chromium alloys strengthened with titanium and aluminium

E. A. Fell, B.Met., A.I.M., W. I. Mitchell, M.A., Ph.D., and D. W. Wakeman, B.Sc., Ph.D.

The main structural features in three commercial alloys are shown to be a general distribution of a stable precipitate of the phase $Ni_3(Ti,Al)$ within the grains, with a precipitate of a carbide phase, or phases mainly at grain boundaries, whose nature differs in the different alloys. The grain boundary phase is accompanied by a zone in the neighbouring grains containing less of the $Ni_3(Ti,Al)$ precipitate. The possible correlation of the structure of the alloys with their behaviour in stress–rupture testing is discussed.

INTRODUCTION

OXIDATION-RESISTANT nickel-base alloys containing chromium and strengthened in part by precipitates containing titanium and aluminium are in wide use where stress–rupture resistance at elevated temperatures is required. Although the alloys are resistant to creep at elevated temperature, the resistance to fracture for long times at elevated temperatures, i.e. stress–rupture resistance, is also an important property in a large proportion of engineering applications. The earlier developments were described by Pfeil *et al.*[1]

Subsequent improvements in production techniques enabled the titanium and aluminium contents to be increased, and, together with the addition of cobalt and molybdenum, have led to the development of the alloys Nimonic* 80A, 90, 95, 105 and, recently, 115. Some details of this work and a comprehensive survey of the alloys has been given by Betteridge.[2]

The purpose of this paper is to give an outline of the general structural features of three of these alloys and to attempt to correlate structure and stress–rupture properties. The work described here

* Attention is drawn to the fact that 'Nimonic' is a registered trademark.

The authors are with International Nickel Company (Mond) Ltd, Development and Research Department Laboratory, Birmingham.

forms part of a continuing programme of research on the constitution of nickel-base alloys for high-temperature applications. Some of the present work was described in a recent paper by one of the authors,[3] in which the experimental methods and constitutional details for alloys of lower titanium and aluminium contents are given in greater detail.

EXPERIMENTAL METHODS

The alloys used were obtained in the form of hot-worked bar, either from commercial casts or from casts from a laboratory high-frequency furnace. Typical analyses of the alloys studied are given in Table I. These are the alloys for which lattice parameters are given in Table III, and are not necessarily typical of production material.

After various heat treatments, solid specimens and residues extracted electrolytically from them were studied by X-ray diffraction techniques using a GE.XRD5 Geiger counter unit. Both optical and electron micrographic examinations were also made. The latter used evaporated carbon replica techniques in conjunction with Metropolitan-Vickers EM.3 and EM.6 electron microscopes. Some electron-diffraction studies of extraction replicas were made. Further details of experimental methods are given in the paper by Fell.[3]

EXPERIMENTAL RESULTS

General observations

These alloys are normally put into service after a two or three-stage heat treatment. The heat treaments commonly recommended are given in Table II.[4] These heat treatments are designed for alloys in aircraft gas turbines and other heat treatments may be given for other specific applications, but much of this paper is concerned with material which has received these standard heat treatments.

Other phases are present in addition to the nickel-rich matrix. All alloys contained two face-centred cubic phases of the TiC type, the two phases being frequently associated in the microstructure. One phase was carbon-rich with a lattice parameter around 4·33 Å,

TABLE I Typical alloy compositions

Alloy	Composition % C	Cr	Co	Ti	Al	Mo	Ni
Nimonic 80A	0·05	19·7	0·8	2·6	1·2	...	bal
Nimonic 90	0·07	20·4	19·1	2·4	1·2	...	,,
Nimonic 105	0·07	15·5	19·7	1·3	4·4	5·04	,,

TABLE II Standard heat treatments recommended for Nimonic alloys

Alloy	Heat treatment Stage 1	Stage 2	Stage 3
Nimonic 80A	8 h, 1080°C, AC	16 h, 700°C, AC	...
Nimonic 90	8 h, 1080°C, AC	16 h, 700°C, AC	...
Nimonic 105	4 h, 1150°C, AC	16 h, 1050°C, AC	16 h, 800°C, AC

the other nitrogen-rich with a lattice parameter of 4·24 Å. The nitrogen-rich phase appeared to be unaffected by heat treatment, but the carbon-rich phase was partially dissolved at high temperatures, and could be reprecipitated on subsequent ageing at lower temperatures. There is evidence, which will not be discussed further here, that these phases have no appreciable effect on the stress–rupture properties of the alloys.

All alloys contain a precipitate of face-centred cubic structure which is derived from the Ni_3Al phase of the binary nickel–aluminium system. Titanium can substitute extensively for aluminium in this structure[5, 6] and this phase will be referred to as $Ni_3(Ti,Al)$. Chromium also dissolves in this phase. A typical analysis of an electrolytically separated sample extracted from Nimonic 80A is: 6·2% Cr, 9·5% Ti, 5·2% Al, by weight, balance substantially nickel. The basic hardening mechanism of the alloys discussed in this paper is due to the presence of this $Ni_3(Ti,Al)$ phase. The amount of this phase, of course, increases with increase in titanium and aluminium content. It is taken into solution in the first stage of heat treatment given in Table II, and precipitated in the later stages.

The alloys differ in the carbides, other than TiC, which may be present. In Nimonic 80A, the first carbide present in stage 2 of the heat treatment is chromium-rich and isomorphous with Cr_7C_3, though other elements present in the matrix may substitute for part of the chromium. This phase, on longer ageing at temperatures in the range 500–1000°C, is progressively replaced by another chromium-rich carbide, isomorphous with $Cr_{23}C_6$. In Nimonic 90 only the $Cr_{23}C_6$ type of chromium-rich carbide has been detected. In Nimonic 105 $Cr_{23}C_6$ type carbide is produced initially, but this is subsequently replaced on prolonged ageing by a carbide isomorphous with Ni_3Mo_3C. X-ray fluorescent analysis revealed the presence of nickel, molybdenum, chromium and titanium in this phase which will be referred to subsequently as M_6C. In Nimonic 80A and 90 the temperature of stage 1 of the heat treatment is such that the carbides are not taken completely into solution. If the

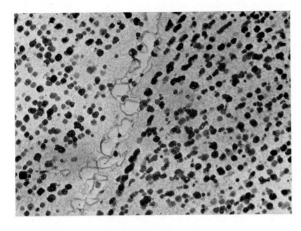

1 *Electron micrograph of Nimonic 80A after standard heat treatment* $\times 20\,000$

carbides are completely dissolved by the use of higher temperatures, extensive precipitation of carbide within the grains can occur in stage 2 of the heat treatment or in service. This is accompanied by deterioration in stress–rupture properties.

Morphology

The electron micrographs in Figs.1–3 indicate the similarity in general microstructure of the three alloys in the standard condition of heat treatment. The generally distributed $Ni_3(Ti,Al)$ phase increases in amount in Nimonic 80A, 90, and 105, and is distributed uniformly through the matrix. Although the titanium and aluminium contents in Nimonic 80A and 90 are similar, the cobalt content of Nimonic 90 decreases the solubility of the matrix for titanium and aluminium and hence increases the amount of $Ni_3(Ti,Al)$ which precipitates on heat treatment. The carbide phases are present mainly at grain boundaries, though occasionally within the grains. The titanium carbide and nitride phases, which are only present in small amounts, are distributed randomly and do not appear on these micrographs. It should also be noted that in Nimonic 80A and 90 there is a narrow region near the grain boundary precipitate which is substantially free of $Ni_3(Ti,Al)$ phase, or in which this phase is present in reduced amounts. This denuded zone is widest in Nimonic 80A, less extensive in Nimonic 90 and essentially absent in Nimonic 105. The grain boundary carbides are not extracted by the replication technique used, and appear light in the micrographs. The carbides in all these alloys can be seen more clearly in optical micrographs where a staining etch can be used to increase contrast.[7]

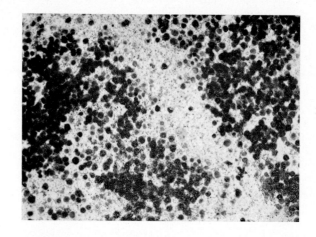

2 *Electron micrograph of Nimonic 90 after standard heat treatment* × 20 000

The increasing amount of $Ni_3(Ti,Al)$ in Nimonic 80A, 90 and 105 respectively is accompanied by an increase in size of the precipitated particles. The higher temperature of the final stage of heat treatment of Nimonic 105 also tends to increase the size of the $Ni_3(Ti,Al)$ precipitate in this alloy compared with Nimonic 80A and 90. Figure 2 also shows some very fine particles of $Ni_3(Ti,Al)$ dispersed over the microstructure: these particles were probably formed during air-cooling from stage 2 of the heat treatment.

Crystallographic relationships

The $Cr_{23}C_6$ carbide in Nimonic 80A can appear within the matrix on (111) phases of the matrix and occasionally on (110) phases.

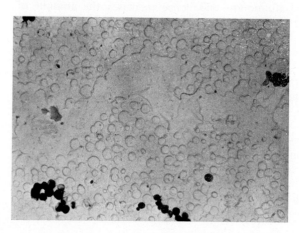

3 *Electron micrograph of Nimonic 105 after standard heat treatment* × 20 000

TABLE III Lattice parameters at 20°C of matrix and Ni₃(Ti,Al) for the alloys of Table I

a parameter	Nimonic 80A	Nimonic 90	Nimonic 105
Matrix	3·566	3·569	3·585
Ni₃(Ti,Al)	3·585	3·588	3·590

Electron diffraction examination of electrolytically extracted $Cr_{23}C_6$ particles showed them to be platelike, and extended in their (111) planes, and occasionally in (110) planes. It is reasonable to deduce that the intergranular precipitate of $Cr_{23}C_6$ is coplanar with the matrix.[3] It was similarly found by use of extraction replicas that the Ni₃(Ti,Al) phases in all the alloys was precipitated along and coplanar with the (100) phases of the matrix in agreement with the results obtained by Manenc.[8] No orientation relationships could be detected between the matrix and the grain boundary carbides, or between the matrix and the TiC and TiN phases.

The lattice parameters of the matrix and the Ni₃(Ti,Al) phases are similar in all the alloys. This is demonstrated in Table III, which gives the lattice parameters at 20°C of the matrix and of Ni₃(Ti,Al) extracted electrolytically from the alloys of Table I. The close similarity of parameter between the matrix and Ni₃(Ti,Al) can be seen; although in the absence of data for the expansion coefficient of the Ni₃(Ti,Al) phase it is not possible to estimate whether the parameters are so closely related at the service temperatures for the alloys. It is also of interest to note that the cell size of the face-centred-cubic carbide $Cr_{23}C_6$ in Nimonic 80A and 90 is about 10·63Å, a near multiple of the lattice parameter of the matrix.

The effect of further heat treatment and of creep strain on constitution

The effect of a range of times and temperatures in both stage 1 and stage 2 of heat treatment of Nimonic 80A and other variations in heat treatment may be summarized as follows. After completion of stage 2 of the heat treatment of Nimonic 80A, Cr_7C_3 is the major carbide phase present. This carbide is not taken completely into solution during stage 1, and carbide precipitation during stage 2 occurs at the grain boundaries and on carbide particles which remain undissolved after the stage 1 heat treatment. On prolonged heat treatment at stage 2 temperature (700°C) for example, 20% of the carbide present is $Cr_{23}C_6$ after 75 h, 50% $Cr_{23}C_6$ after 400 h, and only $Cr_{23}C_6$ is present after times in excess of 2 000 h. Fuller data, in the form of TTT diagrams, of the progress of the dissolution

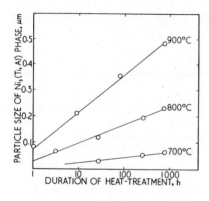

4 *Particle size of $Ni_3(Ti,Al)$ in Nimonic 80A, after solution treatment 8 h at 1080°C, air-cool, aged at times and temperatures shown*

of Cr_7C_3 and precipitation of $Cr_{23}C_6$ are given by Fell.[3] The analogous transformation in Nimonic 105 from $Cr_{23}C_6$ to M_6C proceeds in the same manner, but at a slower rate, though this reaction has not been studied in the same detail as for Nimonic 80A. In Nimonic 105 there is, in addition, at long times of heat treatment some precipitation of a small amount of an additional phase around the grain boundary carbides, and there is some metallographic evidence that this phase is $Ni_3(Ti,Al)$.

The particle size of $Ni_3(Ti,Al)$ phase increased during prolonged heat treatment. This is shown for Nimonic 80A in Fig.4, where the particle size of $Ni_3(Ti,Al)$, estimated from electron micrographs, is given as a function of time at various heat-treatment temperatures. Although few quantitative data are available as yet, the rate of growth of $Ni_3(Ti,Al)$ appears to be less in Nimonic 90 and 105 than

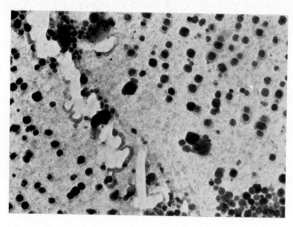

5 *Electron micrograph of Nimonic 80A after creep testing for 230 h at 750°C × 20 000*

142

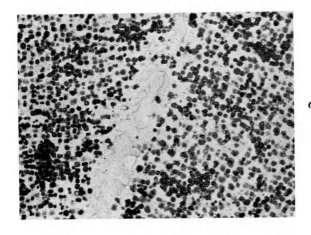

6 *Electron micrograph of Nimonic 09 after creep testing for 250 h at 750°C × 20 000*

in Nimonic 80A, although starting from a larger initial particle size. Creep strain appears to increase to some extent the rate of growth of the $Ni_3(Ti,Al)$ phase, although the acceleration of growth is less marked than in the grain boundary carbides.

The general morphology of the alloys after creep testing for about 200 h at 750°C is illustrated by the electron micrographs of Figs.5–7. These show some changes in the grain boundary carbides and a slight increase in size of the $Ni_3(Ti,Al)$ precipitate, accompanied by a change of shape to a more cubic form. There is also an increase during creep testing in the width of the zone near the grain boundary which is free of $Ni_3(Ti,Al)$, particularly in Nimonic 80A and 90.

A further point is illustrated in Fig.8 from a specimen of Nimonic

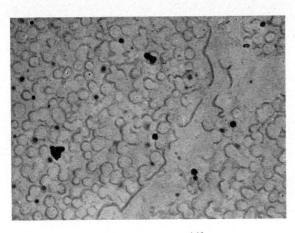

7 *Electron micrograph of Nimonic 105 after creep testing for 430 h at 750°C × 20 000*

143

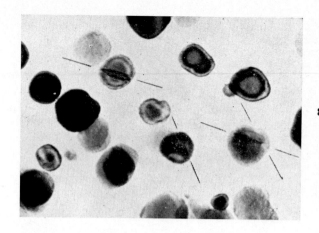

8 *Nimonic 80A at high magnification, showing distortion of Ni₃(Ti,Al) particles ×150000*

80A. This shows at high magnification that some $Ni_3(Ti,Al)$ particles appear to be distorted, possibly by slip, and others show internal structure, which may be stacking faults. These are indicated by lines in the figure.

DISCUSSION

The assessment of the influence on mechanical properties of the structural phenomena described above must be somewhat speculative, but certain qualitative deductions may be made.

It was noted that the $Ni_3(Ti,Al)$ phase, which has an ordered face-centred cubic structure, is very similar in lattice spacing to the matrix and is precipitated in parallel orientation. Since it is formed at a relatively high temperature, it is likely that the interface between precipitate and matrix is in the form of a dislocation array. This would be equivalent to a low angle boundary of low surface energy which could be responsible for the slow rate of growth of $Ni_3(Ti,Al)$ particles illustrated in Fig.4. Thus the basic resistance to creep deformation is probably provided by the obstacle to dislocation movement inherent in an array of $Ni_3(Ti,Al)$ particles of relatively stable size.

For many applications at high temperatures a long time to rupture is more important than low rates of deformation in creep as such. Franklin and Betteridge[7] have shown for Nimonic 80A that fracture can occur during creep testing at a relatively small extension if an unfavourable carbide distribution is present, so that life to fracture may be short despite a low creep rate. In particular, alloys with less than 0·03% carbon show this behaviour. Alloys with carbon in excess of 0·1% show high creep rates and excessive extension at fracture, and may also have a short life to fracture. It is, however, sometimes possible to obtain good creep properties in high carbon alloys by specialized heat treatments. Similar considerations are known to apply to Nimonic 90. In general, variations in stage 1 of the heat treatments, which have little effect on the size and distribution of the $Ni_3(Ti,Al)$ phase, but which affect most strongly the distribution of the carbide phase, can also affect life to fracture.

Since the carbide precipitate at the grain boundary is chromium-rich, it seems logical to assume that there is a chromium concentration gradient near the boundary. The relevant phase diagram[9] indicates that a decrease in chromium content of the alloy increases the solubility of titanium and aluminium in the matrix. As a result, there will be a zone near the grain boundary where less $Ni_3(Ti,Al)$ precipitate will form. The gradient will tend to be maintained by any reaction involving a migration of chromium to the boundary, such as the Cr_7C_3 to $Cr_{23}C_6$ reaction in Nimonic 80A.

In Nimonic 90, the amount of grain boundary carbide is less after the normal heat treatment, and no carbide reaction takes place: the denuded zone is thus of lesser extent than in Nimonic 80A, as shown in Fig.6. In Nimonic 105, the presence of molybdenum and the complex composition of the M_6C carbide, which may well be lower in chromium, leads to a denuded zone which is even less marked.

It is suggested that the main benefit derived from the grain boundary carbide in these alloys is, in fact, to promote this denuded zone. During creep the deformation of the grains and any grain-boundary sliding will give rise to high local stresses at grain boundaries and grain corners. The presence of a denuded zone, of somewhat lower creep strength, may allow the relaxation of these local stresses. Hence the formation of cracks or voids at grain boundaries and the onset of fracture are delayed so that the time to fracture is prolonged despite a slightly higher creep rate compared with alloys of low carbon content. This agrees with the work mentioned above, where a very low carbon content, associated with a small denuded zone, leads to early fracture at a relatively small extension. The observation that high carbon content, with a correspondingly larger denuded zone leads to a high creep rate, excessive extension at fracture and short creep life, is the converse of this condition. This seems to imply that for a given state of strengthening of the grains there is an optimum degree of weakening at the grain boundary for maximum stress–rupture life. Thus on proceeding from Nimonic 80A, through Nimonic 90 to Nimonic 105, with increasingly strengthened grains, the boundary regions should be correspondingly less weakened. It may be concluded from the electron micrographs of Figs.5–7 that this occurs in practice.

In summary, these alloys consist of a matrix strengthened by a general and stable precipitate of $Ni_3(Ti,Al)$ phase, combined with the formation at the grain boundaries, of zones which are sufficiently weak to permit relaxation of local stresses. This is obviously an over-simplified picture in that, for example, any influence of alloying elements on the properties of the matrix phase itself is ignored. Furthermore, the possibility that slip may occur in particles of the $Ni_3(Ti,Al)$ phase under some conditions, as illustrated by Fig.8, may indicate an alternative mechanism for the relief of local stresses in these alloys. However, the dependence of creep properties on microstructure and heat treatment appears to be consistent with the general picture described above.

ACKNOWLEDGMENT

The authors are indebted to The International Nickel Company (Mond) Ltd for permission to publish this paper.

REFERENCES

1. L. B. PFEIL et al.: 'Symposium on high-temperature steels and alloys for gas turbines', *ISI Spec. Rep. no.* 43, 1952, 37–45.
2. W. BETTERIDGE: 'The Nimonic alloys'; 1959, London, Edward Arnold Ltd.
3. E. A. FELL: *Metallurgia*, in press.
4. 'The Nimonic alloys, engineering data', 1960, 6th edn.; Birmingham, Henry Wiggin and Co. Ltd.
5. J. R. MIHALISIN and R. F. DECKER: *Trans. AIME*, 1960, **218**, 507–515.
6. A. TAYLOR and R. W. FLOYD: *J. Inst. Met.*, 1952–3, **81**, 25–32.
7. W. BETTERIDGE and A. W. FRANKLIN: *ibid.*, 1956–7, **85**, 473–479.
8. J. MANENC: *Rev. Met.*, 1957, **54**, 161–168.
9. A. TAYLOR: *Trans. AIME*, 1956, **206**, 1356–1362.

The metallography of creep-resistant alloys

J. Nutting, M.A., B.Sc., Ph.D., F.I.M., and J. M. Arrowsmith, M.A., Ph.D.

The influence of solute elements in promoting creep resistance is discussed in relation to the mechanism of cross-slip and the formation of stacking faults. The rôle of dispersed phases in preventing dislocation movement is outlined and the methods of obtaining dispersions are described. The factors governing the structural stability of dispersed phase systems are analysed and the importance of the interfacial energy of the precipitate matrix interface and of the specific volumes of the two phases is discussed. The creep ductility of a dispersed phase alloy is shown to depend upon the morphology of the grain-boundary precipitates and the modes of dislocation movement at high temperatures.

INTRODUCTION

IN DEVELOPING creep-resistant alloys, certain well established design principles have emerged. During the past few years, as a result of improvements in metallographic techniques, the underlying science on which these design principles are based has been studied so that it is now possible at least to specify, if not to achieve, the microstructural requirements of an alloy for good creep resistance.

One important constraint which has to be applied to an alloy used for creep resistance is that of oxidation resistance. To achieve this requirement, chemical compositions must be adopted which, from the point of view of creep resistance may lead to unsatisfactory microstructures, and therefore compromises have to be made. The inter-relation of creep and oxidation resistance is not discussed in this paper, but an attempt will be made to outline the various metallographic features necessary in a creep-resistant alloy.

Creep resistance is achieved by producing a complex solid solution, and then distributing throughout this fine particles of another

Professor Nutting is Professor of Metallurgy at The University of Leeds, and Dr Arrowsmith is with Colvilles Ltd.

phase. At the service temperature it is hoped that the dispersed phase will be stable, i.e. the particles will not agglomerate, but in practice such a condition can rarely be obtained. In certain applications, e.g. turbine blades, the amount of creep deformation which can be tolerated is small, whereas in other cases, e.g. superheater tubes, relatively large strains can be accommodated. With the simple microstructural specification outlined above, the alloy should be creep resistant and have a good creep ductility. However, the metallurgical treatments which give good creep resistance are usually associated with poor creep ductility. Most attempts to improve creep ductility, simply by modification of the heat treatment, usually end up by lowering creep resistance. By knowing the microstructural features associated with poor creep ductility, it is possible by minor changes in chemical composition to improve ductility without affecting creep resistance.

One other constraint which has to be imposed frequently is that a creep-resistant alloy should have adequate room temperature properties. In systems based on a face-centred cubic matrix this constraint is not severe. But where a body-centred cubic matrix is used, the alloying elements in solid solution may raise the tough–brittle transition temperature well above room temperature and alleviation of this difficulty invariably leads to a lowering of the creep resistance.

SOLID SOLUTION HARDENING

It is now generally accepted that the creep resistance of a pure metal may be increased by alloying with elements which will go into solid solution. To explain this effect it is generally assumed that the solute elements distort the solvent lattice, so making it more difficult for dislocations to move. Recent metallographic investigations have shown, however, that this simple explanation is not entirely satisfactory. Studies of the deformation structures of alloys based upon iron,[1] aluminium,[2] and copper[3] have shown that with increasing solute content, the slip bands become straighter and the amount of slip in each slip plane increases. These effects indicate that the addition of alloying elements makes cross-slip more difficult. The tendency to cross-slip in fcc alloys is related to their stacking fault energy; if the stacking fault energy is low, the dislocations dissociate and the partials are widely separated, and before cross-slip can occur the partials must re-combine. When the stacking fault energy is high, the partial dislocations are close together and the extra energy required to make them associate is relatively low so that cross-slip is easy.

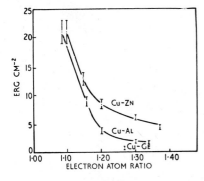

1 *Influence of solute content upon stacking fault energy of Cu-rich solid solutions (after Swann[3]).*

By measuring the radius of curvature of extended nodes produced by dislocation interactions, Whelan[4] has shown that it is possible to determine the magnitude of stacking fault energies. Applying this technique to a range of copper alloys, Swann[3] found that the stacking fault energy depends upon the amount of solute in solid solution and upon the solute valency. The results obtained are given in Fig.1.

Creep resistance is achieved in an alloy by providing barriers to dislocation movements. These barriers may be overcome by the dislocations cross-slipping around them or climbing over them. If the dislocations are widely dissociated, then cross-slip becomes more difficult, similarly, before climb can take place the partial dislocations must associate to allow a vacancy to condense.

It is probable, therefore, that the alloying elements in solid solution confer creep resistance to the system by lowering the stacking fault energy, so enabling the dislocations to dissociate, and hence making it difficult for climb or cross-slip of dislocations to occur.

A further possibility is that the solute elements may segregate to the dissociated dislocations, thus lowering the stacking fault energy further and making it difficult for dislocations to move through the lattice. Suzuki[5] first proposed a hardening mechanism of this type; direct evidence for it has now been obtained by Swann[3] who has found unusual contrast effects in the electron optical images from stacking faults. An example of this effect is shown in Fig.2. Swann postulates that the striations running parallel to the partial dislocations are a form of moiré pattern resulting from local strain in the lattice produced by solute segregation to the stacking fault.

At high temperatures it is possible that such atmospheres would disperse. At lower temperatures of creep testing they are likely to hinder the movement of dislocations through the lattice and the temperature will still be high enough for the soluble elements to diffuse to the stacking faults as they move through the lattice.

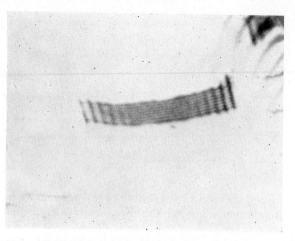

Note: All micrographs have been reduced photographically $\times \frac{3}{4}$

2 *Cu–8%Al alloy, annealed. The stacking fault shows normal striations running perpendicular to the partial dislocations. The fine striations running parallel to the partials are a moiré pattern produced by a local change of lattice parameter at the region of the stacking fault. The change of lattice parameter could occur by segregation of Al to the stacking fault (after Swann*[3]*)   Thin foil* $\times$ *70 000*

THE INFLUENCE OF DISPERSED PHASES

A more permanent barrier to the movement of dislocations may be produced by dispersing particles within a matrix. Barriers of this type may be overcome by shear, when the dislocation will pass through the second phase. An alternative mechanism has been proposed by Orowan[6] in which dislocation loops are produced around the particles. Thomas and Nutting[7] found that cross-slip took place, and more recently Ashby and Smith[8] have found direct confirmation of this mechanism and have shown that in fact prismatic dislocation loops are left around a dispersed phase (*see* Fig.3).

Ansell and Weertman,[9] in considering the rôle of dispersed phases in creep resistance, postulated that different deformation mechanisms would prevail at low and high stresses. At low stresses the dislocations would be held up by the particles until they could climb over them by the absorption of vacancies. The dislocation sources could only produce a new dislocation when climb had occurred. Under these circumstances the creep rate would be proportional to the applied stress. At high stresses the dislocations are forced past the precipitate barriers leaving dislocation loops behind. These loops exert a back stress on the dislocation source and new dislocations will only be produced when the loops have climbed

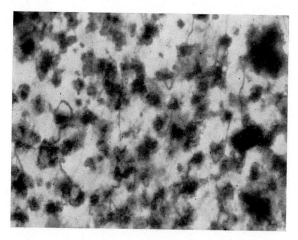

3 *Cu–0·25%Al alloy, internally oxidized for 20 min at 950°C and then deformed 4% in tension at room temperature. Triangular prismatic dislocation loops have formed around the γ-alumina particles (after Ashby and Smith[8])*

Thin foil × 180000

away. Under these conditions the creep rate should be proportioned to the fourth power of the applied stress. Experimental evidence was obtained to support these conclusions.

To maintain creep resistance at high temperatures the dispersed phase must be stable, and at the same time it must be hard so that it will resist shearing by the glissile dislocations. If the particle may be bypassed by climb, then the particle matrix interface must not act as a source of vacancies which would facilitate the process.

Alloys of high supersaturation

In most creep-resistant alloys dispersion is produced by the decomposition of a supersaturated solid solution. In alloys where a high-degree supersaturation can be achieved, the sequence of the reactions which occur is as follows: zones→intermediate precipitate→equilibrium precipitates. A zone may be defined as a region within the matrix lattice in which a change of composition occurs without a change of phase. The transition of a zone into an intermediate precipitate usually occurs at a temperature of 0·4 to 0·5 T_m (where T_m is the absolute melting temperature). As the alloy is likely to be used in this temperature range it follows that the zones would not be stable.

When the intermediate phases form, the interface between matrix and precipitate is initially coherent; this implies that any strain

151

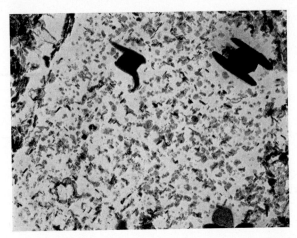

4 *Steel containing 2·7%Mo, and 0·7%V, quenched from the austenitic region and tempered for 50 h at 700°C. A fine dispersion of V_4C_3 in ferrite has been produced. Large needles of M_6C have grown from the large V_4C_3 particles. Carbon extraction replica* × 40 000

developed by misfit between the lattices of the two phases is accommodated by an elastic strain field. As the intermediate phase grows, the coherency strain becomes so large that structural dislocations are nucleated, and the interface is now said to be partially coherent. Most dispersed phase creep-resistant alloys have interfaces of this type. When the intermediate phase forms, the degree of supersaturation of the solvent is usually reduced almost to equilibrium value and the growth of the precipitates is then controlled by the diffusion of solute from the small particles to the large particles.

The equilibrium phase usually forms at temperatures $0·5\,T_m$ and has an incoherent interface with the matrix, with an interfacial energy which approaches that of a grain boundary. Because of the relatively high temperature required for their formation the equilibrium precipitates are usually large in size, and having a high interfacial energy with the matrix they spheroidize rapidly. Examples of rapid spheroidization are the formation of $M_{23}C_6$ and M_6C on the tempering of ferritic alloy steels. Therefore, to achieve good creep resistance with alloys containing incoherent precipitates, the composition has to be adjusted so that the interfacial energy of the particles is as low as possible.

Creep-resistant alloys, in which dispersion is achieved by the decomposition of highly supersaturated solid solutions, are the

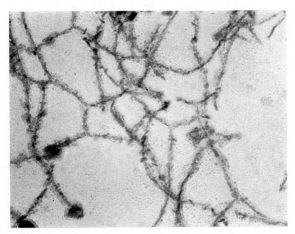

5 *Steel G18B containing 0·4%C, 13%Cr, 13%Ni, 10%Co, 1·8%Mo, 2·5%W, and 3%Nb. Solution treated at 1300°C, air cooled and tempered for 20 h at 700°C. Fine strings of NbC have formed on the dislocation network. Carbon extraction replica* × *160000*

Nimonics, austenitic steels which do not contain very strong carbide-forming elements, and the secondary hardening ferritic steels. A typical microstructure of a ferritic creep-resistant steel is given in Fig.4.

Alloys of low supersaturation

In alloys where the degree of supersaturation which may be obtained on quenching is small, the decomposition of the solid solution does not follow the pattern outlined above. Nucleation is difficult with low degrees of supersaturation, and the new phase can only form at favourable sites such as dislocations. An example of this type of precipitation is shown in Fig.5 where NbC precipitating from an austenite has formed on the dislocations. The dispersions which can be produced in this way are not as uniform as those obtained when decomposing highly supersaturated solid solutions, but they have the merit of producing the particles where they are most needed, i.e. on the dislocations. To achieve a more uniform dispersion of the precipitates the alloy may be deformed at the temperature at which precipitation is occurring. In this way the dislocation density is increased and consequently there are more sites for precipitation. As the total quantity of the precipitated phase will not be changed appreciably by the deformation, the size of the

153

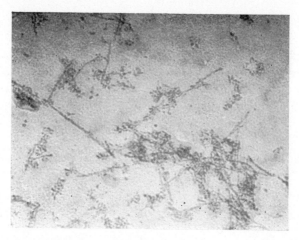

6 *Steel G18B solution treated at 1300°C air cooled and then warm worked at 700°C to give a 10% reduction of area. Very fine particles of NbC have formed on the dislocations. Carbon extraction replica* ×160000

individual particles will be smaller after the deformation treatment. An example of the structure obtained is given in Fig.6. Warm working of this type is known to improve the creep resistance of certain austenitic steels; it is doubtful, however, if it will be very effective in improving the properties of those alloys where the dispersion is obtained by decomposing a highly supersaturated solid solution.

Dislocations may be generated in two-phase alloys on cooling from a high temperature if the coefficient of thermal expansion of the matrix and the dispersed phase differ. An example of this effect has been observed in G18B (an austenitic steel containing 0·4%C, 13%Cr, 13%Ni, 10%Co, 1·8%Mo, 2·5%W, and 3%Nb). At the solution treatment temperature the steel contains massive undissolved NbC.

On cooling, the austenite matrix having the higher coefficient of thermal expansion contracts on to the carbides, high stresses are produced, and dislocations are generated. On tempering the steel at 700°C, NbC precipitates on to the dislocations, so decorating them and allowing their positions to be determined with the aid of an extraction replica. The structure observed is shown in Fig.7.

Examples of alloys in which the dispersion is achieved by dislocation nucleation are the austenitic steels containing strong carbideforming elements such as niobium, and the lowly alloyed ferritic steels which are used in the normalized condition.

7 *Steel G18.B solution treated at 1300°C, air cooled and tempered for 20 h at 700°C. A massive NbC was undissolved at 1300°C and on cooling thermal contraction stresses have given rise to dislocations on two slip systems. On tempering NbC has precipitated on these dislocations. Carbon extraction replica*

× 40 000

Internal oxidation

An alternative method of producing a dispersion is by internal oxidation. Oxygen is allowed to diffuse into an alloy containing a small amount of an element in solid solution which reacts readily to form a stable oxide. The dispersion produced in this way is characteristic of that obtained by decomposing a highly supersaturated solid solution, and because of the stability of the dispersion, creep resistance may be achieved up to relatively high temperatures. However, the alloys usually show poor creep ductility. An example of the structure obtained by internal oxidation is given in Fig.8.

In all the cases discussed so far the dispersed phase has been formed within the grains. An entirely different class of alloys are those of the sintered aluminium powder (SAP) type. The microstructure of these alloys shows a very small grain size, whilst there is a dispersed phase distributed at the grain corners. The microstructure is shown in Fig.9. There is much that is not understood about the metallography of SAP and its mode of creep deformation. But in view of its microstructure it is rather surprising that it has good creep resistance at temperatures up to $0.7\ T_m$. Ansell[10] has proposed that in SAP the effect of the dispersed phase is to inactivate

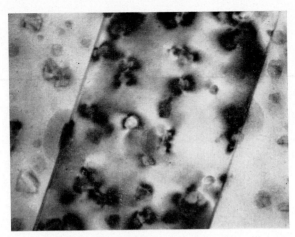

8 *Cu–0·25%Al alloy internally oxidized for 20 min at 950°C. γ-alumina particles are formed, and on cooling the thermal contraction stresses give rise to strain fields in the surrounding matrix. The strain fields are visible in the twin where the orientation is favourable for their detection (after Ashby and Smith[8])*
Thin foil × 180 000

dislocation sources rather than, as in the more normal case of dispersion hardening, hinder dislocation movement.

9 *SAP in the as-extruded condition. Particles of alumina are present at the boundaries of the very small Al grains (after Coiley and Phillips). Thin foil prepared by sectioning with a diamond microtome* × 120 000

THE STABILITY OF THE DISPERSED PHASE

Under conditions of creep testing there are two factors influencing the stability of precipitate dispersions, namely, the temperature and the applied stress. Under actual service conditions one other factor has to be considered: the temperature fluctuations. The higher the temperature the greater the rate of diffusion of the solute, hence the greater the tendency to approach the equilibrium state. Under the action of stress, dislocation movements and multiplication occur. The dislocations probably facilitate diffusion; they certainly provide sites for precipitate nucleation. Temperature fluctuations may result in the generation of stresses far higher than those normally applied under service conditions and these stresses will give rise to unusual dislocation distributions which in turn may modify locally the growth of the dispersed phases.

The mechanism of precipitate growth

At the creep-testing temperatures the solute content of the solid solution will be almost the equilibrium value, and under these conditions the growth of the dispersed phases will occur by the small particles going into solution and the large particles growing larger.

This process may be considered in relation to the equation which relates the solute concentration in the matrix to the particle size

$$\ln \frac{C_r}{C_\infty} = \frac{2V\gamma}{rRT} \quad . \qquad . \quad . \quad . \quad . \quad \text{(i)}$$

where C_r is concentration of solute elements adjacent to a particle of radius r and composed of the solute elements; C_∞ is concentration of solute adjacent to a particle of infinite radius, i.e. the equilibrium concentration; V is volume per mol. of the dispersed phase; γ is the interfacial energy of the dispersed phase and the matrix; r is particle radius; T is temperature; and R is gas constant.

From equation (i) it follows that if there is a wide size range in the particles of the dispersed phase, large solute concentration differences may be set up within the matrix, consequently diffusion will occur readily and growth will be rapid. Uniformly sized dispersions will be obtained by rapid heating of the supersaturated solid solutions to the precipitating temperature.

Although an increase in temperature will decrease the value of C_r/C_∞ the exponential dependence of diffusion rate upon temperature will more than offset this decrease, and as a result rates of spheroidization are likely to increase with temperature. Experimental evidence to support this has been obtained by Hyam and Nutting[11] when examining the tempering of plain carbon steels.

If the surface energy of the precipitate matrix interface is high, the ratio C_r/C_∞ will be large, consequently large concentration differences will be set up, diffusion will occur readily, and this will lead to rapid particle growth. The surface energy will depend upon the nature of the precipitated phase. If it is a metastable intermediate phase, it is likely to be partially coherent with the matrix and consequently have a low surface energy; if it is an equilibrium phase it is likely to have an incoherent interface and a high interfacial energy. It is possible to change the particle matrix interfacial energy by adding another alloying element which may be soluble in either the matrix, the precipitate, or both. The lattice parameters of the precipitate and the matrix may then be changed so that the degree of mismatch across the interface is lowered and consequently the surface energy decreased. An example of this effect, discussed by Smith and Nutting,[12] and Baker and Nutting,[13] is the rapid rate of growth of V_4C_3 in ferritic steels when the V/C ratio exceeds 4. The excess vanadium in solid solution beyond that required to form V_4C_3 changes the lattice parameters of the ferrite so that matching does not occur so readily. By adding Mo, which is soluble in both the ferrite and the V_4C_3, to the steel, the growth rate of V_4C_3 may be decreased.

To keep the growth rate low the value of C_∞ should be low. This implies that the free energy of the precipitated phase should be low, i.e. a stable compound should be formed, preferably with ionic binding rather than a terminal solid solution. Other solutes may be added to give solid solution strengthening of the matrix provided they do not hinder the formation of the dispersed phase. Chromium in Nimonic alloys, apart from giving oxidation resistance, must exert a solid solution hardening effect whilst the precipitated γ' phase does not contain much of this element.

Changes in specific volume

Up to now it has been considered that the rate-controlling process for the growth of the dispersed phase is the diffusion of the solutes through the matrix. This may not always be the case. If the dispersed phase has a greater specific volume than that of the matrix, then as the small particles go into solution, vacancies will be created at the interface, and as the large particles grow, stresses may be produced which could lead to the generation of dislocations and the formation of interstitials. Growth could continue by the migration of vacancies to the particles, and this would be the rate-controlling process. If the specific volume of the dispersed phase were smaller than that of the matrix, the growing particles would be the sources of vacancies and the dissolving particles the sinks.

Whilst these effects may be of merely academic interest in relation to the stability of the dispersion, they are of importance when considering creep behaviour. Unless the specific volumes of the dispersed phase and the matrix are the same, with an unstable dispersion, there is bound to be an extra source of vacancies at the precipitate matrix interface. These vacancies are produced at sites where they are most likely to favour the climb of dislocations over obstacles, therefore, in order to obtain good creep resistance, such vacancy sources should be avoided. The rapid creep rates found in certain ferritic steels, when there is a change from one carbide type to another, could be accounted for by this effect. It would seem, also, that carbides are not ideal as a dispersed phase for conferring creep resistance to steels, since the specific volumes of carbides are always much higher than those of the matrix solid solutions of austenite or ferrite.

Instability during creep

The influence of stress upon the growth of precipitated phases may be determined experimentally by examining specimens after differing creep treatments. This has been attempted in the complex austenitic steel G18B. The form of the NbC after 10% reduction of

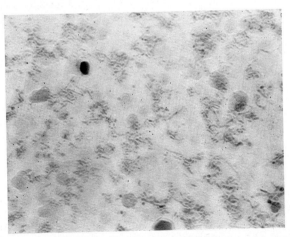

10 *Steel G18B solution-treated at 1300°C air cooled and warm worked at 700°C to give 10% reduction of area, then tempered for 2000 h at 700°C. The NbC particles are almost identical in size with those shown in Fig.6. Carbon extraction replica* × 160000

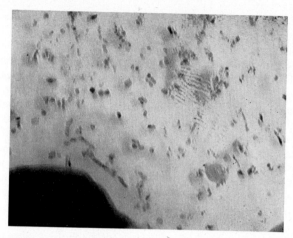

11 *Steel G18B after same heat treatment as Fig.10, but then creep-tested at a stress of 3 tons/in² for 2 000 h at 700°C giving 0·3% strain. Some growth of the NbC has occurred (cf. Fig.10)* × 160 000

area by warm working at 700°C is shown in Fig.6. On tempering for a further 2 000 h at 700°C there was negligible growth of the NbC, as shown in Fig.10. However, when the steel was creep-tested for 2 000 h at 700°C, under a stress of 3 tons/in², although only a strain of 0·3% was obtained, some growth of the NbC occurred as shown in Fig.11.

By increasing the stress to 8 tons/in² at 700°C a creep strain of 14·6% was obtained in 18 000 h, and after this treatment the NbC had grown considerably and was present chiefly on the slip planes of the austenitic matrix, as shown in Fig.12.

It seems that the effect of stress is to accelerate the growth of precipitates, but it is also probable that the amount of dislocation movement, i.e. the strain, will also play an important rôle. There is still much to be learnt about the influence of creep-testing conditions upon the morphology of precipitated phases.

CREEP DUCTILITY

In dispersed phase creep-resistant alloys the total elongation at failure is found to depend upon the prior heat treatment of the alloy and the creep-testing conditions. The heat treatment will influence the microstructural type, whilst the modes of creep deformation will depend upon the microstructure and the applied stress.

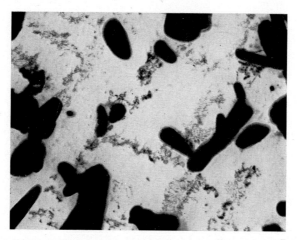

12 *Steel G18B after same heat treatment as Fig.10 but then creep-tested at a stress of 8 tons/in² for 18 000 h at 700°C giving a strain of 14·6%. Fine particles of NbC are formed on the slip planes of the austenite. The massive particles are Fe₂(MoW) precipitated after the long heat treatment. Carbon extraction replica* × 40 000

The influence of microstructure

During the decomposition of highly supersaturated solid solutions, preferential nucleation may occur at the grain boundaries, and as a result large precipitates grow there and denude regions adjacent to the boundary of solute elements. Another possibility is that on cooling from the solution-treatment temperature, the excess thermal vacancies will diffuse to the grain boundary leaving a vacancy-denuded region adjacent to the boundary. On decomposing the supersaturated solid solution, precipitate nucleation will be difficult in the vacancy-denuded zone. In each case a precipitate-free region will be found adjacent to the boundary, but in the former case this region will be denuded of solute, whilst in the latter it will be solute rich. Thomas and Nutting[14] have shown that solute-rich regions are likely at low ageing temperatures, whilst at high ageing temperatures grain boundary precipitates and solute-deficient regions are to be expected. An example of precipitate-free region close to a grain boundary is shown in Fig.13.

If an alloy is aged at a relatively low temperature and then creep-tested below this temperature, dislocations moving near the grain boundaries will be passing through solute-rich regions and, therefore will not move much more readily than through the body of the grain; a good ductility would therefore be expected. When the

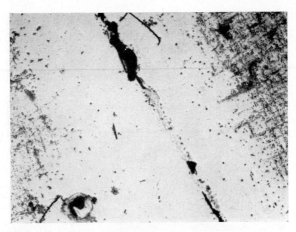

13 *Steel containing 0·4%C, 13%Cr, 13%Ni, 10%Co, solution treated at 1300°C, air cooled and then tempered for 20 h at 700°C. $M_{23}C_6$ particles have formed at the grain boundaries and have spheroidized during tempering. This is a precipitate-free zone adjacent to the boundary whilst within the grains there is a fine dispersion of $M_{23}C_6$. Carbon extraction replica* ×3 200

alloy is aged at a higher temperature there will be a precipitate-free and solute-deficient region adjacent to the boundary; consequently dislocations will move much more readily here than through the body of the grain, whilst it will be difficult for dislocations to be forced through the boundary because of the almost continuous chains of particles which have been precipitated there. As a result, high local strains develop which give rise to intercrystalline fracture even though the macroscopic elongation is small.

By increasing the ageing temperature, the grain-boundary precipitates spheroidize and grow chiefly along the grain edges and corners rather than along the grain surfaces, whilst the precipitates within the grains become larger and more widely dispersed. The precipitate-free regions at the grain boundaries are no longer so apparent, consequently dislocation movement can take place readily within the grains whilst dislocation movement across the boundaries is not greatly impeded; thus a large elongation is obtained before fracture occurs. However, the creep resistance of the alloy will have been decreased by the high ageing temperature giving rise to a coarse precipitate dispersion.

To achieve good ductility whilst still maintaining creep resistance it is necessary to modify the grain-boundary precipitates. In certain alloy steels and Nimonics, low creep ductility is associated with the form of the $M_{23}C_6$ at the grain boundaries. The addition of small amounts of boron to these alloys, which because of its atomic size segregates to the boundaries, modifies the morphology of the $M_{23}C_6$ and leads to an improved creep ductility.

In alloys where the degree of supersaturation is low, adequate creep ductility is to be expected after ageing, for although grain-boundary precipitates are formed and there are adjacent precipitate-free zones, the precipitates within the grains are dislocation nucleated, and the density is not sufficiently large to hinder greatly dislocation movement through the grains. However, as Younger and Baker[15] have shown in the case of 18%Cr, 12%Ni, 1%Nb steels, if the dislocation density is increased within the grains there is an increase in the number of NbC precipitates, and these may so hinder dislocation movement through the grains that highly localized flow occurs at the grain boundary leading to fracture with low macroscopic elongations.

Influence of creep-testing conditions

In alloys which have been heat treated to give adequate creep ductility when tested at a high stress, it is frequently found that failure occurs with a low elongation if the stress is decreased.

The general pattern of behaviour is as shown in Fig.14. At high stresses failure occurs in a short time with a high elongation, at very low stresses failure occurs in a long time again with high elongation, but at intermediate stress levels failure occurs with low elongation. With pure metals it is generally found that the elongation at failure decreases with decreasing stress. This probably means that as the stress decreases there is a difference in the mode of creep deformation. To deform a metal at room temperature a relatively high stress is required and it is probable that dislocation sources both within the grains and at the grain boundaries are active. The boundary displacements shown by Brandon and Nutting[16] could be

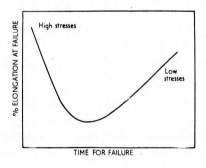

14 *Dependence of the elongation during creep testing at constant temperature upon the time for failure.*

accounted for by the grain boundaries acting as dislocation sources. Similarly, at elevated temperatures and high stresses the two types of sources would be active. At low stress levels and high temperatures it is probable that grain boundary sources will become inactive, and consequently creep deformation will occur chiefly by the grains rolling over each other rather than by an overall change of grain shape. This implies a highly localized strain at the grain boundary regions, which leads to intercrystalline failure with a low total elongation.

The increase in ductility found in the dispersion hardened alloys as the stress is reduced still further, could be accounted for by microstructural instability. To produce failure at low stress, a long time at temperature is required and this may be sufficient to spheroidize the grain-boundary precipitates.

CONCLUSIONS

1. Alloying elements which go into solid solution improve creep resistance by making cross-slip and climb more difficult. In fcc materials the effect of the alloying elements is to change the stacking fault energy. Solute elements may segregate to the stacking faults and so make it difficult for the partial dislocations to move through the lattice or to associate.

2. Dispersion hardened creep-resistant alloys are of two main types, those containing a uniform dispersion of precipitates obtained by decomposing a highly supersaturated solid solution, and those containing precipitates chiefly on the dislocations, a type of dispersion which is obtained when decomposing only slightly supersaturated solid solutions.

3. Thermal contraction stresses in the region of massive undissolved phases may lead to dislocation generation. This effect is an important source of dislocations acting as precipitate nucleating sites in certain alloys. Stresses of this type may be important as dislocation sources under actual service conditions where frequent temperature fluctuations occur.

4. The thermal stability of a dispersion-hardened system will be increased by lowering the interfacial energy between the precipitate and the matrix and by lowering the free energy of the precipitated phase.

5. In a thermally unstable system enhanced creep resistance is likely to result if the specific volumes of the matrix and the precipitate are equal.

6. Creep ductility in dispersion-hardened alloys can be correlated with the morphology of the grain-boundary precipitates, the extent

of the precipitate-free region adjacent to the boundary, and the degree of dispersion of the precipitates within the grains.

7. The stress dependence of the creep ductility is associated with a change in mode of creep deformation. High stresses tend to favour the boundaries acting as dislocation sources whilst low stresses favour grain boundary sliding.

ACKNOWLEDGMENTS

One of the authors (J.M.A.) would like to thank the British Iron and Steel Research Association for the award of a bursary. They would both, also, like to thank the MG/J Committee of BISRA for much useful advice, and Mr H. Child of Jessop-Saville Ltd for the supply of steel and creep-tested specimens.

REFERENCES

1. J. C. Suits and J. R. Low jun.: *Acta Met.*, 1957, **5**, 285–289.
2. G. Thomas and J. Nutting: *J. Inst. Met.*, 1956, **85**, 1–7.
3. P. Swann: Ph.D. Thesis, Cambridge University, 1960.
4. M. J. Whelan: *Proc. Roy. Soc.*, 1958, (A), **249**, 114–137.
5. H. Suzuki: *Sci. Rep. Res. Inst. Tohoku Univ.*, 1952, (A), **4**, 455–463.
6. E. Orowan: 'Internal stresses in metals and alloys', 447 (discussion); 1948, London, Inst. Met. Monograph No. 5.
7. G. Thomas and J. Nutting: *J. Inst. Met.*, 1957, **86**, 7–13.
8. M. F. Ashby and G. C. Smith: *Phil. Mag.*, 1960, **5**, 298.
9. G. S. Ansell and J. Weertman: *Trans. AIME.*, 1959, **215**, 838.
10. G. S. Ansell: *Trans. AIME.*, 1959, **215**, 294–5.
11. E. D. Hyman and J. Nutting: *JISI*, 1956, **184**, 148–165.
12. E. Smith and J. Nutting: *ibid.*, 1957, **187**, 314–329.
13. R. G. Baker and J. Nutting: 'Precipitation processes in steel', *ISI. Spec. Rep.* no. 64, 1–22, 1959.
14. G. Thomas and J. Nutting: *J. Inst. Met.*, 1959, **88**, 81–90.
15. R. N. Younger and R. G. Baker: *JISI*, 1960, **196**, 188–194.
16. D. G. Brandon and J. Nutting: *Acta Met.*, 1959, **7**, 101–110.

The effect of structure on the creep properties of titanium alloys

*A. L. Dalton, M. Met., D. Webster, A.I.M., and
H. C. Child, B.Sc., F.I.M.*

*A study has been made of the electron microstructures of
several commercial titanium-base alloys and these have
been correlated with their creep strength. Factors which
have been shown to affect the creep properties are (a) solid-
solution hardening of the alpha phase, (b) dislocation locking
promoted by silicon, (c) the nature of the decomposition
products of prior beta. It is concluded that of these, (a) and
(b) are probably the most important, particularly for creep
resistance in the higher temperature range (400–500°C).*

DURING the short history of titanium production, considerable
efforts have been directed towards the improvement of the creep
properties of titanium alloys. The earliest titanium alloys contained
elements for the solid-solution hardening of both the alpha and
beta phase and, in general, were duplex alloys at room temperature.
Examples of such alloys are the 4%Al–4%Mn and the 6%Al–4%V.
Further developments on this type of alloy led to the selection of more
effective alloying elements for the solid solution hardening, i.e.
manganese was replaced by molybdenum, and aluminium by
mixtures of aluminium and tin, and sometimes zirconium. Precipitation hardening elements such as silicon were also added. The
earliest of these complex alloys, Hylite 50,[1] contains 4%Al, 4%Mo,
2%Sn, and $\frac{1}{2}$%Si. Such an alloy consists of at least 80% alpha at
room temperature, and has a creep strength substantially greater
than that of the 4%Al–4%Mn alloy (*see* Table I). Another example
of an alloy of this type, Hylite 60, which contains Al, Sn, Zr, Mo,
and Si, has further improved creep strength due to a more careful
balance of the alloying elements.

A second class of alloy which was wholly alpha at room temperature relied entirely on the solid solution hardening of elements
such as aluminium and tin for the strengthening effect. An example

Mr Dalton and Mr Child are with the Research Department, Jessop-Saville Ltd.
Mr Webster was formerly with Aeon Ltd.

of this was the 5%Al, 2½%Sn alloy. Further developments in this field included the better choice of alpha-strengthening elements, including the addition of zirconium, and, similarly to the alpha–beta alloys, the addition of precipitation-hardening elements. Here again, silicon has proved to be the most successful strengthening element for titanium-base alloys. An example of such a complex alloy containing Al, Sn, Zr, and Si, is Hylite 55 (*see* Table I). As before, the addition of precipitation-hardening elements has resulted in a substantial improvement in creep properties.

The aim of the present paper is to try and explain the improved properties obtained with these developments in terms of microstructure.

EXPERIMENTAL TECHNIQUE

Specimens for either optical or electron microscopic examination were prepared in a conventional manner by grinding on 240, 400, and 600 grade silicon carbide papers, electropolished using a methyl alcohol, butyl cellosolve, and perchloric acid electrolyte, and finally were etched. The etchant used depended upon the composition of the alloy, 1% hydrofluoric acid–2%nitric acid in water being used for the alpha–beta alloys, and 2% hydrofluoric acid in saturated oxalic acid solution for the alpha alloys.

Direct carbon extraction replicas were prepared for electron microscopic examination using the technique developed by Smith and Nutting,[2] the carbon film being removed by immersion in a hydrofluoric acid (1 part) nitric acid (1 part) water (30 parts) solution.

The structure of Hylite 50 in the quenched condition was examined by three further electron microscopic techniques, namely, (i) shadowed replicas, (ii) cut sections, (iii) thin foils.

(i) Pt–C *shadowed replicas*
    The specimens were electropolished and etched in a 2% HF in oxalic acid solution. After etching a mixture of platinum and carbon was evaporated on to the specimen at an angle of 45°, using the method outlined by Bradley.[3] This ensured that the presence of any particles would be revealed even if the particles themselves dissolved during removal of the carbon film.

(ii) *Cut sections*
    Thin sections about 1000Å thick were cut from massive specimens with a diamond knife on an ultra microtome. These sections were transparent to electrons in the microscope and allowed the structure to be seen and diffraction

167

TABLE I Composition and properties of the alloys together with figure references

Alloy	Composition	Heat treatment	0·1%PS tons/in²	UTS tons/in²	El.% L=4√A%	R of A %	Temp., °C	Stress to give 0·1% strain in 100 h	Figure references†
Hylite 30	2%Al-2%Mn	½ h, 810°C, FC, 700°C, AC	35·6	44·0	20·0	40	{350, 400}	18·25 / 10·0*	
Hylite 40	4%Al-4%Mn	½ h, 810°C, FC, 700°C, AC	58·3	64·0	18·0	43	{350, 400}	25·6 / 14·0*	O Fig.1 E Fig.2
		½ h, 900°C, AC, aged 24 h at 500°C		64·8	20·2	45	350	29·6	O Fig.3 E Fig.4
Hylite 45	6%Al-4%V	½ h, 900°C, AC, aged 24 h at 500°C		65·9	18·6	56	400	20·0	E Fig.5
T.48	4%Al-4%Mo-2% Sn	½ h, 900°C, AC, aged 24 h at 500°C		68·0	20·0	54	400	16·2	E Fig.6
Hylite 50	4%Al-4%Mo-2% Sn-0·5%Si	½ h, 900°C, AC, aged 24 h at 500°C	71·5	80·0	15·0	40	{400, 450, 500}	35·7 / 16·5 / 4·0	O Fig.7 E Fig.8
Hylite 60	Complex αβ alloy containing Al, Sn, Zr, Mo & Si	½ h, 1000°C, AC, aged 24h at 550°C	60·9	72·0	16·0	36	{400, 450, 500}	35* / 26·0 / 19·5	O Fig.20 E Fig.21
Hylite 20	5%Al, 2·5%Sn	½ h, 900°C, AC, aged 24h at 500°C	45·6	55·4	20·9	40	{400, 500}	22 / 10	O Fig.22
Hylite 55	Complex α alloy containing Al, Sn, Zr & Si	½ h 1000°C, AC, aged 24h at 500°C	56·8	62·9	17·3	37	{450, 500}	26·5 / 18·7	E Fig.23

Note: Properties determined upon $\frac{5}{8}$ in. dia. rolled bar material.
* Approximate values   †O Optical micrograph   E Electron micrograph

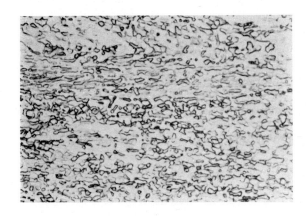

1 *Hylite 40,
annealed at
810°C,
optical
micrograph
× 500*

patterns to be taken without complications arising from chemical attack.

(iii) *Thin foils*

A sheet of titanium about 0·009in thick was thinned by electro-polishing until portions of it were transparent to the electron beam. This method has the advantage over the sectioning technique in that distortion of the structure due to the cutting process is eliminated.

RESULTS

The tensile and creep properties of the various alloys considered are summarized in Table I which also gives references to the relevant optical and electron micrographs for each alloy.

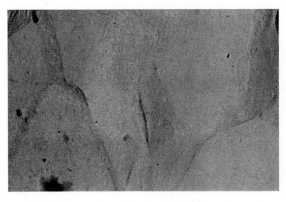

2 *Hylite 40,
annealed at
810°C,
carbon
replica
electron
micrograph
× 15 800*

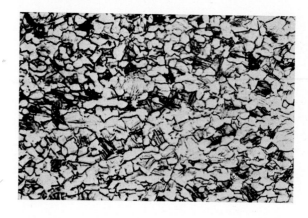

3 *Hylite 40, ½ h
at 900°C, AC,
aged 24 h at
500°C,
optical
micrograph
× 500*

Alpha–beta alloys

In the case of the 2%Al–2%Mn and the 4%Al–4%Mn alloys in the annealed condition, which is the heat treatment normally used in service, optical examination indicated that the structure consisted predominantly of alpha but also contained elongated globules of a second phase (Fig.1). The corresponding electron micrograph (Fig.2) shows that this second phase is a solid solution and there is no evidence of a duplex structure. X-ray examination proved that the second phase was beta titanium and consequently the structure of the alloys in this heat treated condition consists of homogeneous solid solutions of alpha and beta titanium.

When the 4%Al–4%Mn alloy was normalized at 900°C and aged at 500°C, the structure consisted of primary alpha in a transformed

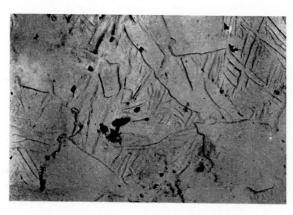

4 *Hylite 40,
½ h at 900°C,
AC, aged
24 h at
500°C,
carbon
replica
electron
micrograph
× 4600*

170

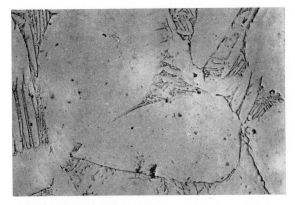

5 *Hylite 45,*
½ *h at 900°C*
AC, aged
24 h at
500°C,
carbon
replica
electron
micrograph
×4 600

beta matrix (Figs.3 and 4). There is less primary alpha after normalizing than after annealing because of the increased solution treatment temperature whilst the more rapid cooling rate has suppressed the beta to alpha transformation temperature to a point where secondary alpha forms in an acicular manner. The acicular nature of the beta decomposition product can be faintly seen in the optical photograph and is somewhat more clearly delineated in the electron micrograph.

The 6%Al–4%V alloy, and the complex alloys T.48 and Hylite 50, are used in the normalized and aged condition. With this heat treatment, like the 4%Al–4%Mn alloy, they have a structure of primary alpha in a matrix of beta transformation products. In the case of the 6%Al–4%V alloy, the beta transformation products (Fig.5) are very

6 *T.48, ½ h at*
900°C, AC,
aged 24 h at
500°C, carbon
replica electron
micrograph
×15 808

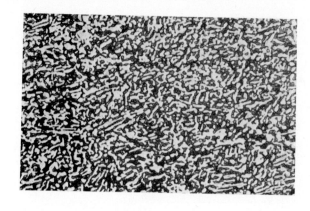

7　*Hylite 50, ½ h*
at 900°C,
aged 24 h at
500°C,
optical
micrograph
　× *500*

similar to those of the 4%Al–4%Mn alloy. In the case of the complex alloys, however, the beta transformation products are of a substantially different nature from those found in the 6%Al–4%V alloy. This may be seen both from the optical micrograph of Hylite 50 (Fig.7) and the electron micrographs Figs.6 and 8, when compared with Fig.5. The transformation products are coarsely acicular in nature, this being more obvious in the case of Hylite 50 than in the case of T.48.

The structure of a Hylite 50 specimen which had been creep tested for 9650 h under a stress of 21 tons/in² at 450°C, is shown in Fig.9. After the prolonged ageing under stress, there is marked evidence of a 'precipitate' within the primary alpha grains (cf. Fig.8) This precipitate, which was in the form of thin laths about 300Å. wide by 3000Å long, could not be identified by electron diffraction

8　*Hylite 50, ½ h*
at 900°C, AC,
aged 24 h at
500°C,
carbon replica
electron
micrograph
　× *15800*

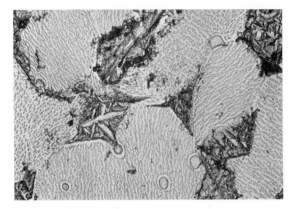

9 *Hylite 50, ½ h at 900°C, AC, aged 24 h at 500°C, then creep tested for 9 650 h at 450°C with applied stress of 21 tons/in² carbon replica electron micrograph × 9 200*

and was at first thought to be etch pits left from the removal of an intermetallic phase, possibly Ti_5Si_3. The beta decomposition products have undergone further modification and are less acicular in nature.

T.48 and Hylite 50 have also been examined in the quenched and quenched and aged condition. In the quenched condition, T.48 (Fig.10) has a structure of primary alpha in a matrix which had been beta at the solution treatment temperature, the relative amounts of the two phases were 40:60. There is also evidence of a finely dispersed precipitate some 250Å in diameter within the primary alpha grains. Hylite 50, however, again shows pronounced evidence of a second 'phase' within the alpha grains (Fig.11), and as the only difference in composition between T.48 and Hylite 50 is the addition

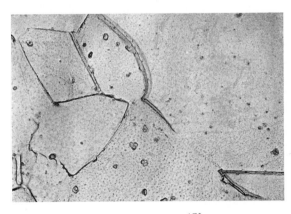

10 *T.48, ½ h at 900°C, WQ, carbon replica electron micrograph × 15 800*

173

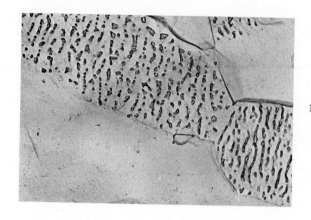

11 *Hylite 50, ½ h at 900°C, WQ, carbon replica electron micrograph* × *15 800*

of 0·5 % Si to the latter, this phase was thought to be Ti_5Si_3. Ageing T.48 at 500°C causes the prior beta to decompose into fine globular decomposition products (Figs.12 and 13). This reaction is nucleated at the boundaries of the prior beta grains and then spreads inwards. A general area diffraction pattern from the replica shown in Fig.12 gave the following results:

Dia., Å	β phase	TiC
2·52		2·51
2·29	2·32	
2·17		2·18
1·62	1·64	
1·54		1·54
1·32	1·34	
1·02	1·03	
0·98		0·97

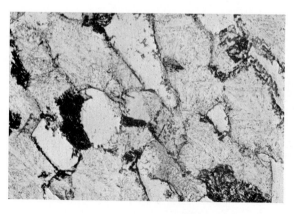

12 *T.48, ½ h at 900°C, WQ, aged 24 h at 500°C, carbon replica electron micrograph* × *4 600*

174

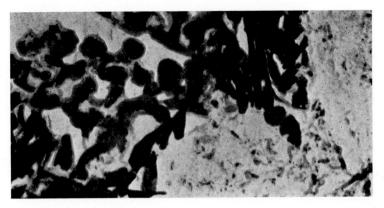

13 *T.48, ½ h 900°C, WQ, aged 24 h at 500°C, carbon replica electron micrograph*
× 38 000

It can be seen that much of the beta phase (bcc lattice parameter 3·27Å) has been extracted together with some TiC.

Ageing Hylite 50 at the same temperature caused the precipitates present in the primary alpha to disappear. The beta transformation products of Hylite 50 (Fig.14) were similar to those of T.48, but the extracted phases were less evident. When aged at 300°C (Fig.15) the prior beta showed evidence of the beginning of decomposition, and again this was most marked at the alpha/beta interface. The primary alpha grains still showed evidence of the precipitates found in the case of the quenched material. When aged at 600°C the prior beta decomposed to a coarser acicular structure (Fig.16) similar to that found in the normalized and aged material (Fig.8).

In order to determine the nature of the apparent precipitate

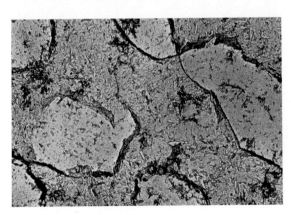

14 *Hylite 50, ½ h at 900°C, WQ, aged 24 h at 500°C, carbon replica electron micrograph*
× 15 800

175

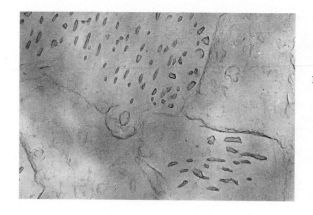

15 *Hylite 50,*
½ h at 900°C,
WQ, aged
24 h at 300°C,
carbon
replica
electron
micrograph
× 15 000

within the alpha grains found in Hylite 50, the water quenched sample was examined, using Pt–C shadowed replicas, cut sections, and thin foils. The platinum shadowed replicas (Fig.17) were much more revealing than the carbon extraction replicas previously used. The thread-like structure in the alpha grains could be seen by the position of its white shadow, to be standing proud of the surface. This proved conclusively that the structure was not formed of pits, which was a possibility on previous evidence. In fact, the thread-like structure was composed of a collection of small spherical particles. Much larger mounds of material scattered uniformly over the whole structure were revealed. The evidence suggests that these large

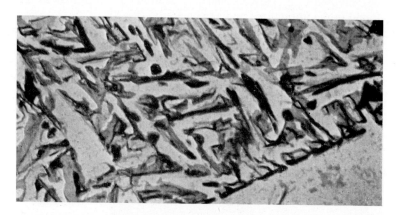

16 *Hylite 50, ½ h at 900°C, WQ, aged 24 h at 600°C, carbon replica electron micrograph* × 38 000

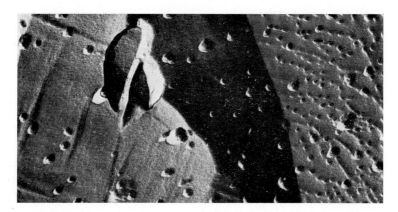

17 *Hylite 50, ½ h at 900°C, WQ, Pt–C shadowed replica electron micrograph* × 30 000

particles are etch products, whilst the fact that in the alpha grains these large particles always occur on the thread-like structure indicates that these, too, are formed by etch products. Another interesting effect revealed by the shadowing is a needle-like structure in the beta regions.

An examination of both the cut sections and foils (Figs.18 and 19) revealed no evidence of a precipitate within the alpha grains. This observation is confirmed by selected area diffraction. Although

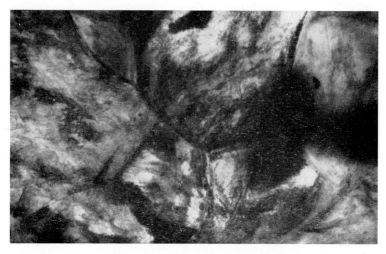

18 *Hylite 50, ¼ h at 900°C, WQ, thin foil electron micrograph* × 15 000

177

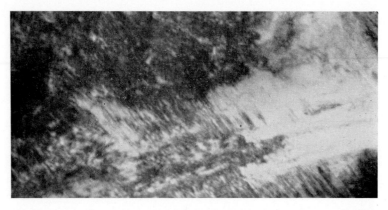

19 *Hylite 50, ¼ h at 900°C, WQ, thin foil electron micrograph* × 80 000

the foil and sections clearly show the alpha and beta grains, selected area diffraction gives only hexagonal patterns of alpha from both regions.

The results indicate that the thread-like structure within the alpha grains is not a genuine precipitate but an etching structure due at least in part to the effect of silicon.

The hexagonal pattern from the beta region suggests that the beta may have undergone a shear transformation to alpha prime. The needle-like structure of the retained beta regions supports this view. This alpha prime must then decompose on ageing to acicular alpha plus beta.

Hylite 60, the complex alloy, is normally solution treated at 1 000°C, and at this temperature is entirely beta. Consequently, the

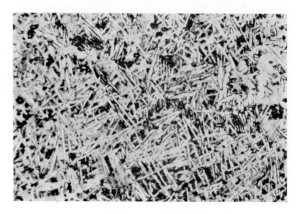

20 *Hylite 60, ½ h at 1 000°C, AC, aged 24 h at 550°C, optical micrograph* × 500

178

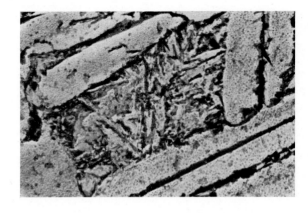

21 *Hylite 60, ½ h at 1000°C, AC, aged 24 h at 550°C, carbon replica electron micrograph × 15 800*

structure in the aged condition consists of alpha fingers arranged in a Widmannstäten pattern inside the prior beta grains, as may be seen from the optical micrograph (Fig.20). It may be noted that this alloy can be treated in the beta field without grain coarsening occurring. Beta transformation products are formed at boundaries of the alpha plates, as shown in Fig.21.

Alpha alloys

The 5%Al–2·5%Sn alloy on solution treating at 900°C remains completely alpha ($a \rightarrow a + \beta$ transition temperature is about 980°C) and after ageing for 24 h at 500°C the structure consists of fairly small equi-axed alpha grains (Fig.22).

The complex alloy, Hylite 55, which was normalized at 1000°C and aged 24 h at 500°C had a structure which was essentially alpha

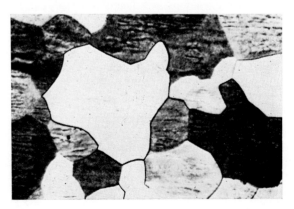

22 *Hylite 20, ½ h at 900°C, AC, aged 24 h at 500°C, optical micrograph × 500*

179

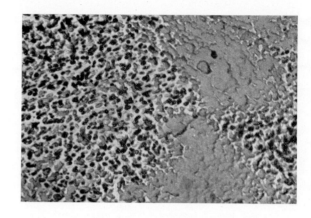

23 *Hylite 55, $\frac{1}{2}h$ at 1000°C, AC, aged 24 h at 500°C, carbon replica electron micrograph × 38 000*

with a fine dispersed precipitate about 400Å dia. (Fig.23). There were also some larger particles 10 000Å dia. These could not be extracted and identified by electron diffraction, but they may be Ti_5Si_3.

DISCUSSION

Apart from solid-solution strengthening, the mechanical properties of alpha–beta titanium alloys are dependent on the nature of the decomposition products of the beta phase present at the solution treatment temperature. The decomposition process has been studied extensively[4-8] and can occur in several ways.

1. Beta retained upon quenching precipitates alpha on ageing.

$$\beta \xrightarrow{\text{quenching}} \beta \xrightarrow{\text{ageing}} \alpha + \beta$$

2. Some omega forms on quenching and then decomposes to give beta+alpha as above.

$$\beta \xrightarrow{\text{quenching}} \beta + \omega \xrightarrow{\text{ageing}} \alpha + \beta$$

3. Martensitic alpha forms on quenching and then decomposes on ageing to give alpha+beta.

$$\beta \xrightarrow{\text{quenching}} \alpha' \xrightarrow{\text{ageing}} \alpha + \beta$$

With cooling rates slower than water quenching, some alpha may be precipitated during cooling to room temperature. For eith r conditions (1) or (2) to apply there must be a considerable amount of a beta stabilizing element, e.g. Mo, Mn, V, present. In most commercial alpha–beta titanium alloys, e.g. 6%Al–4%V, there is insufficient beta former present, hence martensitic alpha forms from beta upon quenching. This applies when the alloy is quenched from the beta region or from a temperature in the two-phase region but close to the transus. At lower temperatures in the two-phase field the beta phase contains sufficient vanadium for it to be retained on quenching.

In practice, none of the commercial alloys is used in the quenched condition but they are either annealed or normalized. Under these conditions, it would be expected that beta decomposition would be direct to the alpha phase. Under certain circumstances, i.e. with the more complex alloys and the faster cooling rates which occur in thin sections, it would be expected that martensitic alpha might also occur which in turn decomposes to alpha and beta on subsequent ageing.

The micrographs shown in Figs.18 and 19 are very similar to those obtained by Kelly and Nutting[9] when examining martensite in high-carbon steels. There is evidence of striations which could be interpreted as narrow twins produced by a shear transformation. Therefore, it must be accepted that condition (3) applies to the Hylite 50.

An interesting facet of this investigation has been the observation that when the martensitic alpha decomposes the new alpha which forms is continuous with the primary alpha. Dupouy et al.[4] have postulated that martensitic alpha decomposes simply by the precipitation of beta. Under these circumstances, the remaining alpha would not be continuous with the primary alpha.

The structure of the 2%Al–2%Mn and the 4%Al–4%Mn alloys in the heat treatment normally used is one of homogeneous solid solutions. Strengthening would, therefore, be expected to be limited to solid solution hardening, and the low creep properties at 400°C are consistent with this hypothesis.

In the case of the 6%Al–4%V alloy, the creep strength is considerably enhanced, and this is to be expected from the higher concentration of alpha solutes, whilst it should be noted that vanadium has a much higher solubility in alpha titanium than manganese (maximum solubility of approximately 3% compared with 0·5% for Mn).

T.48 has been included amongst the alloys as an example of a silicon-free alloy of the Hylite 50 type, although it is not used commercially. In this alloy in the normalized and aged condition, the prior beta decomposition products are acicular in nature, and it would be anticipated that they would have higher creep strength than the previous alloys considered. This is borne out in practice as the alloy is substantially stronger than the 4%Mn–4%Al alloy.

In the normalized and aged condition, the complex alloy, Hylite 50, has a beta decomposition structure similar to T.48, but, if anything, the structure is even more acicular in nature. Experimental heat treatments have shown that the structure within the alpha grains is not a genuine precipitate but an etching structure due, at least in part, to the effect of silicon. The etching structure could be associated with a dislocation decorating effect and therefore it is possible that the improved creep properties of this alloy could be a result of dislocation atmosphere locking of the type postulated by Glen[10] to account for the creep behaviour of low alloy ferritic steels.

The complex alloy, Hylite 60, has the highest creep strength of known alpha–beta titanium alloys, and the structure of this alloy consists of interweaving alpha laths containing a dispersed precipitate with a small amount of interspersed beta.

It may be noted that Hylite 60 has a comparable creep strength at 400°C to Hylite 50. At higher temperatures, however, the Hylite 60 alloy is much superior. Previous experience has shown that alpha alloys, even of the solid-solution hardened type such as Hylite 20, had at higher temperatures, e.g. 500°C, a creep strength superior to most alpha–beta alloys. The structure observed on Hylite 60 which is essentially alpha in nature with dispersed precipitant would, therefore, be expected to give good creep properties at 500°C, as is the case.

The only example of an alpha-type alloy studied has been the complex alloy, Hylite 55. This has creep properties superior to the 5%Al–2·5%Sn alloy referred to above. The structure of this alloy closely resembles the electron microstructure of nickel-base creep-resistant alloys,[11] having a matrix of alpha with a uniformly dispersed precipitate of about 400Å dia., and as such would be expected to be creep resistant.

CONCLUSIONS

The electron microstructures of several commercial titanium-base alloys have been studied and correlated with their creep strengths. The following factors have been shown to affect the creep properties:

 (i) solid solution hardening of the alpha base
 (ii) dislocation locking promoted by silicon
 (iii) the nature of the decomposition products of prior beta.

The first two factors are probably the most important, particularly for creep resistance in the higher temperature range (400–500°C).

ACKNOWLEDGMENT

The authors wish to thank Professor J. Nutting for his helpful advice and guidance in the interpretation of the electron micrographs, and Mr G. T. Harris for his support and encouragement.

REFERENCES

1. G. T. HARRIS *et al.*: *J. Inst. Metals*, 1959–60, **88,** 112–120.
2. E. SMITH and J. NUTTING: *Brit. J. Appl. Phy.*, 1956, **7,** 214–217.
3. D. E. Bradley: *Nature* 1958, 181, 875–877.
4. J. M. DUPOUY *et al.*: *Trans. ASM*, 1960, **52,** 221–232.
5. P. J. FOPIANO *et al.*: *J. Metals*, 1960, **12,** 727.
6. R. F. DOMAGALA and W. ROSTOKER: *Trans. ASM*, 1956, **48,** 762–772.
7. P. D. FROST *et al.*: *ibid.*, 1954, **46,** 1056–1071.
8. 'Symposium on advances in electron metallography,' 1; ASTM Spec. Tech. Publ. no. 275.
9. P. M. KELLY and J. NUTTING: *Proc. Roy. Soc.* (A), 1960, **259,** 45.
10. J. GLEN: *JISI*, 1958, **190,** 114–135.
11. 'Precipitation processes in steels,' *ISI Spec. Rep.* no. 64, 1959.

Discussion 2

The four preceding papers were presented and discussed at this session.

Dr **G. L. J. Bailey** (International Nickel Co. (Mond) Ltd): As our Chairman has said, in contrast with the hypothetical, or if not hypothetical, metallurgically more simple, materials that were discussed at session 1, the papers at this session have all been concerned with the more complex situations which exist in alloys of practical engineering use. The simple materials seem to offer the most attractive starting point for working out the basic factors which influence creep behaviour, while the engineering alloys in the main have had to be developed by empirical efforts to meet specific engineering needs, and it will be much more difficult to achieve a rational and detailed understanding of the creep characteristics of these more complex materials; Professor Nutting has made an excellent shot at doing so, but it will I am sure, still be useful to have the discussion at the first session in mind in trying to account for the reported facts.

May I briefly remind you of the main points from the earlier papers. First, Professor Cottrell made the point that the creep/rupture life of material particularly involves consideration of structures, processes, and events at grain boundaries, though the deformation of the grains themselves cannot be ignored. Dr McLean and his colleagues were more concerned with creep rate than rupture life, and this is, in the first place, a function of the more highly ordered structure within the grains, with the grain boundaries in the subsidiary role. Davies and Wiltshire developed the connexion between boundaries and grains and between creep rate and rupture life which appears in pure metals and in some simple solid solutions.

In the more complex alloys we are now concerned with, there are more opportunities for marked differentiation of composition, structure and properties as between the grain boundary regions and the grains themselves. Creep rate and rupture life are to some extent independently variable, therefore, as the paper by Mr Fell *et al.* indicates. The possibilities for producing differentiation between grain boundaries and grains, so gaining a degree of freedom for better or worse, are perhaps particularly marked in systems where more than one kind of precipitation process can occur.

Mr Child is to be warmly congratulated for reporting a monumental programme of systematic alloy manufacture and testing which I think very well illustrates the approach that, when guided as far as possible by the current theoretical background, still gives the quickest results when one has to develop engineering materials against specified property targets. As he said, he has not, however, been able to go very far in relating his structural observations with the results of his mechanical property tests.

In view of the importance of grain boundary structure in relation to the development of rupture, it is not perhaps surprising that he should find no marked correlation between rupture life and any feature of the structure of the grains themselves. In this context, and speaking of solid solution hardening, I notice that Child uses the terms 'lattice parameter' and 'lattice strain' interchangeably. I was not quite sure what he meant by 'lattice strain' expressed in this way. I had the idea that a random distribution of solute atoms in the parent lattice would in fact do little to interfere with dislocation movement, and that solid-solution hardening is more likely due to circumstances such as clustering of solute atoms around dislocations, or other sorts of short-range order, or regular irregularities, as Professor Nutting discussed in some detail. That being so, a simple correlation of creep rate with lattice parameter is perhaps hardly to be expected, and correlation with rupture life or data derived from life, seems even less likely. We certainly need more enlightenment on this point of how far solid-solution hardening can improve any of the creep parameters, and of the reasons why.

Child, nevertheless, attaches importance to solid solution hardening, and in this his conclusions contrast with those of Fell *et al.* who are concerned with a relatively simpler situation involving only one kind of precipitate Ni3(Ti,Al), and the subsidiary effect of carbide phases.

Fell and his colleagues conclude that the basic resistance to creep deformation in their alloys is provided by a relatively stable array of precipitated particles. They required to use the high resolution of the electron microscope to distinguish these particles, and indeed, the theoretical implications seem to be that in practical terms the finer the dispersion the more creep resistant will the alloy be. But they would still like to know how much the creep resistance of their alloys owes to solid solution hardening.

I suspect that, had Child examined his alloys at higher resolution than is permitted by the light microscope, he might also have detected finely dispersed precipitates in some of his more creep-resistant alloys.

It seems that high-resolution electron microscopy is an essential tool for studying the structure of creep resistant alloys profitably. Certainly, the grosser precipitates visible with the light microscope seem to give no benefit to creep resistance. The general structure of two different alloys illustrated by Child's Figs.3c and *l* are very similar in respect of overall degree of precipitation, and also particle size of precipitate. Nickel-base alloys of the kind described by Fell can be heat-treated to have a similar structure. The creep properties of these alloys, however, are all very different indeed.

One of Child's conclusions is that optimum creep properties are associated with the addition of a given element in an amount just beyond the limit of solid solubility. This recalls the so-called 'marginal solubility hypothesis' which was postulated during the earlier development of the nickel-based alloys. It was then suggested that the optimum amount of solute element was slightly in excess of the solubility limit at the test temperature. It was considered that in these circumstances the alloy would have maximum solid solution hardening, and that it would also have the most desirable age-hardening response from the point of view of creep resistance. Further additions of solute element would render the alloy susceptible to over-ageing and result in deterioration of creep resistance. It was believed that a prerequisite of continued creep resistance was that the structural configuration should be as stable as possible. This did in fact prove a very useful concept of the 'necessary but not sufficient' type.

In the work on titanium alloys described by Dalton *et al.*, correlation of composition and structure has been attempted with the property of creep resistance rather than rupture life. Again it is found that as the solid-solution hardness is increased, in their case by progressive additions of aluminium and manganese, there is a corresponding general increase in creep strength.

Special interest attaches to the effects of silicon and Dalton *et al.* suggest that this is due to dislocation locking promoted by silicon. This would seem very reasonable, and they are saying essentially that silicon atoms are acting in the same way as a fine precipitate, though the authors say that they could not find one. Have they considered the possibility that the etching markings associated with silicon represent something akin to Preston Guinier zones?

Are the silicon sites centres of coherent precipitation in the early stages, which are not necessarily revealed by the electron microscope?

TABLE 1 Creep of binary titanium alloys with equiaxed and acicular alpha microstructures (10 tons/in^2 at 500°C)

Composition	Equiaxed alpha (20 h at 800°C, furnace cooled)			Widmanstätten alpha ($\frac{1}{3}$ h at 1100°C air cooled+ 1 h at 700°C, furnace cooled)		
	% initial plastic strain	% creep strain in 300 h	% total plastic strain in 300 h	% initial plastic strain	%creep strain in 300 h	% total plastic strain in 300 h
6%Al	nil	0·218	0·218	nil	0·079	0·079
15%Sn	nil	0·205	0·205	nil	0·103	0·103
12½%Sb	nil	0·363	0·363	nil	0·088	0·088
21%Zr	nil	0·925	0·925	nil	0·664	0·664

I have left comment on the paper by Professor Nutting and Dr Arrowsmith till last. This attack on the basic understanding of the factors influencing creep behaviour from the difficult departure point of real engineering alloys is one which I am sure is warmly welcomed by all those like Mr Child and other contributors to this symposium who have to meet the demands of engineering users for better and better alloys. Thanks to these authors we can recognize the structural characteristics we want and see when we have got them.

Now we need to know how, in any particular system, to modify undesirable precipitation characteristics to produce the ideal dispersion of stable particles. I wonder if Professor Nutting can tell us some more about how to go about this important task apart from doing without carbides? Perhaps this is one of the most brightly coloured panels that Professor Nutting dangles above our heads on his very attractive and provocative kite.

TABLE 2 Creep of titanium Ex.013 (Sn–Al–Zr) with nucleation and growth or martensitic-type acicular alpha microstructures

Creep test conditions	Widmanstätten alpha ($\frac{1}{3}$ h at 1100°C, air cooled+ 1 h at 700°C, furnace cooled)			Mainly martensitic alpha ($\frac{1}{3}$ h at 1100°C, quenched+ 1 h at 700°C, quenched)		
	% initial plastic strain	% creep strain in 300 h	% total plastic strain in 300 h	% initial plastic strain	% creep strain in 300 h	% total plastic strain in 300 h
35 tons/in^2 at 400°C	1·359	0·065	1·424	0·032	0·142	0·174
15 tons/in^2 at 500°C	nil	0·050	0·050	nil	0·270	0·270

% Mo	Creep tests under 35 tons/in² at 400°C			Creep tests under 15 tons/in² at 500°C		
	% initial plastic strain	% creep strain in 300 h	% total plastic strain in 300 h	% initial plastic strain	% creep strain in 300 h	% total plastic strain in 300 h
nil	1·359	0·065	1·424	nil	0·050	0·050
0·5	0·157	0·077	0·234	nil	0·132	0·132
1·0	nil	0·096	0·096	nil	0·202	0·202

Mr **W. P. Fentiman** (ICI Metals Division): I should like to comment on the conclusions of the titanium paper by Dalton *et al.* We believe that the nature of the decomposition products of prior beta has a much greater importance than the authors have allowed.

Creep performance of titanium alloys is normally defined as the stress which may be applied at a particular temperature to produce, usually, 0·1 % total plastic strain in a specific time. On this definition it is only at the higher temperatures and the longer times that creep performance depends solely on creep rate. At lower temperatures and shorter times some compromise between low creep rate and high elastic limit is necessary to obtain best creep performance. In our experience the addition of beta stabilizers, such as molybdenum, raises the elastic limit but also increases the creep rate, particularly when retained beta is formed. For this reason I should like to refer briefly to the effect of microstructure on the creep resistance of alpha type titanium alloys.

Generally speaking with alpha-type titanium alloys acicular structures give

TABLE 4   Effect of heat-treatment on creep of an alpha titanium alloy with and without 0·22 %Si

Heat-treatment	% total plastic strain in 300 h. Under 15 tons/in² at 500°C (all creep strain)	
	Ex 013 (alpha)	Ex 013 + 0·22 %Si (alpha + compound)
8 h at 800°C air cool	0·112	0·202
1 h at 850°C air cool + 24 h at 500°C	0·090	0·240
⅓ h at 1100°C air cool + 1 h at 700°C furnace cool	0·050	0·045
⅓ h at 1100°C air cool + 24 h at 500°C	0·100	0·025

TABLE 5 Effect of beta heat treatment on creep properties of titanium 679 (Sn–Al–Zr–Mo–Si)

		Creep properties at 500°C		Tensile properties after creep testing		
Solution treatment temperature, °C (All specimens air cooled and aged 24 h at 500°C)		Stress tons/in²	% total plastic strain in 300 h	UTS tons/in²	% Elong. on 4√A	RA %
900°C	Alpha+ beta	15	0·111	75·0	16	40
975°C	Beta	20	0·117	77·0	14	26
1 000°C	Beta	20	0·095	73·4	12	20
1 040°C	Beta	20	0·085	79·0	10	10

rise to lower creep rates than equiaxed structures. This point is illustrated in Table 1 for four simple binary alloys. In all the examples a creep test period of 300 h has been used. Beta heat-treated commercial purity titanium even when quenched decomposes largely by nucleation and growth to Widmanstätten type structures. However, as alpha alloying elements are added the nucleation and growth reaction tends to be suppressed and, at high cooling rates, microstructures containing appreciable proportions of martensitically formed alpha can be obtained. Materials containing martensitic alpha are stronger, and have higher elastic limits than materials consisting of Widmanstätten alpha, but their creep rates are also higher. This is illustrated in Table 2 for a complex alpha alloy titanium Ex.013.

This difference in creep properties between Widmanstätten and martensitically formed alpha is important when considering the effect of additions of beta-stabilizing elements on the creep properties of an alpha base. At any specific cooling rate, addition of beta stabilizers tends to shift the decomposition products of beta from nucleation and growth to martensitically formed alpha, and, eventually, to retained beta. This process leads to an increase in both elastic limit and creep rate. The initial stages of this process are illustrated in Table 3, where small additions of molybdenum were made to titanium Ex.013, heat-treated to produce acicular structures, that is, they were air-cooled from 1100°C, reheated to 700°C and furnace cooled.

Generally, as with alpha alloys, a change in microstructure of alpha beta type alloys from acicular to equiaxed, or from Widmanstätten to martensitic alpha is reflected in an increase in creep rate although the elastic limit may also be raised. Reactions which depend upon retention of beta from the solution treatment followed by low temperature precipitation of omega or alpha, do not in our experience effect much improvement in creep resistance above about 350°C.

The addition of compound-forming elements, such as silicon, to alpha alloys does not reduce creep rate when solution-treatment temperatures are restricted to those at which large proportions of alpha are present. It is only when appreciable beta is present that creep rate is lowered, silicon appearing to take part

TABLE 6 Creep properties of alpha, alpha+compound, and alpha+beta+ compound titanium alloys

Alloy	Heat treatment	Stress to give 0·1% total plastic strain in 300 h tons/in²		
		400°C	450°C	500°C
Titanium Ex 013 (Sn–Al–Zr)	⅓ h at 1000°C, air cool +1 h at 700°C, air cool	27	24½	19
Titanium Ex 013B (Sn–Al–Zr–Si)	⅓ h at 1000°C, air cool +24 h at 500°C	30	26½	23
Titanium 679 (Sn–Al–Zr–Mo–Si)	1 h at 900°C, air cool +24 h at 500°C	36½	25	13½
	Forge to thin strip at 950°C, air cool+24 h 500°C	44	33	20

in the beta to alpha reaction. This point is illustrated in Table 4, where creep properties of titanium Ex.013 with and without silicon are compared for different heat treatments. Solubility of silicon in this alloy is somewhat less than 0·2% at 850°C and around 0·3% at 1100°C.

The first heat treatment represents solution treatment in the alpha and compound field near to the phase field boundary. The second is an attempt to produce supersaturated alpha followed by precipitation of compound at lower temperature. Both of the last two heat treatments represent beta solution treatment followed by transformation to Widmanstätten alpha by air-cooling. An hour at 700°C is sufficient to temper the acicular alpha, and in this example, was followed by furnace cooling to precipitate the compound. Twenty-four hours at 500°C does not temper the acicular alpha, but as the creep of the alpha +compound alloy is improved, some precipitation or pre-precipitation or compound is presumably occurring.

Alpha beta alloys are normally heat-treated in the alpha beta phase field to maintain high ductility. Silicon is effective in improving creep rate under these conditions, but it appears improbable to us, from our experiments with alpha alloys, that it is the presence of silicon in the alpha phase which is responsible for the improvement in creep. It appears more likely that silicon affects the beta decomposition, although the nature of the influence is not yet clear.

In the presence of compounds which restrain beta grain growth it is possible to heat-treat alpha beta alloys in the beta field and yet retain reasonable ductility. In the presence of these compounds the alpha precipitates in the form of short stubby plates somewhat similar to Fig.20 of Dalton's paper. These structures are not easy to control in commercial-scale fabrication, but, as might be expected, the transition from equiaxed to Widmanstätten structures results in a considerable lowering of the creep rate as illustrated in Table 5.

There is a third increase in stress on going from alpha+beta to beta solution treatment. If you combine this type of microstructure with a heavy deformation after solution-treatment, you can obtain a very high level of creep performance for titanium alloys. By suitable working of this type one can produce a very fine Widmanstätten alpha microstructure with a comparatively high strength. Creep properties are shown in Table 6.

Properties are here compared with those for rod in the alloy with the normal alpha beta-type solution treatment. Also in Table 6 we have also included properties for typical alpha and alpha plus compound alloys to illustrate how the preceding considerations affect creep performance.

For the alpha alloy creep rate is low, but so is the elastic limit and performance at 400°C is limited. For the alpha+compound alloy creep rate is reduced and there is also some increase in elastic limit with a resultant overall improvement in performance. For the alpha+compound+beta alloy creep rate is increased but elastic limit is raised, so that performance at 400°C is improved whilst that at 500°C deteriorates.

In all three alloys creep performance is markedly affected by the nature of the decomposition products of prior beta.

Mr F. B. Pickering (The United Steel Companies Ltd): I should like to make two fairly short comments. The first is in connexion with the paper of Professor Nutting and Dr Arrowsmith in which they say that with alloys of low super-saturation, such as an austenitic stainless steel stabilized with Ti or Nb, one should get precipitation mainly on dislocations, whereas in alloys of high supersaturation such as unstabilized austenitic stainless steels, one would tend to get general precipitation throughout the grains. This is not necessarily the case because we have found that in austenitic stainless steels containing 0·2% and 0·4%C solution-treated at 1050°C and aged at 700°C a very marked precipitation of $M_{23}C_6$ can occur on dislocations. This alloy, however, is one of a high degree of supersaturation in which general precipitation would be expected to occur. It must be admitted, however, that in this alloy a considerable amount of general precipitation also takes place. On the other hand, it is possible to increase the degree of supersaturation in an Nb-stabilized steel by increasing the solution treatment temperature, and to produce a structure after ageing in which a large amount of precipitate occurs both generally and on dislocations, whereas at lower solution treatment temperatures when the degree of supersaturation is low, precipitation mainly appears to be general rather than on dislocations. It may be that in alloys of low supersaturation, the density of precipitates along the dislocations is relatively small and consequently the extraction replica does not show a structure in which recognizable precipitation on dislocations occurs. It seems therefore, that generalizations about the mode of precipitation in austenitic steels cannot be made, as it depends on other factors besides supersaturation. One of the causes of grain boundary denudation has been quoted by Professor Nutting as being the removal of nuclei near to the grain boundaries due to the grain boundaries themselves acting as vacancy sinks. We have occasionally seen evidence for this hypothesis, in which dislocations have been observed to be passing through heavily denuded regions near to grain boundaries and have resulted in marked precipitation on themselves. This indicates that the solute atom concentration was present, but not the requisite nuclei for precipitation.

The second point I would like to deal with is that of rupture ductility. It has been said in session 1 that particles on the grain boundaries could behave either in a detrimental or beneficial manner depending upon the nature of the particle. Furthermore, Dr Bailey and his co-workers believe that grain boundary denudation effects in Nimonic alloys have a beneficial effect on creep ductility, whilst recent evidence on 18–13–1 Nb stainless steels would suggest that grain boundary denudation is very detrimental. Perhaps the picture is not quite so simple as these two factors would lead one to expect and that in fact the degree of strengthening produced by any precipitation in the matrix is by far the most important effect. When considering austenitic alloys for example, the Nimonic alloys and 18–13–1 Nb have distinct similarities. Both are face centred cubic alloys, both precipitate $M_{23}C_6$ at grain boundaries, and both have cubic types of precipitate in the matrix. One wonders, therefore, why grain boundary denudation should apparently behave differently in the two alloys. We may rationalize this by suggesting that the real controlling factor is the relative strength between the grain boundary regions and the matrix, and when there is a heavily strengthened matrix, much of the strain is thrown on to the boundary so that grain boundary denudation can prove very detrimental. This might be related to the degree to which the matrix is strengthened by precipitation in the two alloys. If the relative strengthening of the grains compared with the grain boundary regions is large, presumably low ductility will result. This seems to be the case in 18–13–1 Nb. On the other hand, if the relative strengths were less in Nimonic alloys, the grain boundary denudation need not impair the ductility. This raises the question of the relative effectiveness of NbC precipitates in 18–13–1 Nb and $Ni_3(AlTi)$ precipitates in Nimonic alloys in increasing the strength during creep, and particularly the effect of creep testing conditions on such strengthening.

Mr **A. Dunlop** (Jessop-Saville Ltd): In the two papers presented by Dr Wakeman and Professor Nutting, the great importance of the form and distribution of the dispersion phase has been emphasized. Dr Bailey in his comments asked how to control this. I can tell him one way of making it very bad!

In alloys of the Nimonic type which are subjected to two-stage heat treatment, generally if any mechanical work, hot or cold, is done between these two treatments, the creep properties are greatly impaired. Some results which came to me are as follows: a nickel base alloy containing 20%Cr, 20%Co hardened with 6%Mo, $2\frac{1}{2}$%Ti and $1\frac{1}{2}$%Al in the normal heat-treated condition, quenched from 1 100° and aged at 750°, would give 100 h to fracture under a load of 15 tons at 815°C. Applying cold or warm working between solution treatment and hardening temperature, say, of 20%, the creep rupture time is reduced to less than 30 h. This can be rectified by short time treatment after cold or warm working of 5–10 min at 1 050°. This is important because of the practical application. It was the practice to machine turbine blades in the solution-treated condition followed by ageing. We noticed on occasion, however, masses of small creep cracks on the surface of the blades. The reason was soon obvious. The cold working of the blade surface by machining had produced this condition, which we demonstrated by work hardening the whole bar right through, and it was overcome by short-time heat treatment.

I should like Professor Nutting's comments on the mechanism whereby this type of cold or warm working damages the dispersion hardening, bearing in mind that alloys of the G18B type benefit by warm working.

I should like some comments on the mechanism of the improvement in creep rupture on the nickel-base alloys by the addition of a small amount of boron and zirconium. If we understand this thoroughly there may be other ways of making dispersion hardening better.

Mr **R. N. Younger** (BWRA): If Table I of the paper by Fell *et al.* is interpreted in the light of Professor Nutting's remarks, it is interesting to note that of the two groups of precipitation systems the C–Cr–Ti system has a very low degree of supersaturation, and the Ni–Al–Ti system has a high degree of supersaturation. It would therefore seem likely that in this material we will get precipitation of the

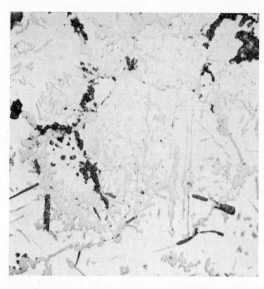

A *Microstructure of air creep test piece, unetched* × 500

carbide phases on dislocations and of the intermetallic phases through zones. This introduces the important question of the relative effect, on creep strength and creep ductility, of precipitates on dislocations and of those distributed throughout the matrix.

Have selected etches been used to determine the relative extent of these two types of precipitation?

Mr **J. E. Northwood** (National Gas Turbine Establishment): The effect of atmosphere on creep properties does no strictly fall within the scope of this symposium, but when the atmosphere under which the test is carried out modifies the structure of the material (Nutting and Arrowsmith's paper discusses the effect of internal oxidation) it is felt that some comment is pertinent to the discussion.

Creep tests have been carried out at the National Gas Turbine Establishment with different atmospheres and some interesting results have been obtained on Nimonic 90. These tests have been conducted in air, argon, or vacuum between 950° and 1000°C, temperatures rather higher than normally used for tests on this alloy. More extensive work on the effect of atmosphere on creep tests has been carried out in the USA by Shahinian and Achter[1,2] on pure nickel and a nickel-base alloy containing chromium and aluminium, and has shown similar results.

Figure *A* summarizes data obtained to date. Duplicate tests at 1000°C and 0·5 tons/in² were carried out in air, argon, or vacuum. The most significant feature occurred in the tests in air. These showed normal primary, a short secondary, and a long tertiary creep stage, but instead of extending to failure in a similar manner to the argon and vacuum tests, the tests in air went into a 'quaternary' creep stage of decreasing creep rate. Similar tests at a stress of 0·25 tons/in² appeared to remain in the secondary creep stage showing no indication of a similar effect after 4000 h. A feature of the tests was the very high creep strain of about 20% which seemed to be a criterion for the 'quaternary' creep stage to take place.

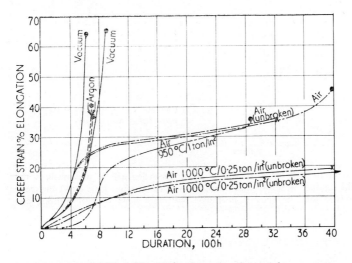

All tests at 1000°C, 0·50 ton/in² unless otherwise stated.
Tests in air made in normal creep furnaces lightly packed with asbestos flock at each end.
Tests in vacuo better than 0·01 μm.
Tests in argon under 15 lb/in² minimum pressure

B *Tests on Nimonic 90 in air, argon, and vacuo*

In the work carried out in the USA a so-called 'air strengthened' region was obtained, and this was dependent on the temperature and stress of the test. The test at 950°C and 1 ton/in² shows that the quaternary creep stage occurs after a longer time than in 1000°C tests.

Metallographic examination of specimens taken from creep tests have indicated that appreciable intergranular cracking occurred in the secondary creep stage, and oxidation had then penetrated along the cracks. The extent of this oxidation on a test at 1000°C and 0·5 ton/in² and 3963 h duration is shown in Fig.*B*. This shows a mid-plane section of the centre of the gauge length of a 0·357in dia. test piece. Oxidation has penetrated across the whole section, and there is a precipitate of oxides or nitrides together with oxides tending to fill cavities. This condition is reached towards the beginning of the quaternary stage of the creep tests in air. Corresponding tests in vacuum and argon have shown a similar degree of intergranular cracking but without any oxide phases. It is thought that the dispersion of oxides and possibly nitrides in the matrix and at grain boundaries locally inhibits crack propagation.

It is appreciated that this effect has limited and obscured practical possibilities in view of the high creep strain at which it occurs, but it is possible that it may give a lead to further development of materials of the metal/oxide dispersion types which will have properties superior to the simple metallic materials.

Mr **W. E. Duckworth** (BISRA): In his exposition of what we used to know as solid-solution hardening, Professor Nutting pointed out that alloying elements which lower the stacking fault energy of the matrix element will improve its creep properties. I have it on his own authority that nitrogen lowers the stacking

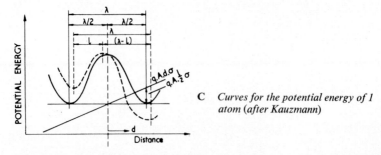

C   *Curves for the potential energy of 1 atom (after Kauzmann)*

fault energy of iron, yet in the paper which Dr Allen will be presenting in the following session he shows that nitrogen in pure iron has little effect on creep properties. I shall be glad of Professor Nutting's views on this seeming discrepancy.

WRITTEN CONTRIBUTION

Dr **W. Siegfried** (Battelle Memorial Institute) wrote: Recently, much progress has been made in explaining the influence of changes in structure on the creep of metals. A great number of processes can take place in the structure of a metal during the creep process, and the difficulty is to know what kind of process will take place at a certain moment under a certain stress and temperature. Generally speaking, we have no possibility of predicting what kind of process will take place after a certain time, and this makes all methods for the determining of long-time properties by extrapolation of tests of short duration nearly impossible.

In any case, where different processes are in competition with each other, in a general manner thermodynamic reflections can determine what kind of process is taking place. Nearly all metallurgical science is based on the thermodynamical functions for the equilibrium.

During the creep process there is no equlibrium, so that the thermodynamic functions can not be applied under the assumption of the existence of an equilibrium. In physical chemistry there has already been development of new methods which allows the use of thermodynamical considerations for processes which are not in equilibrium. This is the method of the activated complexes. The important point is that all these processes take place in such a manner that a threshold of energy has to be surpassed; they are described by an equation of the Arrhenius type. In this equation

$$v = \frac{2\,kT}{3\,h}\,l^{\,\Delta S^*/R}\,.\,l^{\,-\Delta H^*/RT}\,.\,\sinh\,(q.A.l.\sigma/_{kT}) \qquad . \qquad . \qquad . \qquad (1)$$

Figure C shows the meaning of several terms: $\Delta H^* =$ activation energy, $q =$ the stress-concentration factor of the microstructure, $A =$ the surface area for a dislocation unit displacement, $l =$ the distance between two atoms, $\Delta S^* =$ the entropy of activation which is determined by the degree of freedom of the system under consideration. If, for instance, the creep process changes in such a manner that new possibilities of deformation by the introduction of new gliding systems are given, then there will be a rise in activation energy. On the other hand, if there is for example a limitation on the creep process on a small zone in the grain boundaries, then a diminution in the value of the entropy of

194

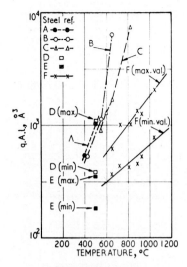

D *Values for q.A.l as a function of temperature, following different methods of evaluation*
(*Note* Λ = steel A)

Steel ref.	Steel type	Method of evaluation	Composition, %
A	Kauzmann No.9	Kauzmann	0·34C
B	Kauzmann No.10	Kauzmann	0·5Mo; 0·2Mn; 1·4Si
C	Kauzmann No.11	Kauzmann	18–10 Cr–Ni
D	Thum and Richard No.5	} Analysis of time-to-rupture curves	0·33C; 0·3Si; 0·64Mn
E	Thum and Richard No.10		0·165C; 0·29Si, 0·77Mn; 0·58Mo
F	Grant and Bucklin S590		0·4C; 20Cr; 20Ni, 20Co; 4Mo; 4Nb

activation is expected. Changes in structure introduced by heat treatment will first affect the structural factor $q.A.l$ determining the influence of the applied stress on the activation energy.

For this reason, I thought that it could be of help in the determination of the influence of changes in structure on creep, if the thermodynamical functions are determined by analysing the creep/rupture curves. This method is not new; Larsen and Miller, and Zener and Holomon already use this kind of analysis for the extrapolation of creep tests to very long durations. For this purpose, they made the following simplifications of the Arrhenius equation:

(*a*) *Larsen – Miller*
ΔS^* = constant, ΔH^* = function of the stress, but not of the temperature, $q.A.l$ = constant.

(*b*) *Zener – Hollomon*
ΔS^* = function of stress, but not of the temperature, ΔH^* = constant, $q.A.l$ = linear function of the temperature.

Recently, the validity of these simplifications had been checked by Kauzmann who analysed by determinations of the minimum creep rates, made at different temperatures and with different stresses, and by myself by the analysis of time-to-rupture curves. The mean results of these investigations can be seen in Fig.*D* Here, the factor $q.A.l$ had been plotted as a function of the temperature in the logarithmic scale, and one can see that the factor $q.A.l$ rises exponentially with the

195

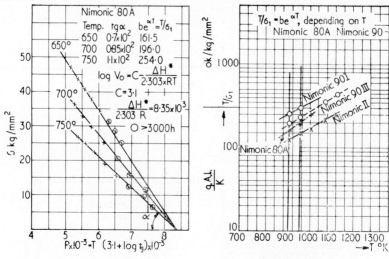

E *Results of creep-to-rupture tests, Nimonic 80 (after Betteridge)*

F *Temperature dependence of structural factor q.A.l*

temperature. This is the reason why the results of the extrapolation by the methods of Larsen – Miller or Zener – Hollomon are very often inexact.

Derivation of the method to determine the thermodynamical constants by using the Arrhenius equation.

We start from the following form of the Arrhenius equation:

$$v = \frac{1}{t} = \frac{2\,kT}{3\,h} \cdot l^{\Delta S^*/RT} \cdot l^{-\Delta H^*/RT} \cdot l\frac{q.A.l}{kT}\,\sigma \quad . \quad . \quad . \quad (2)$$

This equation can be transformed into the following:

$$\frac{\Delta H^*}{2 \cdot 3 . R} - T\underbrace{\left[\log\frac{kT}{3\,h} \cdot l^{\Delta S^*/R} + \log t\right]}_{c} = \frac{q.A.l}{2 \cdot 3 . K}\,\sigma \quad . \quad . \quad (3)$$

$$\frac{\Delta H^*}{2 \cdot 3 . R} - \underbrace{T\,(c + \log t)}_{p} = \frac{q.A.l}{2 \cdot 3 . K}\,\sigma \quad . \quad . \quad . \quad . \quad (4)$$

$$p = T\,(c + \log t)$$

For the case where ΔH^* = constant and ΔS^* = constant, we can plot the tension as a function of the parameter $p = T\,(c + \log t)$, and we get for different temperatures straight lines which all intersect at the same point on the *p-ax* at the value $\frac{\Delta H^*}{2 \cdot 3 . R}$. The factor $q.A.l$ is given by the relation: $\frac{q.A.l}{2 \cdot 3 . K} = -\,tg\,\alpha \quad . \quad . \quad (5)$

196

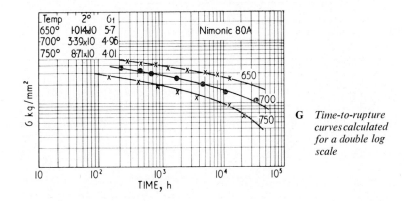

G *Time-to-rupture curves calculated for a double log scale*

There are a number of results of creep tests. We can determine in a very easy way the time and the temperature dependence of the thermodynamic functions. We plot these results in the diagram $p-\sigma$, and the values can be determined according to the equations (4) and (5). In Fig.*E* the results of the creep-to-rupture tests of Betteridge for Nimonic 80A are given. For this alloy all the values are determined by a constant value of ΔH^* and a constant value of ΔS^*. The temperature dependence of the structural factor $q.A.l$ is shown in Fig.*F*. One sees that there is a linear relationship between the logarithmic $q.A.l$ and the temperature. In Fig.*G* the time-to-rupture curves have been calculated for a double-logarithmic scale. In the same diagram, the points of the tests of Betteridge have been given. One sees that all points fit very well in this representation. Figure *H* shows the results of the tests with Nimonic 90, also made by Betteridge. Here it was no longer possible to represent all points by one value of activation energy, but it was necessary to subdivide the creep process into three regions with different activation energies and one and the same value for the activation entropy. A small change in the entropy of activation from one creep process to another could be determined, but it was so small that it could be neglected to a first approximation. The values of the factor $q.A.l$ are also different for the different regions but are, as can be seen on Fig.*F* also given by an exponential function of the temperature of time.

Figure *I* shows the time-to-rupture curves, calculated from Fig.*H* in double-logarithmic scale. Simultaneously, the points determined by Betteridge have been plotted in this diagram. The concordance between the test results and the calculated curves is good, and what is astonishing is the fact that also certain irregularities are very well reproduced.

It is now interesting to discuss the results of Fell *et al.* with the aid of the thermodynamic functions, which had been determined by analysing the creep-to-rupture curves of Betteridge and to compare the alloys Nimonic 80 A and 90.

The work done by these authors showed that in these two alloys the Ni_3 (Ti, Al) phase is precipitated, and that there is in the neighbourhood of the grain boundaries a zone containing less of the Ni_3 (Ti, Al) precipitate. This zone is larger in Nimonic 80A than in Nimonic 90. The authors think that this grain boundary zone is due to a precipitation of chromium carbide in these regions which diminishes the chromium content of the matrix and changes the conditions for the precipitation of the Ni_3 (Ti, Al) phase.

197

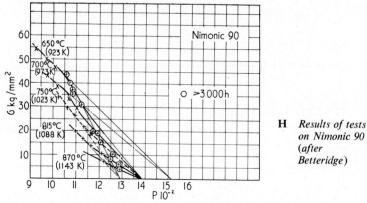

H   *Results of tests on Nimonic 90 (after Betteridge)*

What are the results of the thermodynamical analysis of creep-to-rupture curves?

(i) *Entropy of activation*

The constant c which has the value

$$c = \log \frac{kT}{3\,\mathrm{h}} \cdot l^{\,\Delta S^*/R} \quad\quad\quad\quad\quad (6)$$

has for Nimonic 80 A the value 3·1 and for Nimonic 90 8·0.

(ii) *Activation energy*

The activation energy for Nimonic 80 A is given by the expression:

$$\frac{\Delta H^*}{2\cdot3.R} = 8\cdot3 \,.\, 10^3 \quad\quad\quad\quad\quad (7)$$

and for Nimonic 90:

$$\frac{\Delta H^*}{2\cdot3.R} = 15\cdot2 \,.\, 10^3 \quad\quad\quad\quad\quad (8)$$

(iii) *The structural factors q.A.l*

are not very much different from one alloy to the other.

This behaviour can be explained by considering the results of Fell *et al.* as follows. In the alloy Nimonic 80 A, there is a grain boundary very weak in com-

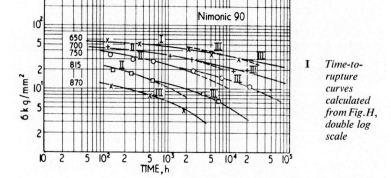

I   *Time-to-rupture curves calculated from Fig. H, double log scale*

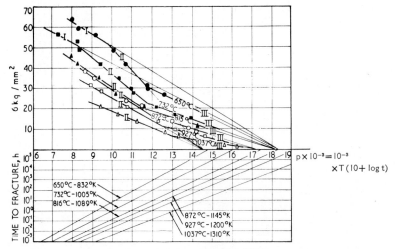

J   *Results of analysis (S590 results of Grant and Bucklin)*

parison with the resistance of the grains, and creep proceeds mainly by the deformation of the grain boundaries. The small value of activation energy is due to the small amount of Ni_3 (Ti, Al) precipitated in these grain boundary regions.

Owing to the big difference in the resistance to deformation between the grain and the grain boundary, the degree of freedom of the whole system is reduced, so the entropy of the system is small.

In the alloy Nimonic 90, there is less difference between the resistance of the grain boundary and the grains, so the freedom of the system is higher, and the entropy is higher, too. The higher resistance of the grain boundary regions due to the amount of Ni_3 (Ti, Al) precipitated is expressed by the higher activation energy. The relatively small difference in the structural factor $q.A.l$ suggests that there is no difference in principle in the arrangement of the dislocations, because the mechanical resistance is due to the precipitation of the same phase.

There are not enough results at our disposal for the discussion of the observations which had been made with the alloys Nimonic 80 A and 90 by variation of the heat treatment, but I have the feeling, that it would be possible to get interesting indications by such an analysis. I would like to show another example giving the influence of an annealing-treatment on the thermodynamical constants of a heat-resistant alloy. For this reason, I analysed the results on the alloy S 590 published by Grant and Bucklin. With this alloy, long time-to-rupture tests had been executed at 650°, 732°, 816°, 872°, 927°, and 1037°C. The samples tested at 650° and 732°C had been annealed at 760°C; the samples tested at 816°C had been annealed at 816°C, and the samples for the tests at 872°, 927° and 1037°C had been annealed at 732°C. Figure *J* shows the results of the analysis. The value of the constant c is 10, and all test-points can be represented by three regions with different values of activation energy. There is a difference in the activation energy between the samples annealed at 760° and 732°C. Figure *K* shows the temperature dependance of the structure factor $q.A.l$, and can be seen that there is quite a remarkable difference between the two annealing treatments. Figure *L* shows the calculated curves for this alloy together with the

199

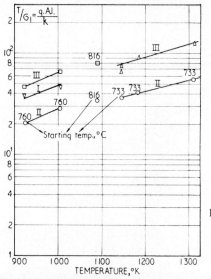

K *Temperature dependence of structure factor q.A.l (S590 results of Grant and Bucklin)*

experimentally determined points, and it is astonishing how well all details of the time-to-rupture curves can be given by this kind of presentation.

Fell *et al.* shows that for the explanation of the creep phenomena it is not sufficient to know the composition and the equilibrium diagram of the precipitated phases, but that the microscopical and the submicroscopical distribution is also of importance. The determination of the thermodynamical functions by analysing the form of the time-to-rupture curves enables us to get some information about the distribution of the precipitated phases and the changes in this distribution during the creep process.

AUTHORS' REPLIES

Mr Ch ld: Dr Bailey has rightly drawn attention to the absence of electron microscopical studies. There is little doubt that if such work had been carried out in parallel with the extensive creep testing, a much better insight would have been obtained into the precipitation process involved.

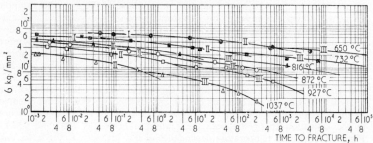

L *Calculated curves for the alloy, together with experimentally determined points (S590 results of Grant and Bucklin)*

As far as solid-solution strengthening is concerned, I have regarded the 'lattice parameter' of an alloy to be a practical measure of 'lattice strain'. If one assumes a regular substitution of a solid-solution hardening element in the matrix, then one may of course calculate the lattice strain of the solid-solution hardened alloy relative to the standard base alloy. In practice this is not completely justifiable because of such effects as super lattice formation and interatomic attractions between certain elements. For these reasons I have preferred only to use the lattice parameter as a measure of solid-solution hardening.

I think that Fell *et al.* would also agree that solid-solution hardening is important in the case of the nickel-base alloys they have studied, as the more recent alloys developed for commercial applications all contain substantial additions of molybdenum which does not occur as a precipitate and presumably is effective by solid-solution hardening.

Mr Fell: With reference to the paper by Professor Nutting, in the Nimonic alloys both the high supersaturation and the low supersaturation conditions can operate. In these alloys it is particularly important to avoid the introduction of internal stress before ageing, either by cold working, warm working, or rapid quenching from the solution heat treatment temperature. Otherwise, an ageing, carbide precipitation on dislocation arrays can occur adjacent to grain boundaries and large precipitate particles, which results in reduced creep ductility. In answer to Mr Pickering, during creep testing, similar carbide precipitation on dislocation arrays can occur but, in this case, the arrays do not extend to the actual boundary and creep ductility is relatively unaffected.

Dr Wakeman: Mr Dunlop noted the bad effects of hot working between two stages of heat treatment. One would suggest that hot working introduces boundaries away from existing particles, introduces a great deal of extra nuclei and produces carbide precipitation more extensively within the grain rather than grain boundaries. Hence, the denuded zone boundaries would not be reproduced and the alloy would break at a fairly low elongation. Ten minutes at 1050° would be adequate to move the dislocations out of the way and renew the carbides at the boundaries.

I was interested in Dr Siegfried's contribution. There are many extrapolation methods for extending creep curves. He gives a method which may well be superior to many of the other methods. At least it seems to have a more respectable thermodynamic background than some of the others may have. As to its usefulness in practice, I am doubtful. One cannot stretch this extrapolation formula too far. On the other hand it gives a set of three numbers which may have some thermodynamic backing, and possibly numbers such as this can be correlated with the structural factors, and put what are qualitative theories on a more quantitative ground in this matter.

AUTHORS' WRITTEN REPLIES

Messrs **Dalton**, **Webster** and **Child** wrote: In reply to Dr Bailey we think that the effect of silicon in Hylite 50 in the solution treated and aged condition bear some similarities to the formation of Preston-Guinier zones in that it is a pre-precipitation phenomena and moreover increases creep strength by restricting the free movement of dislocations. However, silicon gives rise to etching markings in the alpha grains of Hylite 50 which are revealed in electron micrographs taken from direct and extraction carbon replicas of etched surfaces. It is feasible that they denote silicon-enriched sites in the matrix but this was not proved by our techniques and thus there is only indirect evidence that this is so. On the other hand the appearance of Preston-Guinier zones is not an etching phenomenon. In extensive studies on age-hardening alloys these zones have been shown to be definite structures observed by direct transmission electron microscopy of thin metallic films. That they are visible at all is primarily due to the coherency strain field they induce in the parent lattice, which gives rise to diffraction contrast in addition to differential absorption of electrons.

Furthermore the fine etching markings occur almost exclusively on alpha grains although the Pt-C replication shows large amounts of etch-product randomly dispersed over the alpha–beta field. The two forms are believed to be of similar origin but the finer markings on the alpha grains are of prime interest. The structure of alpha titanium is hexagonal close packed and we are not aware of the Preston-Guinier zone phenomena being observed in a hexagonal lattice before. It has been widely studied in binary and ternary aluminium alloys but these are based on fcc structures. The hexagonal close-packed structure has fewer degrees of freedom for the vacancy and dislocation movement necessary for the initial solute atom clustering (three slip systems as opposed to twelve in the fcc structure).

Thus we think that the effect of silicon is to promote dislocation locking by a dislocation decorating effect rather than by the formation of Preston–Gunier zones.

Mr Fentiman is to be congratulated on his contribution on the effect of structure on the creep strength of titanium alloys. A very interesting observation is the increased creep strength produced by solution treating the ICI 679 alloy in the beta temperature region followed by heavy deformation at 950°C and finally ageing at 500°C. We wonder if any difference in the coarseness of the microstructure can be partially responsible for the observed difference in creep strength?

Mr Fentiman has shown that the mode of the beta decomposition has marked effect upon the microstructure of alpha–beta titanium alloys, particularly upon solution treating in the beta temperature region. In our experience many alpha–beta titanium alloys including T.48, when solution treated in the alpha–beta temperature region and aged, have a similar structure when examined under the optical microscope to that of Hylite 50 shown in Figure 7 of our paper, although the creep strengths may differ widely (the creep strengths of T.48 and Hylite 50 are compared in Table I of our paper). It is only when the alloys are examined at a much higher magnification in the electron microscope that any difference in microstructure can be detected. Comparing T.48 with Hylite 50 we observed differences both in the structure of the primary alpha grains and also in the mode of the beta decomposition.

By solution-treating in the beta temperature region Mr Fentiman and his co-workers have developed coarse microstructures and this has enabled them to study the beta decomposition by optical microscopy. However, our work has shown that the mode of the beta decomposition on subsequent ageing is influenced by the primary alpha grains present, and thus observation on structures produced by quenching from the beta temperature region may not be applicable to material quenched from the alpha+beta temperature region.

By analogy with his work on alpha alloys containing silicon Mr Fentiman feels that the major effect produced by silicon additions is to influence the mode of the beta decomposition. However, we do not think that the difference in decomposition products of T.48 and Hylite 50 upon normalizing from 900°C and then ageing for 24 h at 500°C can be solely responsible for the marked difference in creep strength at 400°C. Thus we believe that the dislocation locking within the primary alpha grains promoted by silicon must also contribute to the increased creep resistance.

One might comment in conclusion that in the UK all the titanium alloys being used or considered for applications at 400°C and above contain silicon because of its accepted importance in promoting creep strength.

Professor **Nutting** wrote: Dr Bailey has asked a very interesting question but it is difficult to give a satisfactory answer. Our methods of controlling microstructure are relatively crude; we can vary the solution treatment and ageing temperatures, introduce a few dislocations by mechanical working or change within fairly restricted limits the alloy composition. Usually, these methods do not give us the precise control of the microstructure we require, e.g. we cannot with certainty change the size, shape and distribution of the grain boundary precipitates whilst maintaining at a constant size the precipitates within the grain. Trace element additions which segregate to grain boundaries offer some hope of boundary precipitate control, but our understanding of the action of these additions is limited at the moment, and it may be that we are not making full use of these possibilities. The quantity of a dispersed phase we can produce in an alloy is governed by the solid solubility of the precipitating components at the solution treatment temperatures. If we could produce powders in the sub-micron range then by powder metallurgical techniques we may be able to make dispersed phase alloys in which we had direct control of the quantity of the dispersed phases, and materials with enhanced creep resistance may then be produced.

In differentiating between the modes of precipitation from solid solutions of low and high degrees of supersaturation, Dr Arrowsmith and I were putting forward limiting cases. Mr Pickering has given us some facts which do not seem to support completely the generalizations we have made. There are on the other hand many facts which do support the conclusions we have reached, and it may be as Mr Pickering points out that factors other than the degree of super-saturation have also to be taken into account, particularly when considering austenitic steels.

There could be a relatively simple explanation of the phenomenon described by Mr Dunlop. When the alloy is worked the subsequent ageing reactions are greatly accelerated, consequently after treatment at 750°C the cold-worked material would have a coarser microstructure and a different grain boundary precipitate distribution than alloy aged directly after solution treatment. Similar microstructural changes have been observed in Al–4%Cu alloys. In this alloy and the alloy described by Mr Dunlop, generalized precipitation occurs by decomposition of highly supersaturated solid solution. In an alloy of the G18B type only low degrees of supersaturation are found, consequently precipitate nucleation is difficult and the effect of warm working is to introduce dislocations to act as extra precipitation sites. For a given ageing treatment, the precipitate density is increased and better creep properties are found.

The results of Mr Fisher at Cambridge and of a more recent investigation by Mr Dulieu at Leeds indicate that nitrogen lowers the stacking fault energies of iron and austenitic steels. It now seems that part of this lowering could be accounted for by segregation of the solute elements to the stacking faults. As the temperature is raised, it is to be expected that the segregated regions will disperse. There may, therefore, be a temperature above which a particular solute element will cease having much effect on the creep resistance of an alloy. This may be the reason for some of the anomalies mentioned by Mr Duckworth.

REFERENCES

1. P. Shahinian and M. R. Achter (Ed. R. F. Hehemann): 'High temperature materials', 448–465; 1957, New York, John Wiley.
2. P. Shahinian and M. R. Achter: *Proc. ASTM*, 1958, **58**, 761–774.

An investigation of the creep ductility of 18–12–1 Nb and related steels

H. W. Kirkby, A. Met., F.I.M. and
R. J. Truman, A. Met., A.I.M.

The effect of solution treatment on the high temperature ductility of 18–12–1Nb *steel has been investigated by means of short-time tensile and creep–rupture methods. From the data obtained, it appears that increasing the solution temperatures has a markedly deleterious effect on the level of ductility generally and on the ductility/time pattern after creep–rupture testing. Secondary treatments following a 1350°C solution treatment were found to restore in varying degrees the ductility as determined by the short-time tensile method of testing, but these treatments did not appear to be particularly beneficial in terms of the ductility/time patterns obtained by the stress–rupture testing method. Slow cooling from 1350°C, compared with the air-cooled counterpart, showed considerably better ductility after short-time tensile testing, and a superior ductility/time pattern after stress–rupture testing. The general pattern of ductility behaviour in the case of the short-time tensile tests appears to follow a particular type of solution and precipitation phenomenon, but the position in regard to the ductility behaviour under creep–rupture conditions appears to be more complex in that the secondary type of treatment after an air-cooled 1350°C treatment is largely ineffective in improving the ductility/ time pattern, and hence may account for the wide scatter in creep ductility experienced with 18–12–1Nb steel. No completely satisfactory explanation has been found to date for the creep–rupture ductility behaviour. The paper also includes some creep–rupture results obtained on a 16–12–1Nb-type with a $1\frac{1}{4}$%Mo addition. This latter appears to exert a significant and beneficial effect on creep–rupture ductility.*

INTRODUCTION

AN EXAMINATION of the published creep–rupture data obtained from investigations on the 18–12–1 Cr–Ni–Nb austenitic type of steel

The authors are at the Brown-Firth Research Laboratories, Sheffield.

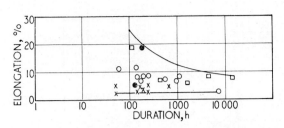

1 *Ductility behaviour of 18–12–1Nb bar material, British data*[1] *at 650°C*

suggests that the creep ductility behaviour of material of this composition is likely to be variable, with some examples exhibiting quite low ductility, e.g. of the order of 1–2% elongation. These features are illustrated in Figs.1 and 2, which summarize published collective UK[1] and US[2] data respectively, on a ductility (elongation %) v. log time to rupture basis, for test temperatures of 650°C. Results obtained at other test temperatures, but not reproduced, showed similar trends.

Whilst this variable and low ductility behaviour has been known for some time, it is only relatively recently that investigations have been directed towards a better understanding of the mechanisms involved, largely as a result of the stimulation provided by cracking troubles in service. These latter were experienced in the USA[3–7] and later in UK[8] power stations, where the 18–12–1Nb type of steel had been used for components such as steampipes, headers, valve bodies, etc. The cracking in these cases was confined largely to heavy weldments, the cracks being located at weld metal/parent metal junctions. Preliminary studies indicated that low ductility at temperature was in some way involved, and later and more detailed work supported this conclusion. The results of some of this work were published recently in a small symposium of papers.[9–12]

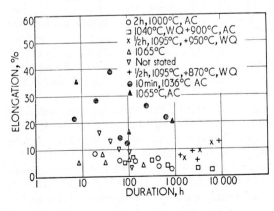

2 *Ductility behaviour of 18–12–1Nb (type 347) material, US data*[2] *at 1200°F*

205

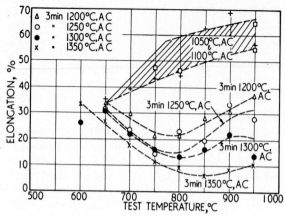

3 *Effect of solution treatment temperature on short-time tensile ductility of 18–12–1Nb bar material*

Perhaps the outstanding feature shown in some of these papers was the deleterious effect of high-temperature solution treatments on the short-time tensile ductility behaviour of 18–12–1Nb steel over a wide range of testing temperatures. A marked ductility trough was noted at 800–850°C, and this was attributed to a strain-assisted precipitation of niobium carbide, the intensity and effect of this being a function of the solution temperature (*see* Fig.3). Thus, using solution treatment temperatures similar to those attained at a weld junction (i.e. about 1350°C), the precipitation of niobium carbide appeared to exert its maximum effect when tensile specimens were deformed at about 800–850°C, such that surface intergranular cracking was observed with applied strains as low as 1%. This particular behaviour observed at 800–850°C was associated with the weld junction cracking observed at weld junctions.[9] A second low-ductility zone, obtained at around 1100°C, was considered to be due to a different set of circumstances peculiar to the testing procedure and this particular phenomenon will not be discussed further in this paper.

Two of the previous papers[9,11] demonstrated the beneficial influence of secondary treatments on the ductility/temperature curve, particularly in the 800–850°C region, i.e. where the strain-induced precipitation of niobium carbide appeared to have the greatest effect on the ductility. It was shown that soaking at temperatures of the order of 850–900°C, after a 1350°C solution treatment, but before testing, considerably improved the ductility in the region

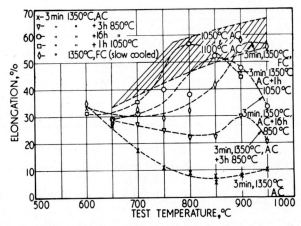

4 *Effect of various secondary heat treatments on the short-time tensile ductility of 18–12–1Nb bar material*

of 800–850°C. More recent results have also shown that a 1050°C* secondary treatment is even better for improving the ductility in this temperature region, this being illustrated in Fig.4, along with the other results mentioned above.

The earlier papers[9,11] concluded that the beneficial effects of these secondary treatments were due to an initial precipitation of niobium carbide in a relatively coarse form, which reduced the degree of super-saturation and hence the amount of subsequent strain-induced precipitation at the particular temperature of testing. From Fig.4 this initial precipitation is obviously time/temperature dependent.

To sum up the results of this work to date, it appears that after a high solution treatment of 18–12–1Nb steel, the strain-induced precipitation of niobium carbide has a catastrophic effect on short-time tensile ductility at temperature, but prior secondary treatments of 850–1050°C restore the loss of ductility in varying degrees. As shown in Fig.4, the 1050°C secondary treatment restores duc-

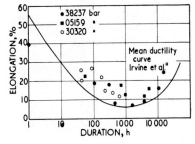

5 *Rupture ductility of 18–12–1Nb bar material (1050°C AC condition) at 650°C*

TABLE I Bar material analyses and grain size

Cast no.	Dia. in.	Analysis, % C	Si	Mn	S	P	Ni	Cr	Nb	Mo	N₂	Heat treatment, AC from temp.,°C	ASTM grain size
05159	⅜	0·06	0·64	1·44	0·006	0·008	12·65	17·68	0·88	...	...	1050	5–7
30320	¾	0·07	0·75	1·51	0·003	0·011	12·00	17·84	0·95	0·19	0·036	1050	8–9
												1150	Mixed 2–8
												1250	Mainly 2–3
												1350	Mainly 0–1

tility almost completely in the 800–850°C region, i.e. the ductility behaviour is similar to that obtained on as rolled + air cooled 1050°C treated bar without the 1350°C treatment.

Parallel with the above investigation, the ductility behaviour of 18–12–1Nb steel under the longer time stress–rupture type of testing conditions was also undergoing examination from the special viewpoint of explaining variable and low ductility of the type illustrated in Figs.1 and 2. The following information has been obtained at the time of writing this paper.

Creep–rupture tests on 18-12–1Nb steels

Using fine-grained test pieces prepared from relatively small diameter rolled bar, say ¾–1⅛in diameter, and solution treated or softened by air cooling from 1050°C, the evidence[11],[13] indicates that the 'normal' form of the ductility (elongation) v. log time to rupture curves for test temperatures of 650° and 700°C is approximately similar to those given in Figs.5 and 6 respectively. Some additional unpublished data are given in these figures on other casts of 18–12–1Nb steel. Details are given in Table I.

*Normal solution and softening temperature for 18–12–1Nb steel.

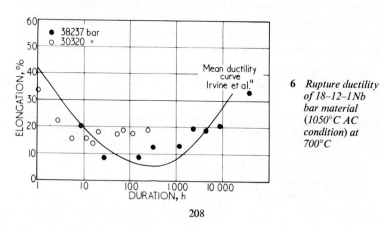

6 *Rupture ductility of 18–12–1Nb bar material (1050°C AC condition) at 700°C*

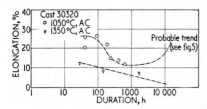

7 *Effect of solution treatment on rupture ductility of 18–12–1Nb bar material at 650°C*

From Figs.5 and 6 it will be observed that a minimum ductility is reached at both temperatures, with decreasing stress (increasing rupture time), followed by an increase in ductility with a further decrease in stress (and increase in rupture time). As with a number of other steels, the minimum ductility occurs at different testing times for the two testing temperatures in question; the higher the testing temperature the shorter the time. This aspect of creep–rupture ductility for 18–12–1Nb steel has been discussed in one of the more recent symposium papers[11] referred to earlier, where it was suggested that the minimum ductilities for the test temperatures considered (550–700°C) were also due to strain-induced precipitation of niobium carbide. That is, dislocations are generated by plastic straining on loading, niobium carbide precipitation on the dislocations follows and this has a strengthening effect on the matrix, with the result that most of the straining occurs at the boundary regions, with consequent overall loss of ductility.

It should be noted that these particular findings were obtained from material which had been solution treated from 1050°C only. However, the conclusion appears to be the same as that reached from the work carried out using the short-time tensile testing method[9] referred to earlier, where the effect of solution treatment temperature on hot ductility was brought out.

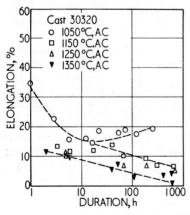

8 *Effect of solution treatment on the rupture ductility of 18–12–1Nb bar material at 700°C*

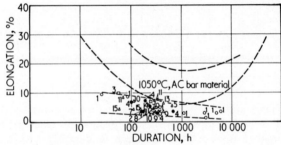

See Table II for pipe ref. no.

9 *Comparison of rupture ductility behaviour of 18–12–1Nb bar material and pipe material (1050°C AC) at 650°C*

In view of this, it was decided to study the effect of solution treatments in excess of 1050°C on the longer time creep–rupture ductility of the 18–12–1Nb steel, at test temperatures of 650° and 700°C. Details of the cast used are given in Table I.

Figures 7 and 8 show the ductility results obtained to date at 650° and 700°C on material solution-treated at various temperatures from 1050° to 1350°C. This work is still in progress and incomplete, but it is already evident that solution temperatures in excess of 1050°C have a significant effect on the ductility generally and on the ductility/time curve. These curves appear to fall into two main categories when the 700°C test results are considered (Fig.8); an upper 'band', made up of the results obtained after a 1050°C treatment, and a lower band of the results obtained using solution treatments of 1150–1350°C. These latter plots indicate that minimum ductilities are lower than those obtained on 1050°C treated material and appear to be displaced to longer times. It is clear that much longer testing times are needed to differentiate between the 1150–1350°C solution treatments in terms of the time for minimum ductility and the behaviour thereafter.

Prior to this work, it had been observed that creep–rupture tests on test pieces cut from 18–12–1Nb pipes* (and some forgings) resulted in creep ductilities lower than might be expected from bar material which had been finally heat treated by a 1050°C air-cooled treatment, i.e. the 'standard' heat treatment usually accorded to this type of material. These results are given in Figs.9 and 10 for test temperatures of 650° and 700°C, and in the same figures comparison is made with the ductility band obtained on rolled and air cooled 1050°C bar material (from Figs.5 and 6). Details of the pipes are given in Table II.

* 8in bore × 1–1¼in thick.

210

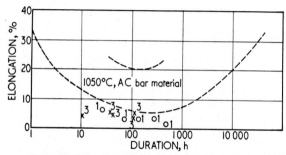

See Table II for pipe ref. no.

10 *Comparison of rupture ductility behaviour of 18–12–1Nb bar material and pipe material (1050°C AC) at 700°C*

It will be seen from the plots (Figs.9 and 10) that the behaviour of the pipe material is more akin to that of bar material solution-treated at a high temperature, say 1150–1350°C, this being shown more clearly in Figs.11 and 12, where the band of the pipe results obtained at 650°C and 700°C is plotted with the test results obtained on the bar treated at 1350°C. Included in the same figures are a few results obtained on one of the pipes solution-treated at 1350°C, which come within the band of the results obtained on 1050°C treated pipes.

The pipes in question are reported to be pierced and drawn in a temperature range of the order of 1210–1150°C. This might well be considered to constitute a solution treatment of 1150°C+. From the data which have been presented, it is clear that solution treatments of this type could exert a significant influence on short-time tensile

TABLE II **18–12–1Nb pipe analyses, grain sizes, etc.**

Ref. no.	Cast no.	Analysis, % C	Si	Mn	S	P	Ni	Cr	Nb	ASTM grain size*
1	37478	0·12	0·37	1·21	0·005	0·014	11·65	18·54	1·30	Mainly 5–6
2	...	0·07	0·71	1·58	...	...	11·45	17·08	1·02	,, 3–4
3	...	0·09	0·41	1·66	...	...	12·50	17·36	0·93	,, 3–4
4	43273	0·11	0·66	1·24	0·005	0·016	11·40	18·20	1·33	,, 2–4
5	38520	0·06	0·69	1·38	0·004	0·009	11·45	18·12	1·05	,, 3–4
6	38520	0·06	0·69	1·38	0·004	0·009	11·45	18·12	1·05	,, 2–4
7	38083	0·06	0·68	1·15	0·012	0·009	11· 5	17·84	0·90	,, 3–5
8	38083	0·06	0·68	1·15	0·012	0·009	11·15	17·84	0·90	,, 2–4
9	36004	0·07	0·70	1·52	0·004	0·013	12·05	18·00	1·09	,, 2–4
10	36338	0·06	0·77	1·52	0·012	0·013	12·15	17·72	1·12	,, 2–3
11	36323	0·06	0·87	1·54	0·006	0·013	11·90	17·92	1·08	,, 2–4
12	36021	0·07	0·71	1·67	0·004	0·010	12·20	17·92	1·06	,, 2–4
13	36347	0·07	0·75	1·33	0·008	0·015	11·60	17·36	0·99	,, 2–4
14	35819	0·07	0·60	1·57	0·009	0·010	11·80	17·60	0·97	,, 1–3
15	34073	0·08	0·64	1·50	0·006	0·012	12·00	17·52	1·02	,, 2–3

* All the above pipes were given the normal treatment of 1050°C AC. Grain sizes tended to be mixed, but the majority of grains in each pipe conform to the range specified.

211

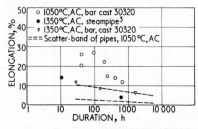

11 *Effect of high solution treatments on rupture ductility of bar and pipe material at 650°C*

and particularly on the longer time creep–rupture ductility behaviour, if no further heat treatment was carried out. All the pipes were, in fact, given a solution treatment of 1050°C air cooled as a final heat treatment before testing. From the results of the short-time tensile tests on bar (Fig.4), it might be expected that this final AC 1050°C treatment has beneficial effects on the short-time tensile ductility, and this is actually the case as seen in Fig.13, which shows the ductility/temperature plot for pipe material in both the 1050° and 1350°C solution-treated conditions, with a comparison being made with bar material in the plain 1050°C air-cooled condition. Whilst the 1050°C treated pipe material generally has lower ductility than that of the corresponding bar material, the results obtained are very much superior to those obtained with the 1350°C treated pipe test pieces.

As the precipitation mechanisms operating in the two different types of test, i.e. short-time tensile and the longer-time creep–rupture, are thought to be the same, it would seem reasonable to expect 1050°C treated pipe material to show some improvement in the longer-time creep ductility behaviour compared with, say, material 1350°C treated, but, as shown, this is not the case at 650°C or 700°C. The same was found to apply when secondary treatments were given to the 1050°C treated pipe material. Thus, additional treatments of 850°C for 3 h had no substantial effect on the longer time ductility at 650°C, as shown in Fig.14. A few results obtained

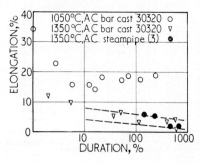

Note: Broken line indicates scatter-band of pipes as in Fig.11

12 *Effect of high solution treatments on rupture ductility of bar and pipe material at 700°C*

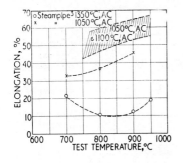

13 *Comparison of short-time tensile behaviour of 18–12–1Nb bar and pipe material*

on pipe samples after a 16 h, 850°C treatment are also included in the same figure, and these suggest a similar conclusion, though more points are required. Some of the pipe material was also treated from 950°C AC followed by 1050°C AC and the results obtained are given in Fig.14, from which it will be seen that the general ductility pattern is similar to that of the 1050°C treated pipes. The results obtained at 700°C are given in Fig.15 and are of interest in showing the effect of 16 h, 850°C on the shorter time end of the ductility/time curve and the rapid fall-off in ductility with time. Longer testing times are necessary to determine whether the 16 h, 850°C treatment modifies the shape of the ducility/time curve.

Using bar material from cast no. 30320, it was decided to try the effect of secondary treatments after an initial 1350°C AC solution treatment, namely a treatment which gives maximum solubility of niobium carbide and also a ductility/time pattern similar to that of the pipe material in the 1050°C treated condition. The secondary treatments tried were (*a*) 850°C for 16 h, (*b*) 1050°C for 1 h, air cool, and the results obtained at 700°C only are given in Fig.16. The corresponding 650°C tests are in progress, but insufficient data are available for plotting.

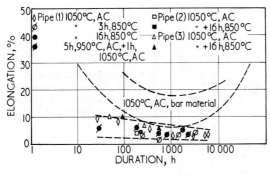

14 *Effect of secondary treatments on rupture ductility of 18–12–1Nb pipe material at 650°C*

213

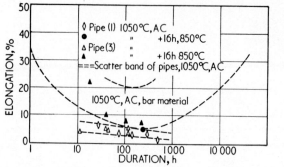

15 *Effect of secondary treatments on rupture ductility of 18–12–1Nb pipe material at 700°C*

The results given in Fig.16 show a ductility/time pattern more in keeping with the 1350°C behaviour, but there are indications that both the 1050°C and the 16 h, 850°C secondary treatments have slightly improved the ductility; more test points and longer testing times are required. In general, the behaviour of the bar which has been given the 1350°C plus the secondary treatments is similar to that of the corresponding pipe material, indicating that once 18–12–1Nb steel has received a high solution treatment, secondary treatments of the type used do not restore the creep ductility pattern to that expected from fine-grained bar material treated at 1050°C.

In an earlier paper,[9] the authors drew attention to the effect of the cooling rate from 1350°C on the short-time tensile ductility/temperature plot. In this paper it was argued that if pre-ageing treatments of 850°C (and higher) eliminated the ductility trough at around 850°C, then some suitable slower cooling rate from the initial high solution treatment temperature should achieve a somewhat similar result. With a particular cooling rate,* a ductility curve was obtained, and is reproduced in Fig.4, comparison being made with the various other treatments referred to earlier.

Figure 4 shows that the ductility pattern of the slow cooled, i.e.

* Cooling rate 400°C/h at 1100°C and 220°C/h at 850°C.

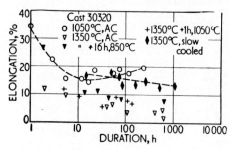

16 *Effect of secondary treatments on rupture ductility of 18–12–1Nb bar material at 700°C*

214

furnace cooled, 1350°C condition around 800–850°C is superior to that obtained with the AC 1350°C + 16 h 850°C treatment, though not quite as good as the plain AC 1050°C and the AC 1350°C + AC 1050°C treatments.

Creep–rupture tests have also been carried out on bar from cast 30320 after the furnace cooling 1350°C treatment and the results so far available at 700°C are plotted in Fig.16 along with the results of the other treatments. From the plot it is evident that the furnace cooling has improved the ductility considerably and modified the ductility/time pattern as compared with the results on material treated at 1350°C AC, and also 1350°C AC followed by various times at 850°C or 1050°C. It does not appear, however, that the restoration of the ductility behaviour is quite complete in terms of the plain AC 1050°C pattern, the trend of the curve being, if anything, downwards. Results well in excess of 1000 hours are required to complete the picture.

Results of microexamination

A survey of the microstructures, before testing, of the bar cast 30320 and one of the steampipes (ref.3) has been made by normal optical and by electron microscopy. Specimens of bar material in the various initial solution-treated conditions (1050°, 1150°, 1250°, 1350°C AC, and 1350°C slow cooled) and of the steampipe in the normal 1050°C AC condition were examined along with specimens covering the effect of secondary heat treatments (16 h, 850°C AC and 1 h, 1050°C AC, following the initial 1340°C AC).

The grain sizes resulting from these various heat treatments are reported in Tables I and II. Massive niobium carbide particles were found in all specimens, along with 'dot' carbides uniformly dispersed throughout the matrix in the 1050°C AC samples. The 'dot' carbides appeared to have been taken into solution at temperatures of 1150°C and over, but the massive carbide particles were obvious through the whole series although becoming positively less in amount and somewhat smaller with increasing solution treatment temperature.

Electron microscopical examination showed a general dispersion of spheroidal niobium carbide particles of varying sizes throughout the matrix in the 1050°C AC bar sample. These were the 'dot' carbides referred to earlier. After 1350°C AC, there was a general absence of the smaller spheroidal particles and only occasional clusters of small particles were observed from which no reasonable electron diffraction pattern could be obtained. Some coarse boundary carbides had apparently formed during air cooling from 1350°C;

these confirm the findings of Moore and Griffiths[12] on similar specimens where $M_{23}C_6$ type boundary carbides were identified.

A secondary treatment of 16 h, 850°C AC following the 1350°C AC resulted in an increase of the boundary phase and of the formation of clusters of fine cubic particles throughout the matrix along with a marked formation of a complex form of precipitation along crystallographic planes. Both types of particles within the grain were identified as niobium carbide. There was an obvious depletion of precipitation in regions adjacent to grain boundaries. The general precipitation of small cubic particles, and the precipitation on crystallographic planes was more intense than that reported by Moore and Griffiths[12] on a specimen aged for 3 h at 850°C after 1350°C solution treatment. These workers also reported boundary depletion zones.

A secondary treatment of 1 h, 1050°C following the 1350°C AC treatment showed coarser boundary particles than with the 850°C secondary treatment, along with a general dispersion of somewhat coarser cubic particles of niobium carbide in the matrix. There was a tendency for these particles to form clusters and stringer formations, and a boundary depleted region was still obvious.

Slow cooling from 1350°C resulted in an increased amount of the grain boundary phase compared with the 1350°C AC + 1050°C treated specimen, but the main feature was the coarse dispersion of niobium carbide particles within the matrix. These particles were appreciably coarser, both in size and dispersion, than either the 1350°C AC + 850°C or the 1350°C + 1050°C specimens.

Only one steampipe sample (1050°C AC condition) was examined, and this showed a general dispersion of cubic-shaped particles throughout the matrix. There was a general similarity between the structure of this specimen and the 1350°C AC + 1 h, 1050°C AC bar specimen, in that the matrix precipitation was very similar in form and size, although the dispersion was somewhat different; with the steampipe specimen the precipitation showed more of a stringer formation on what appeared to be a sub-grain structure.

Preliminary examinations have been made on a number of test pieces from bar material after short-time tensile testing and creep–rupture testing, to confirm the mode of fracture. In regard to the short-time tensile tests, specimens tested at 650° and 800°C have been examined to check the effects of 1050° and 1350°C AC, 1350°C slow cooling, and various secondary treatments following 1350°C AC.

At 650°C, all the tests fractured with high ductilities (*see* Fig.4) and all the fractures were found to be predominantly transgranular.

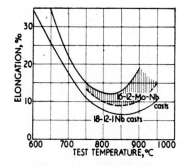

17 *Comparison of short-time tensile behaviour of 18–12–1Nb and 16–12–1MoNb materials*

A few intergranular voids were noted on boundaries, but these had apparently formed after considerable deformation of the grains.

At 800°C, the specimen originally treated at 1350°C AC showed low elongation and a mode of fracture which was predominantly intergranular. The specimens initially treated 1050°C AC, 1350°C AC with secondary treatments of 850°C and 1050°C, and 1350°C slow cooling all showed high elongations at 800°C, with fractures which were predominantly transgranular.

The longer time creep–rupture tests at 700°C, following the above initial and secondary heat treatments, had fractures which were mainly intergranular or had started in an intergranular manner. This confirms earlier examinations made on 1050°C AC bar material creep–rupture tested at 650°C.[13]

Molybdenum-bearing austenitic steels

One of the authors has reported in an earlier paper[14] the apparently beneficial effects on creep ductility when molybdenum is added to an 18–12–1Nb type of steel, and this aspect is discussed further in the present paper.

The composition of the steel in question is as follows:

Steel	Analysis, %				
	C	Ni	Cr	Mo	Nb
F.V.548					
(16–12 MoNb)	0·1	12	16	1·25	1·0

It should be noted that the chromium content is a little lower than is usual for 18–12–1Nb steel in order to minimize the formation of sigma phase, but this modification has no bearing on the behaviour of molybdenum-containing steel, since a 16–12–1Nb composition has the same ductility characteristics as 18–12–1Nb steel, both as regards short-time tensile and creep–rupture behaviour.

Short-time tensile tests at elevated temperatures of the type shown in Fig.3, have been carried out on the molybdenum-bearing steel, and the

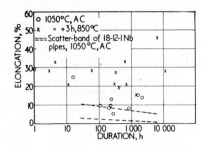

18 *Rupture ductility of 16–12–MoNb pipe material at 650°C*

temperature/ductility curve is shown in Fig.17 alongside the 18–12–1 Nb counterparts. The ductility characteristics of both types of steel after a high solution treatment are similar, the molybdenum-bearing steel being only slightly better around 800–850°C. Examination of tensile test pieces deformed at 850°C showed surface intergranular cracks at around 1 % elongation, i.e. similar to the 18–12–1Nb steel. Whilst not shown, the molybdenum-bearing steel also responded similarly to 18–12–1Nb steel when subjected to secondary treatments such as 3 h at 850°C AC, 1050°C, i.e. after the 1350°C treatment.

The creep–rupture ductility behaviour of the molybdenum-bearing steel differed, however, in that a pipe of the same dimensions as those described earlier and given the same thermal cycle in its manufacture was found to have much better ductility properties than the 18–12–1Nb counterpart, as shown in Figs.18 and 19. These figures show the results obtained on pipe material of the two compositions in question in the 1050°C AC condition and 1050°C AC + 3 h, 850°C at 650° and 700°C. It is clear from Figs.18 and 19, particularly Fig.19, that the creep ductility of the molybdenum-containing steel is much better than that of the 18–12–1Nb counterpart. Furthermore, comparing the results in the AC 1050°C + 3 h, 850°C condition, the ductility of the molybdenum-bearing steel is

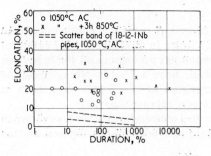

19 *Rupture ductility of 16–12–MoNb pipe material at 700°C*

further improved, particularly at 650°C, as a result of the 850°C treatment, which was not the case for the 18–12–1Nb pipe material. This superior behaviour of the molybdenum-bearing steel has been confirmed on other casts of the same composition, showing that the molybdenum has an important influence on creep ductility.

DISCUSSION

Whilst a contribution of this type tends to pose more questions than answers, the evidence presented shows quite clearly that the ductility properties of 18–12–1Nb steel at elevated temperatures can vary between wide limits, depending upon the thermal history of the steel. This behaviour has been revealed on material submitted to both the short-time tensile and the longer time creep–rupture methods of testing, although the picture is by no means complete in regard to the latter type of test. The information is probably sufficient, however, to account for quite a lot of the scatter observed in creep ductility referred to in the introduction to this paper, though other causes may exist.

The deterioration in ductility with increasing solution treatment has been observed to be associated with a fine precipitation of niobium carbide on dislocations generated by plastic straining, this feature strengthening the matrix relative to the boundary. Consequently, most of the straining occurs at the boundaries, leading to intergranular cracking and low ductility, depending upon the intensity of precipitation. In addition, boundary depletion effects, which have also been observed, may contribute to the loss in ductility.

Turning to the temperature/ductility patterns obtained by the short-time tensile (or bend)[9,11] method of test, they would appear to be in keeping with a solution and precipitation phenomenon of the type described. That is, the higher the treatment temperature and the greater the amount of niobium carbide taken into solution, the lower the subsequent ductility and the more marked the ductility trough at intermediate temperatures. The ductility behaviour is clearly temperature/time/strain dependent, which is shown also by the response to secondary or pre-ageing treatments.

The ductility behaviour under the longer life creep–rupture conditions would appear to be more complex since the response to the secondary treatments after a 1350°C solution treatment is marked only at the shorter times of testing, this latter being expected from the ordinary short-time tensile data, particularly at 700°C and above. At longer times, the secondary treatments appear to exert only a small influence in terms of ductility level, though longer time/

rupture data are needed to determine the effect of the secondary treatments on the time reached for the minimum ductility and the recovery behaviour.

One heat treatment which stands out from the rest is furnace cooling from 1350°C, which gives a ductility/time pattern superior to all the other treatments, with the exception of the plain 1050°C AC treatment (Fig.16). This improvement could not have been deduced from the short-time tensile data (Fig.4), since the ductilities after 16 h, 850°C or 1050°C (after 1350°C AC) are at least as good as those obtained after 1350°C FC treatment. The only difference noted to date relates to the carbide, which is somewhat coarser and consequently more widely dispersed, but much more work is required before a satisfactory explanation can be given for the differences observed.

The possibility exists, however, that the explanation of the superiority of the 1350°C slow cooling treatment may well depend on the coarser distribution of carbide particles, and probably on a more complete precipitation of niobium carbide by the slow cooling, than by air cooling from 1350°C coupled with secondary treatments of 850° and 1050°C. In addition, the influence of boundary depletion effects is not yet fully understood, and the slow cooling from 1350°C does not appear to show the marked boundary depletion effects found with secondary treatments of 850° and 1050°C, subsequent to rapid cooling from 1350°C. It is interesting also that neither the secondary treatments of 850°C or 1050°C, nor the slow cooling from 1350°C have so far been found to alter the rupture strength significantly, although the influence on long-time behaviour is still unknown.

Work on the effect of longer soaking times at 850°C (after 1350°C AC) is required to determine whether greater carbide spheroidization, and presumably less intense boundary depletion, would improve the creep ductility. The likelihood exists, however, that a temperature of 850°C may still retain a small but sufficient amount of niobium carbide in solution, to cause subsequent precipitation on straining at 650–700°C, thereby adversely affecting ductility. In the case of the short-time tensile test, with its high strain rates, no deleterious effect on ductility was noted at 650–700°C after the secondary treatment of 16 h at 850°C. However, with low strain rates, as obtained in the creep–rupture test, very small amounts of precipitating carbide may be important in affecting creep ductility, particularly where the grain size is large, as in the present case. Within the limits of the treatments carried out, grain size does not appear to exert much influence on the ductility obtained with high strain rates, where the behaviour can be reasonably explained by simple solution and precipitation effects.

The results obtained on the molybdenum-bearing material are very interesting in that the recovery of creep ductility with secondary treatments is quite marked. Further study of the molybdenum-type austenitic steels is being carried out, since it is considered that it may throw light on the general problem of creep ductility in niobium-bearing steels.

ACKNOWLEDGMENTS

The authors wish to acknowledge the help given by their various colleagues at the Brown-Firth Research Laboratories in regard to the experimental work. In particular, thanks are due to Mr H. Hardwick.

REFERENCES

1. W. H. BAILEY et al.: Proc. IME, 1957, 171, 911–942.
2. W. F. SIMMONS and H. C. CROSS: 'Report on the elevated temperature properties of stainless steels,' ASTM Spec. Tech. Publ. no. 124.
3. H. THIELSCH: Combustion, 1956, 27, (11), 67–70.
4. F. P. FAIRCHILD: Trans. ASME, 1957, 79, 1371–1375.
5. R. M. CURRAN and A. W. RANKIN: ibid., 1398–1409.
6. R. M. CURRAN and A. W. RANKIN: Weld. J. 1955, 34, (3), 205–213.
7. E. F. NIPPES et al.: ibid., 1835–1965.
8. F. E. ASHBURY et al.: Brit. Weld. J., 1960, 7, 598–678.
9. R. J. TRUMAN and H. W. KIRKBY: JISI, 1960, 196, 180–188.
10. R. N. YOUNGER and R. G. BAKER: ibid., 188–194.
11. K. J. IRVINE et al.: ibid., 166–179.
12. N. E. MOORE and A. J. GRIFFITHS: ibid., 1961, 197, 29–39.
13. H. W. KIRKBY and R. J. TRUMAN: 'Precipitation processes in steels,' ISI, Spec. Rep. no. 64, 242–258.
14. H. W. KIRKBY: Alloy Metals Rev., 1959, 9, (92).

Some causes of variation in high-temperature strength of steels, with particular reference to the silicon content

J. Glen, D.Sc., A.R.C.S.T., F.I.M., J. Lessells, A.I.M.,
R. R. Barr, B.Sc., A.R.C.S.T., and G. G. Lightbody, B.Sc.,
A.R.C.S.T.

This paper is concerned with emphasizing the importance of active nitrogen on the creep resistance of steel. To study the problem short-time creep tests and high-temperature tensile tests were used. Commercial and experimental steels were tested in the normalized condition and after various stress-relieving treatments. It is shown that after prolonged stress relieving the creep resistance of silicon-killed steels may be seriously reduced owing to the formation of silicon nitride. Very low silicon steels are unaffected. Some of the silicon-killed steels deteriorate more slowly than others and this may be due to a high residual content. Evidence is also given to demonstrate that these effects are not confined to carbon–manganese steels but are equally important in alloy steels.

INTRODUCTION

DURING the last 10 years a much clearer picture of the factors controlling creep has been emerging. These factors have been summarized by Glen and Murray,[1] who suggest that precipitation processes, which occur during testing or which are prior induced by heat treatment, are of paramount importance with regard to creep strength. Solution hardening and grain size are considered to be factors of minor importance.

In considering the problem of creep, it is useful to separate the creep resistance into two components[2,3]; the inherent creep resistance which is related to the microstructure before testing, and the latent creep resistance which depends on precipitation processes occurring during the actual creep test. Strain age hardening effects due to the formation of 'atmospheres' of carbon or nitrogen are included under the general term 'precipitation' and affect the latent creep resistance.

The authors are with the Central Research Department of Colvilles Ltd.

The effect of nitrogen on creep strength has received less attention than carbon and only the more recent contributions have dealt with this subject. Bardgett[4] drew attention to the deterioration in creep strength which is obtained in aluminium grain-controlled steels and related this to loss of active nitrogen by the formation of aluminium nitride. Attention has also been focused on the adverse effect of vanadium additions due to the formation of vanadium nitride.[1]

More recently, Glen and Murray[1] have noted that silicon nitride may be formed during the tempering of carbon–manganese steels containing as little as 0.15%Si. This was confirmed by Irvine[5] who showed by internal friction measurements that interstitial nitrogen was removed from solution by tempering. He also showed by means of electron micrographs that a precipitate had formed and identified it as silicon nitride. These latter findings are of great practical importance, as nearly all steels used for high-temperature components are of the silicon-killed type and these components are usually given a stress-relieving treatment. Thus a greater or less formation of non-coherent silicon nitride can be expected.

The present paper is concerned primarily with emphasizing the importance of active nitrogen content on the creep resistance of steel. If large variations in active nitrogen content can be shown to exist in nominally similar steels, one of the most important reasons for scatter in creep properties will have been found.

EXPERIMENTAL TECHNIQUES
Variations in inherent creep resistance can be detected by comparatively short-time creep tests. The latent creep resistance on the other hand may not develop fully until after very long testing times. Fortunately, however, although active nitrogen influences latent creep resistance its effect occurs within the first few hours of testing and thus short-time creep tests give sufficient information for the purposes of this paper. For this reason creep tests were mainly confined to 50 h duration at a stress of 8 tons/in² and a temperature of 450°C. The creep rate chord between 24 and 48 h was measured as defined in BS. 1271, 1945. All the creep test results, however, were also analysed using log strain/log creep rate curves since in this way variations in initial and latent creep can be detected.

Since the presence or absence of active nitrogen was thought to be of prime importance, another method of evaluating the behaviour of interstitial elements was considered necessary. Internal friction measurements are being increasingly employed in this connexion, but for the present purpose it was thought that high-temperature tensile tests would be simpler and less costly and in addition would give quantitative results on another strength property. The use of this technique has been previously discussed by one of the authors.[6] This previous work showed that the various peaks obtained in stress/strain curves at different temperatures can be related to alloy precipitates. Only the peak affected by the active nitrogen required study for the present paper and for this reason tensile tests were carried out in most cases only at 20°C and 250°C.

Tensile tests were carried out on a 20-ton multiple lever machine suitably modified to give automatic control of jockey weight travel by means of a servo system. A universal joint system was incorporated to ensure good axial loading and recording of the load/extension curve was completely automatic. The straining rate employed throughout tensile testing was 0·0001 in/in/min as measured on the elastic portion of the curve.

The development of the electron microscope has stimulated the study of precipitates in steel but it should be borne in mind that precipitates may be considered to have relatively little importance in creep when they have coarsened and become non-coherent. The optimum effect on inherent creep resistance occurs with maximum coherency. It is, however, very difficult to judge from electron micrographs whether or not maximum coherency has in fact been obtained. It would appear from this that electron microscopy taken by itself is not sufficient to explain creep processes and will be used to best advantage in conjunction with other supporting tests. No electron micrographs have been used in this paper but it is hoped to carry out such tests and report them later.

Effect of aluminium

The deleterious effects on creep strength obtained by making aluminium additions to a given steel are well known and have been reported in the literature by Bardgett[4] and by one of the present authors.[7] It is now generally accepted that the reduction in creep strength is related to loss of active nitrogen by the formation of aluminium nitride during heat treatment. The extent to which active nitrogen is removed from solution in such steels is dependent to a large extent on the normalizing temperature employed. Since this does not appear to have been sufficiently emphasized in the literature the results shown in Figs.1a and b are of interest. With a high normalizing temperature little or no active nitrogen is lost through the formation of aluminium nitride and creep properties are good. With decreasing normalizing temperature the creep properties become worse owing to the greater loss of active nitrogen.

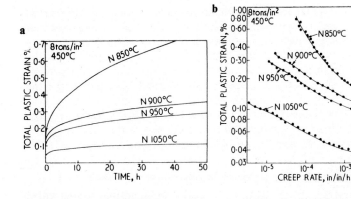

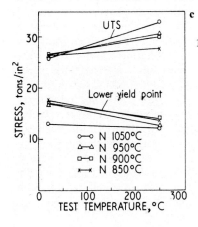

1 *a Effect of normalizing temperature
      on the creep strength of 0·12%C–
      0·50%Mn aluminium grain-
      controlled steel
   b Strain/rate curves for aluminium
      grain-controlled steel
   c Effect of normalizing temperature
      on the tensile properties of
      aluminium grain-controlled steel
   d Relationship between reduction in
      the strain-ageing peak at 250°C
      and creep strength for varying
      normalizing temperatures in
      aluminium grain-controlled steel*

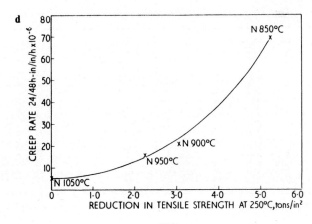

Figure 1c summarizes the tensile results at 20°C and 250°C. With the highest normalizing temperature employed the strain ageing peak is at a maximum and decreases with lowering of the normalizing temperature, indicating loss of active nitrogen. The relationship between the creep strength and reduction in the strain ageing peak (for present purposes taken as the decrease in UTS at 250°C) compared with the UTS at 250°C for the sample normalized from 1050°C for various normalizing temperatures is indicated in Fig.1d. Clearly, a large variation in creep strength can be obtained within the range of commercially acceptable normalizing temperatures.

Effect of prolonged stress relieving on the properties of C–Mn steels

Until very recently it has been generally accepted that silicon-killed C–Mn steels have superior creep and rupture properties compared with equivalent steels deoxidized with aluminium. This assumption is still correct provided the steels are used in the normalized condition or after only a short-time stress relieving treatment at not too high a temperature. The stress-relieving treatment suggested[8] for some nuclear reactor pressure vessels, namely 36 h at 600°C followed by a slow cool, is sufficient to reduce the creep resistance of silicon-killed steel to such an extent that it may be no better or even worse than aluminium grain-controlled steel. This deterioration has been attributed to the precipitation and overaging of silicon nitride.

To study the problem in greater detail a number of commercial steels were tested. Details of these steels are shown in Table I. All the steels were normalized from 900°C and also stress relieved for 36 h at 600°C preceeded by slow heating and followed by slow cooling.

TABLE I   Chemical composition of commercial steels tested

Code no.	Composition, % C	Si	S	P	Mn	Ni	Cr	Mo	Cu	Sn
1	0·15	0·02	0·026	0·021	0·62	0·37	0·12	0·28	0·10	0·01
2	0·13	0·05	0·036	0·011	0·53	0·08	0·03	0·02	0·12	0·02
3	0·17	0·18	0·036	0·020	0·86	0·08	0·03	0·01	0·03	0·009
4	0·17	0·19	0·041	0·021	0·89	0·08	0·03	0·005	0·03	0·005
5	0·10	0·12	0·038	0·030	0·53	0·13	0·035	0·01	0·13	0·02
6	0·145	0·16	0·032	0·015	1·26	0·08	0·03	0·005	0·05	0·009
7	0·14	0·16	0·033	0·015	1·25	0·08	0·03	0·005	0·05	0·006
8	0·135	0·03	0·022	0·024	1·05	0·12	0·09	0·04	0·12	0·02
9	0·155	0·16	0·025	0·024	1·18	0·14	0·06	0·03	0·20	0·021
10	0·195	0·185	0·036	0·018	1·09	0·06	0·03	0·005	0·09	0·007
11	0·145	0·15	0·04	0·026	1·37	0·09	0·045	0·04	0·13	0·009
12	0·24	0·185	0·035	0·016	0·75	0·08	0·03	0·03	0·04	0·006
13	0·22	0·14	0·035	0·027	0·71	0·09	0·05	0·02	0·05	0·007
14*	0·14	0·27	0·009	0·015	1·41	0·13	0·10	0·05	0·08	0·015

* Basic electric arc

TABLE II   Effect of tempering on creep rate of commercial steels

Creep rate, in/in/h × 10⁻⁶, between 24 and 48 h

Code no.	Normalized	Normalized + stress relieved 3 h at 600°C, AC	Normalized + stress relieved 3 h at 650°C, AC	Normalized + stress relieved 36 h at 600°C, cooling rate 12½°C/h
1	1·6			0·4
2	17·6			30·0
3	8·7			104·2
4	7·6			90·0
5	11·7			40·0
6	3·7		35·3	42·4
7	3·0	5·1	29·2	49·0
8	4·9			5·2
9	2·2	2·7	4·1	6·0
10	3·9	4·8	4·2	19·7
11	2·4		3·4	2·3
12	5·7	13·2	38·0	73·0
13	9·0	13·1	85·4	77·5
14*	1·4			10·9

* Basic electric arc

This treatment was adopted as representing extreme conditions of stress relief. A few additional creep tests were carried out after a shorter time treatment at 600° and 650°C to check the effect of a more conventional stress-relieving treatment.

Creep tests were assessed in the first instance on the basis of the creep rate between the 24th and 48th hours. The results obtained are noted in Table II. Curves of log total plastic strain v. log creep rate were constructed in order that a more fundamental examination of creep behaviour might be possible. These curves are further discussed later in this paper. The results of tensile tests at 20°, 250°, and 350°C are listed in Table III and graphs of ultimate tensile strength and lower yield point v. temperature are reproduced for representative samples in Fig.2.

In the normalized condition creep strength as measured by the 24–48 h creep rate showed only variations to be expected from differences in composition. Normalized tensile results (Table III) all indicated an increase in ultimate tensile strength at 250°C as compared to 20°C values. After tempering for 36 h at 600°C a wide variation in creep strength was obtained. Silicon-killed steels gave

TABLE III Tensile results for commercial steels

Code no.	Thickness, in		Normalized					Normalized + stress relieved 36 h at 600°C				
		Test temp., °C	Lower yield or 0.2% PS tons/in²	UTS tons/in²	Elong. %,4√A	R of A %		Test temp., °C	Lower yield or 0.2% PS tons/in²	UTS tons/in²	Elong. %,4√A	R of A %
1	1·0	20	17·9	28·5	32·5	60·4		20	16·2	27·4	50·8	50·4
		250	14·2	34·6	24·0	38·4		250	15·6	30·0	22·5	45·2
		350	11·8	31·7	29·0	49·6		350	11·4	29·4	50·8	50·4
2	¾ dia. bar	20	14·7	24·9	45·0	68·5		20	14·2	23·7	49·0	61·6
		250	13·2	32·4	32·5	52·4		250	11·5	28·2	35·8	58·8
		350	9·6	26·7	37·5	63·6		350	8·6	24·7	50·0	72·8
3	1·0	20	17·4	30·0	38·0	58·0		20	14·2	26·3	42·0	58·0
		250	14·2	34·0	25·0	41·2		250	9·8	24·7	35·0	52·4
		350	11·4	31·7	34·0	48·4		350	9·2	25·4	34·5	58·8
4	1·25	20	17·8	29·4	37·0	54·4		20	15·1	28·2	37·0	62·8
		250	15·3	34·9	30·0	44·8		250	11·2	26·4	32·0	58·8
		350	10·0	30·8	35·0	52·8		350	9·8	26·0	39·0	65·2
5	1·0	20	13·5	23·6	42·0	64·0		20	13·0	23·7	39·0	65·2
		250	12·1	31·3	30·5	48·8		250	10·0	28·3	25·5	46·8
		350	8·7	26·4	37·0	54·4		350	9·6	25·2	28·0	56·4
6	3·0	20	16·2	28·8	42·0	61·2		20	14·8	25·8	41·0	68·0
		250	14·6	35·9	22·5	44·8		250	10·1	24·5	30·0	59·2
		350	11·6	32·6	23·5	42·0		350	9·4	25·2	36·5	63·2
7	3·0	20	16·7	28·8	34·5	62·8		20	14·8	27·3	31·5	63·2
		250	14·6	36·0	25·0	50·0		250	12·8	26·0	20·0	48·4
		350	12·1	32·4	33·0	54·0		350	10·2	30·2	33·0	58·8
8	1·25	20	16·3	27·9	32·3	49·6		20	15·4	26·4	39·0	62·0
		250	12·7	33·9	36·5	59·6		250	13·6	31·2	22·5	41·2
		350	11·2	30·1	25·5	42·8		350	9·8	29·2	31·5	55·2
9	4·0	20	17·4	30·0	30·0	63·6		20	15·8	27·5	39·0	68·4
		250	14·6	36·6	25·0	34·4		250	12·6	26·0	35·0	41·6
		350	13·9	34·8	30·0	42·4		350	11·7	27·3	34·0	54·8
10	1·0	20	17·6	32·4	36·0	62·8		20	15·0	28·1	39·0	65·2
		250	15·4	40·3	24·0	40·4		250	11·8	26·7	33·0	59·2
		350	13·8	35·9	33·0	56·0		350	10·9	26·8	35·5	62·8

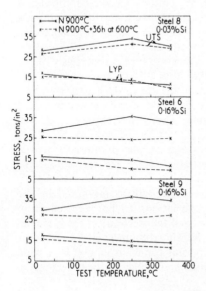

2 *Effect of 36 h at 600°C on the tensile properties of balanced and silicon-killed steel*

creep rates varying from 2·3 to 104·2 × 10⁻⁶ in/in/h. Steels containing small amounts of silicon, on the other hand, showed little or no change. A substantial reduction in ultimate tensile strength at 250°C was obtained in all silicon-killed steels, whereas low-silicon steels were hardly affected. These results indicate that active nitrogen has been decreased to a low level by the formation of silicon nitride. Since silicon seemed to be so important, the deterioration in creep strength due to stress relief was plotted against silicon content as shown in Fig.3. Some of the results reported later are also included in this graph. As will be noted, most higher silicon steels deteriorate substantially after stress relieving.

A few additional creep tests were carried out using a stress-relieving treatment of either 3 h at 650° or 600°C. The results obtained in these cases are also shown in Table II. It will be noted that the effect of tempering for 3 h at 650°C can be just as bad as the effect of 36 h at 600°C. A treatment of 3 hours at 600°C on the other hand, has little effect even on a steel which can deteriorate substantially with a more prolonged treatment.

Examination of Fig.3 reveals that some silicon-killed steels appear to behave anomalously in that these steels do not deteriorate markedly in creep strength after stress relieving for 36 h at 600°C. No anomalous behaviour, however, was indicated by tensile tests since these showed that in all silicon-killed steels, active nitrogen has been reduced to the same extent regardless of behaviour in creep tests. This suggests that whereas in most cases the silicon nitride formed has overaged and become non-coherent, in some cases it was more resistant to overageing and still remained largely coherent after the stress-relieving treatment. Evidence to prove this is given

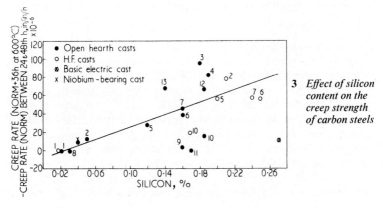

3 *Effect of silicon content on the creep strength of carbon steels*

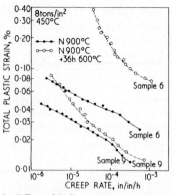

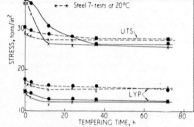

4 *Effect of 35 h at 600°C on the creep strength of silicon-killed steels*

5 *Effect of tempering time on tensile properties of silicon-killed steels*

by the strain/rate curves of two typical steels shown in Fig.4. In the normalized condition both samples show good initial creep resistance as indicated by the low creep rate at very small strains. In each case a transition in creep rate occurred early in the test due to the presence of active nitrogen. After stress relieving, sample 6 shows very poor initial creep resistance and the transition in creep rate due to active nitrogen is no longer present. In other words non-coherent silicon nitride has been formed. After stress relieving sample 9, on the other hand, the initial creep resistance is good, indicating that any silicon nitride which has formed is partly coherent. The shape of the curve, however, indicates that the nitrogen transition has been largely eliminated. This is indicated by the divergence of the curve compared with that of the normalized steel. Thus steel 9 does not deteriorate appreciably on stress relieving because the presence of coherent nitride largely compensates for the loss of active nitrogen.

Effect of tempering time at 600°C

To provide some idea of the rate at which nitrogen is removed from solution during tempering, steels 7 and 9 were tested after various times at 600°C. The former steel is one of the group in which creep strength deteriorated after 36 h at 600°C while the latter behaved anomalously as described in the previous section. The results of tensile tests are summarized in Fig.5. In steel 7 precipitation, as evidenced by reduction in the strain ageing peak at 250°C, starts after 2 h at temperature and is almost complete after about 12 h. No further reduction in ultimate tensile strength at 250°C takes place for times up to 72 h. Corresponding results for steel 9 indicate that

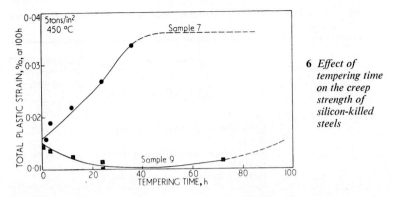

6 *Effect of tempering time on the creep strength of silicon-killed steels*

the rate of removal of nitrogen from solution is much slower in this case, precipitation being complete only after about 36 h. No further change takes place between 36 and 72 h.

Creep tests at 8 tons/in² are not yet available but results at 5 tons/in² are summarized in Fig.6. In both cases, and particularly in sample 9, there is some evidence of coherency with short tempering times. With steel 7, however, deterioration in creep strength is very rapid between 12 and 36 h, whereas in steel 9 the results are good even after 72 h. As indicated in Fig.6 it is not expected that steel 7 will become much worse with longer times at temperature. Similarly steel 9 should eventually reach a value corresponding to steel 7 with sufficiently prolonged tempering.

Comparing steels 7 and 9 it would appear that in each case a coherent nitride forms in the first instance. Further tempering then causes the precipitate to coarsen and creep strength to deteriorate. The essential difference between these steels lies in the rate of formation and subsequent overageing of the precipitate formed. The speed at which these processes occur is very much slower in steel 9.

Effect of normalizing temperature

The standard normalizing tempering used throughout was 900°C. In order to determine whether variation in normalizing temperature was important, two steels (6 and 9) were further investigated after normalizing from 850° and 1000°C.

Whereas it has been shown (Fig.1) that normalizing temperature is important with respect to the creep strength of aluminium-killed steels, no evidence has been found to suggest that this factor is important in silicon-killed steels. The creep results on silicon-killed steels are summarized in Table IV.

TABLE IV Effect of various normalizing temperatures on creep rate of steels 6 and 9

Code no.	Condition		Creep rate, in/in/h $\times 10^{-6}$, between 24th and 48th h
6	Normalized	850°C	3·7
	,,	850°C+stress relieved 36 h at 600°C	55·7
	,,	900°C	3·7
	,,	900°C+stress relieved 36 h at 600°C	42·4
	,,	1000°C	8·9
	,,	1000°C+stress relieved 36 h at 600°C	41·7
9	,,	850°C	2·4
	,,	850°C+stress relieved 36 h at 600°C	4·0
	,,	900°C	2·2
	,,	900°C+stress relieved 36 h at 600°C	6·0
	,,	1000°C	2·5
	,,	1000°C+stress relieved 36 h at 600°C	8·0

Tests on laboratory casts of experimental steels

From results on the commercial steels already mentioned, and those in the literature,[9] it was noted that at least two of the anomalous results were obtained from electric furnace steels. Such steels can have higher nitrogen contents than open-hearth steels.

Thus to study the problem further, a series of 25-lb hf melts using pure raw materials was prepared. In these steels, silicon and nitrogen were the main variables as shown in Table V. Each cast was rolled to $\frac{7}{8}$in dia. bar and was normalized after 1 h at 900°C. Samples were also stress relieved for 36 h at 600°C.

TABLE V Chemical composition of high-frequency casts

Code no.	Composition, %								
	C	Si	Mn	N_2	Ni	Cr	Mo	Cu	Sn
1	0·12	0·02	1·00	0·007	0·03	Tr.	0·01	0·02	0·01
2	0·13	0·21	1·05	0·005	,,	,,	,,	,,	,,
3	0·13	0·50	1·16	0·0055	,,	,,	,,	,,	,,
4	0·13	1·00	1·13	0·0055	,,	,,	,,	,,	,,
5	0·13	0·20	1·10	0·01	,,	,,	,,	,,	,,
6	0·135	0·25	1·21	0·01	,,	,,	,,	,,	,,
7	0·135	0·24	1·00	0·014	,,	,,	,,	,,	,,
8	0·125	0·50	1·13	0·012	,,	,,	,,	,,	,,
9	0·135	0·50	1·10	0·013	,,	,,	,,	,,	,,

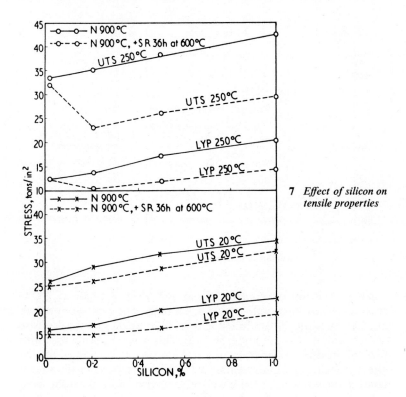

7 *Effect of silicon on tensile properties*

Silicon series

The results of tensile tests on this series are shown in Fig.7. The important point to be noted from this graph is that with only 0·02 %Si present, tensile and yield stress are almost unaffected by stress relieving for 36 h at 600°C.

TABLE VI Creep rate between 24th and 48th h for silicon series of hf casts

Code no.	Sc, %	Creep rate, in/in/h $\times 10^{-6}$ between 24th and 48th h	
		Normalized 900°C	Normalized 900°C+stress relieved 36 h at 600°C
1	0·02	15·0	13·6
2	0·21	3·9	81·7
3	0·50	2·2	47·9
4	1·00	3·8	33·8

233

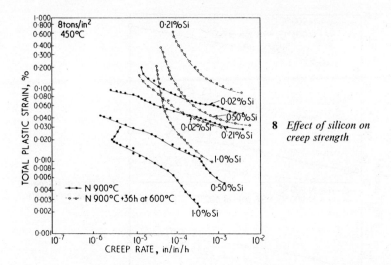

8 *Effect of silicon on creep strength*

Above this silicon content tensile and yield strength at 250°C show a marked deterioration after stress relief. The strain ageing peak at 250°C is particularly affected and it will be noted that the decrease in this peak is constant above 0·2 %Si. This would indicate that with 0·2 %Si present maximum loss of active nitrogen is obtained for the stress relieving conditions employed. Further increase in the silicon content does not have the effect of removing more nitrogen from solution.

The results of creep tests are summarized in Table VI and Fig.8. It is apparent from these that creep strength is closely allied to tensile results in so far as loss of active nitrogen is concerned. With only 0·02 %Si present, creep strength is virtually unaffected by stress relief. With higher silicon contents, however, a marked deterioration is apparent after stress relief.

The effect of silicon in itself is interesting but it is considered that discussion of this point is outside the scope of the present paper.

Nitrogen series

Tensile test results illustrating the effect of nitrogen in 0·2 %Si steel are summarized in Fig.9. These results indicate that in the normalized condition nitrogen up to about 0·01 % has a marked strengthening effect. The magnitude of the strain-ageing peak in UTS at 250°C is particularly affected. It will be noted that the size of the strain-ageing peak is appreciably greater in the steels with higher nitrogen contents.

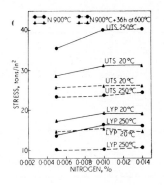

9 *Effect of nitrogen on tensile properties*

After stress relieving no significant strengthening effect due to nitrogen remains since all the steels have the same tensile strength at 20° or at 250°C. However, tensile strength at 250°C is now appreciably below that obtained at 20°C. This indicates that after stress relieving the same active nitrogen content remains in each steel and that 0·2%Si is sufficient to combine with as much as 0·014%N under the stress-relieving conditions used.

Creep results for this series in the form of strain/rate curves are shown in Fig.10 while 24–48 h creep rates are recorded in Table VII.

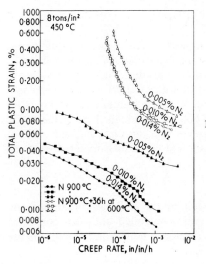

10 *Strain/rate curves for steels with varying nitrogen contents*

235

TABLE VII   Creep rate between 24th and 48th h for nitrogen series of hf casts

Code no.	Total N, %	Creep rate in/in/h $\times 10^{-6}$, between 24th and 48th h	
		Normalized 900°C	Normalized 900°C+stress relieved 36 h at 600°C
5	0·01	1·8	58·5
6	0·01	2·0	58·0
7	0·014	1·7	59·4
8	0·012	1·3	44·0
9	0·013	1·2	42·5

In the normalized condition creep strength increases with nitrogen content, the order of difference between 0·005% and 0·01%N casts being very large. After stress relieving for 36 h at 600°C creep strength shows a very substantial deterioration in all cases. This is related to loss of nitrogen from solution and overaging of silicon nitride as already discussed. As was to be expected from the tensile results very little difference in creep strength is apparent between steels containing 0·005–0·014%N after stress relieving.

These results indicate that even increasing nitrogen content to about 0·014% does not prevent deterioration due to tempering in creep properties of silicon-killed steels. From all the above results it might justifiably be argued that a steel containing little or no nitrogen would give just as bad results even in the normalized condition as do normal silicon-killed steels in the stress-relieved condition.

The above two series of steels were tested in order to determine whether variations in silicon or nitrogen could help to explain the anomalous results discussed earlier. Variations in the quantities of these elements present have a pronounced effect on creep strength in the normalized condition but a much diminished or no effect after stress relieving for 36 h at 600°C. Although these elements are obviously important in themselves the results obtained do not suggest an explanation for the anomalous results obtained on some commercial steels.

Effect of aluminium and silicon

To determine the effect of silicon in the presence of aluminium, a steel which was aluminium grain-controlled and also contained about 0·15%Si was tested. The results of tensile and creep tests are summarized in Table VIII and Fig.11.

TABLE VIII Effect of stress relief on creep and tensile results for 2in thick plate of silicon-bearing aluminium grain-controlled steel

Compo- sition, %	C 0·16	Si 0·15	S 0·025	P 0·030	Mn 1·13	Sol.Al 0·07

Condition	Test temp., °C	LYP or 0·2% PS, tons/in²	UTS, tons/in²	Creep rate, in/in/ h × 10⁻⁶ between 24th and 48th h
Normalized 900°C	20	17·4	29·5	20·3
	250	13·1	27·5	
Normalized 900°C+				
stress relieved	20	16·2	28·1	36·0
36 h at 600°C	250	12·4	26·5	

Tensile tests indicate that in the normalized condition, aluminium has largely suppressed the strain ageing peak at 250°C and no further change was evident after stress relief.

The strain/rate curve shown in Fig.11 for the normalized condition suggests that some active nitrogen may still remain, since the creep rate obtained is not as bad as that of ordinary silicon-killed steel in the stress-relieved condition. It might have been expected that silicon after stress relieving would have removed the remaining

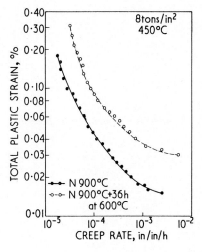

11 *Strain/rate curves for aluminium grain-controlled steel containing silicon*

nitrogen from solution. However, since the creep rate did not show a substantial increase in this condition, it would appear that any silicon nitride which formed remained largely coherent.

While further work on this aspect is clearly warranted, it seems possible that the presence of aluminium can reduce the rate of precipitation and overaging of silicon nitride. Some evidence in the literature[10] tends to support this conclusion.

Effect of niobium

The effect of niobium in steels is arousing considerable interest at this time and it is interesting to note the manner in which creep strength is affected by additions of this element in carbon–manganese steels. A recent contribution to the literature[11] suggested that niobium could form a nitride during stress relieving. To check this point a few tests were carried out. To avoid complications, the steel used contained very little silicon. The results of these tests are also included in Fig.3. Tensile test results are summarized in Fig.12 while creep data are given in Table IX together with compositional and other relevant details.

In the normalized condition, the steel containing niobium shows a less pronounced strain ageing peak than the steel without niobium, indicating the formation of some niobium nitride during normalizing. After stress relieving the ordinary steel containing low silicon showed little change as was to be expected but the niobium steel showed a further drop in tensile at 250°C.

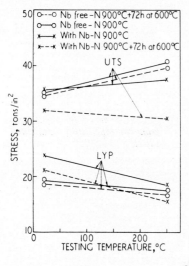

12 *Effect of niobium on tensile properties*

TABLE IX Effect of niobium addition on creep rate of low silicon steel after stress relief

Base composition, %	C 0·19	Si 0·04	Mn 1·44

Code	Condition	Creep rate, in/in/h $\times 10^{-6}$ between 24th and 48th h
Control	Normalized 900°C	5·2
Control	Normalized 900°C+stress relieved 72 h at 600°C	13·8
With niobium (0·06%)	Normalized 900°C	9·9
With niobium (0·06%)	Normalized 900°C,+stress relieved 72 h at 600°C	21·7

These results suggest that insufficient niobium is present to remove completely all the nitrogen from solution. The creep test results confirm this conclusion. Although further work is necessary it would appear from these results that niobium is capable of forming a nitride and therefore, in sufficient quantities, should behave like aluminium.

Residual elements

From the results shown in Tables I and II there was some indication that steels which behaved anomalously had higher residual element contents. To check this, one 25-lb laboratory melt was made to a composition corresponding to that of hf steel 2 with the addition of residual elements. This cast was tested in the normalized and

TABLE X Effect of stress relief on creep rate of hf cast with increased residuals

Composition, %	C 0·13	Si 0·17	Mn 1·00	Ni 0·17	Cr 0·09	Mo 0·04	Cu 0·28	Sn 0·035

	Creep rate in/in/h $\times 10^{-6}$, between 24th and 48th h	
Code	Normalized 900°C	Normalized 900°C+stress relieved 36 h at 600°C
10	2·1	21·6

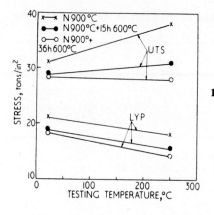

13 *Effect of residual elements on response to tempering. Tensile results on hf steel 10*

normalized and stress relieved conditions. Composition, tensile, and creep results are shown in Table X and Figs.13 and 14.

Tensile results from this cast indicate that the rate of removal of nitrogen from solution is rather slower than would normally be expected and in fact corresponds approximately to that obtained for the anomalous commercial steel 9 (Fig.6). It will also be noted from creep results that the deterioration in creep strength of this steel with the long-time stress relief was not severe, as indicated by the position of this point (hf 10, Fig.3). It would appear from these results that one or more of the added elements may have a significant effect on the rate of removal of active nitrogen from solution and on the resistance to overageing of the silicon nitride precipitated. Further work is being carried out to clarify this point.

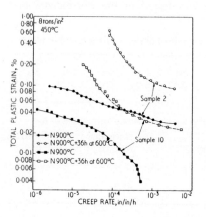

14 *Effect of residual elements on creep strength*

240

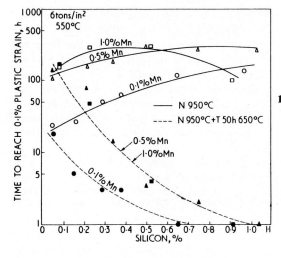

15 *Effect of tempering on 0·5%Mo steels with various silicon and manganese contents*

Tests on 0·5%Mo steels

So far it has been shown that the active nitrogen content largely controls the creep resistance of C–Mn steels. It has also been shown that as little as 0·15%Si is sufficient to tie up most of the nitrogen in steels stress relieved for a sufficiently long time.

All alloy steels contain silicon and it is therefore important to determine whether they behave in a manner similar to that described above for carbon–manganese steels. The effect in 1·0%Cr–0·5%Mo steels has already been considered in some detail by Glen who showed the effect of silicon in large amounts to be detrimental.

In 0·5%Mo steel containing about 0·15%Si the effect of tempering at 650°C has been investigated.[12] Taking the time for 0·10% creep as a criterion in tests at 6 tons/in² and 550°C it was found that a maximum was obtained after about 10 h tempering at 650°C. Murray[13] has suggested from electron micrographs that this corresponds to maximum coherency of molybdenum carbide. The effect of silicon, as shown in the present paper, was not, however, considered in this work.

The results of a series of tests carried out by one of the authors many years ago were available. These refer to tests on hf casts made from very pure materials and nitrogen content was about 0·005%. The steels contained 0·09–0·13%C and 0·48–0·53%Mo. Three series were made with 0·09–0·15%, 0·45–0·55%, and 0·90–1·10%Mn and varying silicon up to 1·0% as shown in Fig.15.

The same criterion of creep strength was used as indicated above

241

and tests were carried out in the normalized 950°C condition and normalized followed by tempering for 50 h at 650°C.

It will be noted that in the normalized condition, the time required to reach 0·10% strain tends to increase with manganese or silicon content. After tempering for 50 h at 650°C, however, there is very little change in the steels containing 0·05%Si but with increasing silicon there is a marked deterioration compared with the normalized results. It is obvious therefore that in a 0·50%Mo steel, the removal of active nitrogen by silicon can be just as important as in a C–Mn steel.

In the normalized condition, molybdenum carbide had not time to form during testing and the creep resistance depends to a considerable extent on the active nitrogen content. After tempering, any molybdenum carbide which has formed is non-coherent and will therefore again have no effect on the initial creep resistance. In the low silicon steels, active nitrogen is not altered by tempering and for this reason the time to reach 0·10% creep strain does not change. With increasing silicon content, more active nitrogen is removed on tempering with a corresponding deterioration in creep resistance.

The maximum in creep resistance previously reported after 10 h at 650°C which was ascribed solely to precipitation of molybdenum carbide must now be considered due to a combination of at least two effects: formation of coherent molybdenum carbide, and precipitation of silicon nitride. Until these effects have been separated, it is not possible to judge the exact tempering time at which molybdenum carbide has its maximum effect.

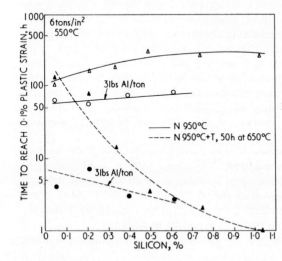

16 *Effect of aluminium on 0·5%Mn–0·5%Mo steel with various silicon contents*

A further series of tests was carried out on 0·5%Mn–0·5%Mo to which 3 lb/ton of aluminium was added. These results are compared with corresponding aluminium-free steels (Fig.15) in Fig.16. It will be noted that since normalizing was carried out at 950°C, aluminium has removed some but not all the active nitrogen since the normalized creep resistances are worse at all silicon levels compared with the steels having no aluminium. After tempering for 50 h at 650°C the creep properties are poor, even at low silicon contents, indicating in this case the formation of aluminium nitride. Some silicon nitride appears to have been formed in the aluminium-killed steels containing silicon, as indicated by the slight worsening of creep strength with increasing silicon.

A few tests were also carried out on 0·5%Cr–0·5%Mo, and 1·0% Cr–0·5%Mo steels containing silicon and these confirmed the results given.

SUMMARY AND CONCLUSIONS

Short-time creep tests in conjunction with high-temperature tensile tests have been used to determine some of the factors affecting the precipitation of nitrogen from solution in C–Mn steels. It has been shown that the amount of active nitrogen in the steel has a very considerable effect upon the creep strength.

In steel deoxidized with aluminium the amount of nitrogen depends upon normalizing temperature; the lower the normalizing temperature the more aluminium nitride forms and the lower the active nitrogen content. In silicon-killed steels the normalizing temperature has no effect since it does not vary the active nitrogen content. If such steels, however, are tempered or given a stress relieving treatment, a greater or less amount of silicon nitride can be formed depending upon tempering time and temperature. In a series of commercial steels tested after stress relieving for 36 h at 600°C (or 3 h at 650°C) it was found that the creep resistance could be seriously affected as shown by short-time creep tests at 8 tons/in² and 450°C. At the same time the strain ageing peak at 250°C disappeared, the tensile strength at 250°C being in most cases less than that obtained at 20°C. This deterioration in strength was attributed to loss of active nitrogen and formation of non-coherent silicon nitride. In steels containing very low silicon, neither creep nor tensile strength deteriorated significantly on tempering since the active nitrogen was unaffected.

A series of small hf casts with 0·02–1·0%Si and 0·005–0·014%N confirmed these observations. In the normalized condition silicon and/or nitrogen increased both the tensile and the creep strength.

After stress relieving for 36 h at 600°C, however, all nitrogen levels gave the same result since most of the nitrogen had been rendered ineffective. It was thus concluded that a steel containing little or no nitrogen would be as bad even in the normalized condition as a normal silicon-killed steel in the stress-relieved condition.

Some of the silicon-killed steels did not deteriorate as much as expected in creep after stress relieving and it was shown that in such cases the rate of decrease in tensile strength at 250°C was slower with time and temperature compared with other steels. This suggests that in these steels the rate of precipitation of coherent nitride and of subsequent overageing was slower. Some evidence is given to show that steels with high residual elements behave in this way.

Three series of hf casts containing 0.5%Mo, 0.1%, 0.5%, and 1.0% Mn together with varying silicon contents up to 1.0% were made. These steels were tested after normalizing from 950°C and after normalizing and tempering for 50 h at 650°C. Creep tests were carried out at 6 tons/in² and 550°C and the time taken to reach 0.10% creep taken as a criterion. No deterioration in creep after tempering was obtained in any of the steels containing about 0.05%Si but with higher silicon contents serious deteriorations occurred due to loss of active nitrogen. Shorter tempering times were not investigated but it is obvious that the reported improvement in creep strength obtained with shorter tempering times does not depend solely on the amount of coherent molybdenum carbide which forms but also on the amount and condition of the silicon nitride. Similar conclusions apply to 0.5%Cr–0.5%Mo, and 1.0% Cr–0.5%Mo, and no doubt to many other alloy steels.

As a matter of interest, a few tests were carried out on a niobium-bearing steel and it was shown that a nitride of niobium can form in the normalized condition and the effect of niobium in sufficient amounts would be expected to be similar to aluminium.

Based on the results of experiments described in this paper, it is evident that a number of factors which might normally be expected to vary in commercial steels can have a profound effect on scatter of creep results. These may be enumerated as follows:

   (i) total nitrogen content
  (ii) normalizing temperature in aluminium grain-controlled steels
 (iii) silicon content in tempered steels
 (iv) tempering time and temperature in silicon-killed steels
  (v) factors, for example residual elements, which affect the response of silicon-killed steels to tempering.

All these factors control the amount of active nitrogen present in the finished product. Active nitrogen may be taken as one of the principal factors affecting scatter in creep testing.

In alloy steels of course, many other factors affect scatter such as the extent and coherency of alloy precipitates which form. These factors, however, are outside the scope of this paper.

ACKNOWLEDGMENTS

The authors wish to express their thanks to Mr W. Barr, o.b.e., director and chief metallurgist of Colvilles Ltd, for his continued encouragement, and to him and his fellow directors for permission to publish this paper.

REFERENCES

1. J. GLEN and J. D. MURRAY, in: 'Symposium on steels for reactor pressure circuits', *ISI Spec. Rep. no.* 69, 1961.
2. J. GLEN: *JISI*, 1958, **189**, 333–343.
3. J. GLEN: *ibid.*, 190, 114–135.
4. W. E. BARDGETT: 'Refresher course on the elevated temperature properties of metals', Institution of Metallurgists, 1958.
5. K. J. IRVINE, in discussion: 'Symposium on steels for reactor pressure circuits', *op. cit.*
6. J. GLEN: *JISI*, 1957, **186**, 21–48.
7. J. GLEN: *ibid.*, 1947, **155**, 501–52.
8. J. M. ROBERTSON and R. W. NICHOLLS, in: 'Symposium on steels for reactor' *op. cit.*
9. R. P. KENT, in discussion: *ibid.*
10. P. WERTHEBACH and H. HOFF: *Stahl Eisen*, 1958, **78**, 736–743.
11. J. E. RUSSELL, in: 'Symposium on steels for reactor pressure circuits', *op. cit.*
12. J. GLEN: *JISI*, 1948, **158**, 37–80.
13. J. D. MURRAY, in: 'Precipitation processes in steels', *ISI Spec. Rep. no.* 64, 1959, 285–291.

Structural aspects of creep-resisting steel

K. J. Irvine, B.Sc., Ph.D., J. D. Murray, A.Met., A.I.M., and F. B. Pickering, A.Met., A.I.M.

The main structural features which influence creep phenomena in steel have been considered, and include solid-solution hardening, grain size, initial microstructure, precipitation hardening, and dispersion hardening and the formation of dislocation atmospheres or grain boundary segregations. Examples of the way in which these factors influence the creep resistance of alloy steels have been given and it has been shown that grain size has much less effect than either solid-solution hardening or the subsequent precipitation effects resulting from high degrees of solid-solution hardening in austenitic stainless steels. In ferritic steels containing nitrogen, the grain size also has less effect than the strengthening effect owing to nitrogen segregation at grain boundaries and dislocations. In transformable ferritic steels the beneficial effects of bainitic structures compared with either ferritic or martensitic structures have been demonstrated and it has also been shown that whereas the initial strength level is markedly influenced by the initial structure, the ultimate strength after long testing periods at high temperatures is largely independent of the initial microstructure. Examples have also been given which show that in a precipitation hardening system, optimum creep properties are developed by a heavy dispersion hardening rather than by coherency hardening. Finally, some examples have been given of the way in which intercrystalline cracks can develop in steels which show low creep ductility at high temperatures

INTRODUCTION

IN ITS WIDEST ASPECTS, incorporating detail down to the atomic structure of the crystal lattice, the microstructure of a metal is the controlling influence on the processes involved during high temperature

Dr Irvine is metallurgical research manager of The United Steel Companies Research and Development Department, Mr Murray is head of the Applied Metallurgy Section, and Mr Pickering is head of the Physical Metallurgy Section.

deformation or creep, because such processes take place by the movement of and interaction between defects in the metal structure and the structure itself. It is the purpose of this paper to illustrate many of the individual aspects of microstructure in both ferritic and austenitic steels, and to relate them to the creep processes and where possible to the shape of the individual creep curve.

In a recent paper, Glen and Murray[1] reviewed many of the metallurgical factors influencing the creep resistance of plain carbon and low alloy steels. In that paper a distinction was drawn between what was termed 'inherent' creep resistance, and 'latent' creep resistance which could be developed at some time during test or service and which usually took the form of a precipitation reaction. The whole purpose of the inherent creep resistance was envisaged as controlling the amount of plastic deformation until such time as the latent creep resistance could become operative.

The main structural features which influence creep metals can be detailed as follows:

(i) solid solution hardening
(ii) grain size
(iii) initial structure, i.e. martensite, bainite, ferrite, etc. This invariably also involves grain size.
(iv) precipitation hardening involving coherent precipitates
(v) dispersion hardening involving non-coherent precipitates
(vi) dislocation atmosphere effects and grain boundary segregations.

Examples of each of these features will be given and their effects on the creep processes will be described. In describing the creep processes, two general concepts will be used which probably require some explanation. The first is the Larsen-Miller[2] method for homologizing time and temperature into one parameter which can then be related to some creep criterion such as rupture strength. This concept enables a considerable amount of creep data to be represented simply on one diagram. The parameter used is $T(20+\log t)$ which is

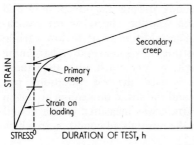

1 *General form of creep curve*

the same as the parameter commonly used for homologizing tempering data.[3] The second concept is based on the form of the creep curve, shown in Fig.1, which enables the deformation processes to be divided into three main stages. Stage 1 is primary creep which has been found to be mainly associated with deformation processes occurring within the grains. In stage 2 or steady state creep, the deformation processes are often associated with grain boundary phenomena although these boundaries may not always be the original grain boundaries and may actually be associated with the sub-boundaries created by the deformation. As Glen[4] has shown, there may be one or several slight changes in slope associated with the steady state as the latent creep effects become operative, i.e. as some form of precipitation occurs during the test. Stage 3, which is not shown in Fig.1 is the final stage leading to ultimate fracture.

These general classifications must not, however, be regarded too rigidly as there may be considerable overlap between the deformation processes involved, but such a generalization is valid in view of the lack of understanding of the basic creep mechanisms, especially in multi-component alloy steels. No discussion of structure and its relationship to creep phenomena is complete without a reference to creep ductility and some examples of structure affecting rupture ductility and also some evidence for mechanisms of intergranular fracture will be given.

Solid-solution hardening

Solid-solution hardening is the result of lattice strain associated with the introduction either of a substitutional atom of a different atomic size from the solvent metal or an interstitial atom into the interstices of the solvent metal lattice. Other effects, however, may also be operative such as clustering of solute atoms at precipitation nuclei, segregation to stacking faults in austenitic structures and segregation to grain boundaries. It is very difficult in steels to obtain unequivocal evidence of solid solution hardening because in most cases the alloying elements react to precipitate either carbides, nitrides or intermetallic compounds during the creep test, and thereby confuse the inherent solid solution effects by the realization of latent creep resistance. The addition of P to low carbon $\frac{1}{2}\%$Mo steels,[5] however, does illustrate only solid solution hardening because the solubility of P in ferrite is very much more than the P contents used. Details of the steels used, the test conditions, primary and secondary creep strains and the strain on loading are given in Table I. The secondary creep strain was measured over a period of 1 000 h. The steel was tested in the normalized condition in which

248

TABLE I Effect of phosphorus on the high-temperature properties of $\frac{1}{2}\%$Mo steel, $9\cdot0$ tons/in^2 at 480°C

Steel no.		1	2	3	4	5
Analysis %,	C	0·06	0·07	0·07	0·07	0·07
	Mn	0·43	0·42	0·42	0·43	0·43
	Si	0·25	0·19	0·19	0·18	0·19
	Mo	0·58	0·58	0·57	0·56	0·56
	P	0·017	0·030	0·046	0·060	0·107
Strain on loading, %		0·0985	0·0962	0·0885	0·0862	0·0839
Primary creep strain $\times 10^{-4}$		5·0	2·8	1·8	1·5	1·3
Secondary creep strain $\times 10^{-4}$		0·7	0·5	0·9	0·9	0·9

the structure consisted of ferrite and bainite and the grain sizes were constant at 6–8 ASTM ferrite grain size. The curves showing the effect of P on the creep strains are shown in Fig.2. It can be seen that P decreased the strain on loading and markedly decreased the primary creep strain, but had no effect on the secondary creep. This shows that solid solution hardening is almost entirely effective in strengthening the grains rather than the grain boundaries, and in this particular case that P does not seem to be segregating to the ferrite grain boundaries. This is in fact precisely the effect which would be expected from a solid solution hardening mechanism.

Grain size

It has been shown by many workers[6,7] that, in pure metals or single phase solid solution alloys, grain size markedly increases the creep resistance and the general impression is that increasing grain size

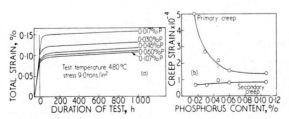

2 a *Effect of phosphorus on creep strain curves;* b *Effect of phosphorus on primary and secondary creep*

has much more effect on the secondary creep strain than on primary creep. In steels, however, both of the ferritic and austenitic types, there is a growing accumulation of evidence to show that grain size has a very small effect compared with other factors.

Glen and Murray[1] have shown some effects of grain size, on the creep properties of Al-killed mild steel. Specimens were soaked at 1100°C for different times which produced different grain sizes, but the active nitrogen was similar in each case. Creep tests were carried out at 450°C at 8 tons/in² and an assessment made of the creep rate. These results are summarized:

Heat treatment time, 1100°C AC, min	Austenitic grain size (aver. dia. $\times 10^{-3}$, in)	Ferritic grain size (aver. dia. $\times 10^{-3}$ in)	Active N content, %	Creep rate 24–48 h chord $\times 10^{-6}$
5	3·82	1·8		
15	4·51	2·5	0·0042	3·3
30	4·50	2·5	0·0042	2·4
60	5·43	1·8	0·0043	2·2
			0·0042	2·2

It is clear that the variation in austenitic grain size did not have any effect on the creep resistance. Additional results were given for steels having a marked variation in ferrite grain size. One sample was normalized from 920°C to give a ferritic grain size of ASTM 8 and another furnace cooled from 1080° to 600°C over 48 h to give a ferritic grain size of ASTM–2; both specimens having similar amounts of active nitrogen. These two samples with widely different ferritic grain sizes had almost identical creep rates.

In austenitic steels, the evidence required to investigate the

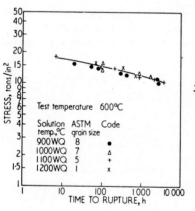

3 *Effect of grain size on the rupture strength of 18%Cr–10%Ni unstabilized austenitic stainless steel (after Ivernel)*

effect of grain size is more difficult to obtain because some precipitation often occurs during testing. Also the increasing solution temperatures required to give larger grain sizes tend to dissolve more of the stable carbides in stabilized steels which increases the initial solid solution hardening and also increases the latent creep due to precipitation occurring during the test. Some evidence is available[8] to show that in unstabilized 18%Cr–10%Ni steels variations in grain size from ASTM 8 to ASTM 1 have no effect on the rupture strength. The rupture results obtained on this steel at 600°C for samples with this wide variation in grain size are shown in Fig.3 and it will be seen that all of the points are on the same rupture line. A similar effect has been obtained on an unstabilized stainless steel of the type 316 composition (17%Cr–12%Ni–$2\frac{1}{2}$%Mo). With test conditions of 10 tons/in² at 700°C the following results were obtained:

Soln. treat. temp., °C	Grain size Average dia. $\times 10^{-3}$ in	Equiv. ASTM	Rupture life, h	Ductility, %
950	0·4	11	117	54
1 050	3·2	5	185	59
1 150	8·0	2	131	28
1 250	16·0	1	184	12*

* Delta ferrite present

Increasing solution treatment temperature had little or no effect on rupture life. The result obtained at 950°C is slightly lower than the others probably because there was undissolved $M_{23}C_6$. It is interesting to note that ductility decreased with increasing solution treatment temperature and this is probably a real effect due to coarsening grain size. The shape of the individual creep curves indicated that increasing grain size had little effect on primary creep but slightly decreased the secondary creep.

Recent American work[9] has shown that fine grain size in stabilized austenitic stainless steels is associated with low creep resistance and it has been suggested that it is the fine grain size which is responsible. Whilst accepting that it is not easy to separate these effects it was difficult to accept that it was grain size which was the controlling factor. Consequently an investigation of type 347 stainless steel (18%Cr–12%Ni–1%Nb) was carried out to investigate the factors controlling the rupture properties.

The effect of increasing solution treatment temperature is primarily to cause NbC to dissolve as shown in Fig.4a. An associated effect is that as the number of NbC particles decreases, the grain

251

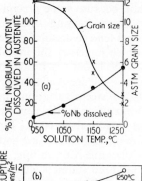

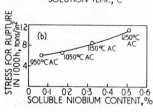

4 a *Effect of solution temperature on solubility of niobium and grain size of 18%Cr–12%Ni–1% Nb steel*
b *Effect of soluble niobium content on the rupture strength of 18%Cr–12%Ni–1%Nb steel*

size increases. Therefore, apart from a grain size effect an increasing solution treatment temperature will markedly increase the solid solution hardening due to Nb and the greater amount of Nb in solid solution will contribute more latent creep. It can be seen in Fig.4*b* that the rupture strength increases with increasing soluble Nb content. When the creep curves are examined closely it is found that the effect is largely confined to the primary creep stage rather than to the secondary creep stage which indicates that the effect of increasing grain size, whilst it is additive to the effect of increased Nb in solution, is definitely of secondary magnitude. As with the unstabilized steels, an increasing solution temperature produced a decrease in ductility as shown by the following results:

Test conditions: 12 tons/in² at 700°C

Sol. temp., °C	Rupture life, h	Elong., %	R of A, %
950	15	20·8	56·0
1 050	44	13·8	24·0
1 150	193	11·4	26·0
1 250	625	9·1	14·0

This is not such a simple example as that quoted for the type 316 stainless steel, since the rupture life is varying considerably. There is no doubt that in this case any effect due to grain size is considerably increased by precipitation of NbC during testing.

Some similar work has also been carried out on Ti-stabilized stainless steel (18%Cr–10%Ni–0·4%Ti). Rupture tests were

252

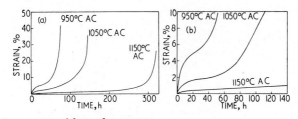

a general form of creep curves
b enlarged low-strain region of curves in (a)

5 *Effect of solution-treatment temperature on creep of 18%Cr–10%Ni–Ti steel*

carried out at 700°C on samples solution treated at 950°, 1 050°, and 1 150°C. The results obtained are summarized below:

Sol. treat. temp., °C	Ti in sol. %	Stress, tons/in²	Grain size, ×10⁻³in	Life, h	Elong, %
950	0·14	8·5	0·27	76	41·6
		10·0		24	37·7
1 050	0·20	8·5	0·54	146	19·1
		10·0		44	35·6
1 150	0·25	8·5	1·14	321	25·8
		10·0		197	19·2

These results are similar to those obtained with the niobium-stabilized steel, with the rupture lives increasing with increasing solution temperature. Once again the rupture ductility decreases with increasing solution temperature and this is no doubt influenced by the precipitation of TiC. The creep curves obtained during these tests are shown in Fig.5 and the main interest is in the low strain region of the curve. Whilst there is some effect of increasing solution temperature on the secondary creep stage it is clear that the major effect is on primary creep, which supports the suggestion that the effect of increasing grain size is small.

The general conclusion from this work is that in a plain carbon ferritic steel, increasing austenitic or ferritic grain size has no effect on the rupture strength. In austenitic stainless steels increasing grain size has little or no effect on the rupture strength of unstabilized steels. In stabilized steels the increasing solution temperature, apart from producing a larger grain size, increases the solubility of Nb or Ti and it is this which is responsible for a marked increased in rupture strength.

Initial structure

In transformable steels, three basic structures can be produced, namely polygonal ferrite, bainite, and martensite. These structures

253

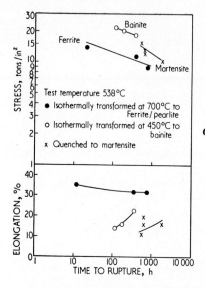

6 *Effect of initial structure on the rupture properties of a 0·1%C–0·5%Mo–B steel*

each have different initial creep resistance as obtained in short time tests, but in the long term they will have a similar level of creep resistance since they will all have similar highly spheroidized structures. The rate at which they approach this limiting strength will depend largely on their tempering resistance, especially under conditions of applied strain.

To show these differences in initial structure, specimens of a low C–½%Mo–B steel were isothermally transformed at 700° and 450°C to produce ferrite–pearlite and bainite structures respectively and also specimens were water quenched to produce an initially martensite structure. These specimens were then rupture tested at a temperature of 538°C and the rupture lives are shown in Fig.6, together with the associated ductilities. The initially bainitic structure had the highest rupture strength followed by the martensite and the ferrite–pearlite structure had the lowest strength. Initially the martensite was the stronger at room temperature, but this structure tempers more rapidly than the bainite so that it gave a lower rupture strength at 538°C. The polygonal ferrite was of an altogether lower rupture strength, as was expected from the low room temperature strength. Some interesting features were shown by the rupture ductility results. The ferrite–pearlite structure had by far the best rupture ductility which is expected because it has the lowest strength. The bainite, however, had rather better rupture ductility than the martensite despite the lower rupture strength of the martensite.

This may not be a real effect, but if it is it may be that since the ductility is increasing with increasing rupture life, the bainite exhibits a minimum ductility at rather shorter times than the martensite.

It has already been stated that, despite initial differences in structures which produce different strength levels in short time or low temperature tests, after long periods of testing or during testing at high temperatures, the strength levels all approach a common and fairly low level of strength due to the heavy spheroidization and recrystallization which eventually occurs.

This effect is most clearly shown in the Larsen-Miller diagram in Fig.7. In this diagram, the stress-to-rupture strength is plotted for:

(i) a $\frac{1}{2}$%Mo steel of a mainly polygonal ferrite initial structure and a tensile strength of approximately 32 tons/in²

(ii) a $\frac{1}{2}$%Mo–B steel with a bainitic structure and a tensile strength of about 40 tons/in²

(iii) a $1\frac{1}{2}$%Cr–$1\frac{1}{2}$%Mn–$\frac{1}{2}$%Mo–B steel having a low temperature bainitic structure with a tensile strength of about 70 tons/in².

The initial microstructures of these three steels are shown in Figs.8a–c. From Fig.7 it can be seen that the short time rupture strength (i.e. at low parameters) increases as the room temperature tensile strength increases. The difference between these steels decreases however, at higher parameters.

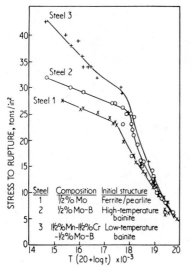

7 *Effect of initial structure on rupture properties*

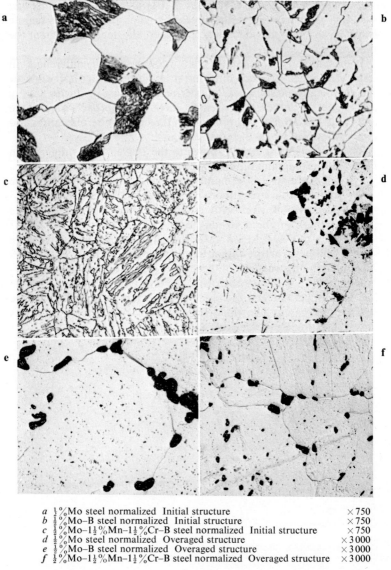

a	½%Mo steel normalized Initial structure	×750
b	½%Mo–B steel normalized Initial structure	×750
c	½%Mo–1½%Mn–1½%Cr–B steel normalized Initial structure	×750
d	½%Mo steel normalized Overaged structure	×3000
e	½%Mo–B steel normalized Overaged structure	×3000
f	½%Mo–1½%Mn–1½%Cr–B steel normalized Overaged structure	×3000

8 *Effect of high-temperature testing on ½%Mo steels with different initial structures*

The $\frac{1}{2}$%Mo ferritic steel only loses strength rapidly at parameter values higher than 17500 by which stage Mo_2C has precipitated and overaged. This reduces the solid solution hardening effect of the molybdenum and since there is only a small amount of precipitate there is little dispersion hardening. The typical overaged structure is shown in Fig.8d.

The $\frac{1}{2}$%Mo–B bainitic steel starts at a higher rupture strength and only loses strength slowly (at about the same rate as the $\frac{1}{2}$%Mo steel) until the parameter value exceeds 18000 when precipitation and coalescence of Mo_2C produces a similar effect to that of the $\frac{1}{2}$%Mo steel and as the parameter value increases still further the strength falls to a similar value to the $\frac{1}{2}$%Mo steel. The overaged structure of this steel is shown in Fig.8e.

The lower temperature bainite structure initially loses strength more rapidly than the $\frac{1}{2}$%Mo–B steel, because of its low tempering resistance. Then at a parameter of 18000 it begins to lose strength very much more rapidly as Mo_2C precipitates and overages. The typical overaged structure is shown in Fig.8f.

During long time or high temperature testing some recrystallization of the ferrite also occurs in the bainitic structure and the carbides spheroidize and the structures of all three steels eventually become identical and they have similar strengths.

A further instance of this effect can be cited for steel containing 0·1%C–2$\frac{1}{4}$%Cr–1%Mo.[10] Various initial structures were produced by different initial treatments as follows:

  (i) furnace cooled 15°C/h to produce an initial structure of coarse pearlite and ferrite containing precipitated carbides
 (ii) furnace cooled 33°C/h to produce fine pearlite and ferrite containing fewer precipitated carbides
(iii) normalized 898°C and tempered at 734°C for $\frac{1}{2}$ h to produce tempered bainite.

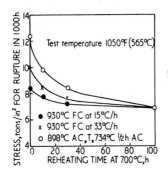

9 *Effect of initial structure and subsequent tempering on rupture strength of 2$\frac{1}{4}$%Cr–1%Mo steel*

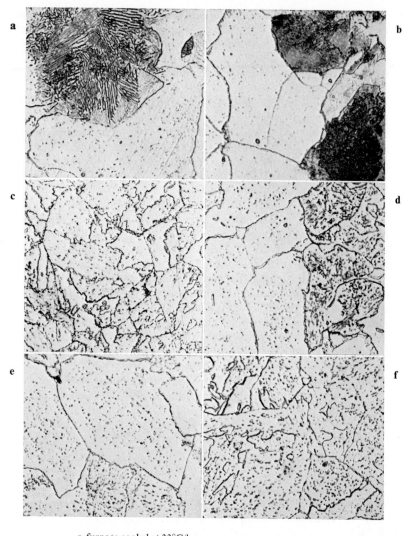

a furnace cooled at 33°C/h
b furnace cooled at 15°C/h
c normalized at 900°C; tempered 734°C/½ h
d furnace cooled at 33°C/h; tempered 700°C/100 h
e furnace cooled at 15°C/h; tempered 700°C/100 h
f normalized at 900°C; tempered 734°C/½ h + 700°C/100 h

10 *Different initial structures produced in $2\frac{1}{4}\%Cr$–$1\%Mo$ steel for rupture testing* ×750

These samples had very different initial 1000 h rupture strengths. Specimens with these structures were then tempered for various times at 700°C and 1000-h rupture strengths were again determined. With increasing tempering at 700°C, the rupture strength of each initial condition decreased, as shown by the curves in Fig.9, the the rate of decrease of strength was more rapid with the initially higher strength structures. Eventually after tempering for 100 h at 700°C the rupture strengths of each of the steels were identical. The structures in the initial condition and after 100 h at 700°C are shown in Fig.10. It can be seen that in spite of the major differences in the initial structures, tempering for 100 h at 700°C has produced very similar structures with heavily spheroidized carbides in polygonal ferrite.

The conclusion therefore is that whilst initial structure can materially affect the short time creep properties, the long time creep resistance of the steel is unaffected by initial structure due to the structural deterioration which occurs. The rate of approach to this ultimate strength will depend very much on the initial structure and how much latent creep resistance can be realized during testing or service.

Precipitation and dispersion hardening

Three examples of the effects of precipitation before and during testing will be given, which illustrate the very complex nature of the changes which can take place and their effect on creep.

1. Tests have been carried out on $2\frac{1}{4}\%$Cr–Mo steel in the normalized and tempered 650°C condition using tempering times up to 100 h. At this temperature, secondary hardening is rapid and

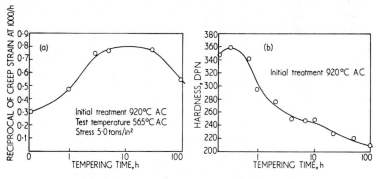

a effect of tempering time on creep strength
b effect of tempering time on hardness

11 *Effect of tempering at 650°C on creep strength and hardness of $2\frac{1}{4}\%$Cr–1%Mo steel*

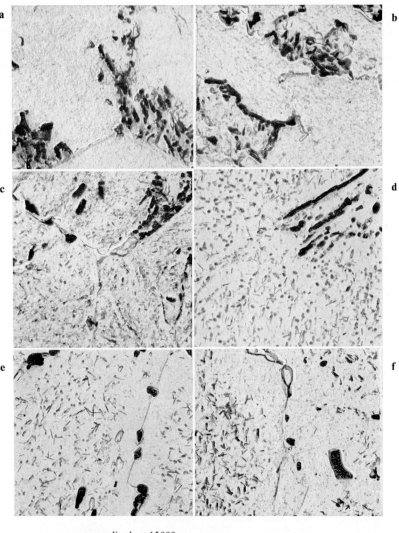

a normalized; ×15000
b normalized; tempered 650°C/20 min
c normalized; tempered 650°C/1 h
d normalized; tempered 650°C/7 h
e normalized; tempered 650°C/20 h
f normalized; tempered 650°C/100 h

12 *Effect of tempering at 650°C on the structures of $2\frac{1}{4}\%Cr-1\%Mo$ steel used for rupture testing* ×1500

overageing and loss of coherency occurs with times in excess of 20 min as can be seen from the tempering curve in Fig.11b.

In Fig.11a the creep strength measured as the reciprocal of the creep strain after 1 000 h at 565°C and a stress of 5 ton/in² is also shown. It is then possible to relate the creep properties with the structures which are shown in Fig.12. Little change in structure is obvious in Figs.12a and b, but after tempering for 1 h Fig.12c shows that the precipitation of Mo_2C has become quite obvious and the larger grain boundary carbides nucleate and grow.

It is clear from the creep strength curve that maximum creep resistance is obtained after tempering 5–10 h at 650°C but Fig.12d shows that at this stage of tempering overageing is well advanced. This suggests that coherency hardening, whilst being responsible for some increase in strength, does not produce the maximum creep resistance. This is not produced until the precipitated Mo_2C carbides have lost coherency and the structure is just about in the maximum dispersion hardened condition. Further tempering at 650°C up to 100 h only causes a decrease in creep resistance of about 20%, and the creep strength is still higher than in the initial normalized condition. Figures 12e and f representing the structures after tempering for 20 and 100 h show that in spite of a considerable degree of overageing there is still sufficient dispersion hardening

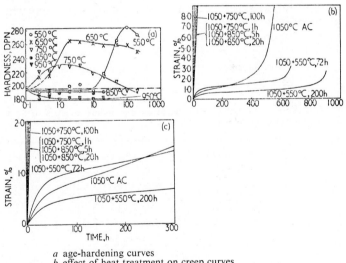

a age-hardening curves
b effect of heat treatment on creep curves
c enlarged portion of low-strain region of (b)

13 *Effect of heat treatment on creep strength of 8%Cr–3%Mo–1½%Ti steel*

to preserve a high degree of creep resistance. The precipitation of alloy carbide from the matrix reduces the solid solution hardening, but this is more than compensated by the dispersion hardening.

2. In an 8%Cr–Mo–Ti age hardening steel[11] very widely different microstructures can be produced by different ageing treatments. A typical series of ageing curves is shown in Fig.13a. At temperatures up to 650°C the precipitating phase is $M_{23}C_6$ and very marked age hardening results. At ageing temperatures above 750°C Fe_2Ti precipitates and grows so rapidly that little or no dispersion hardening occurs and the loss of solid solution hardening actually causes a decrease in the hardness. At 750°C a mixture of $M_{23}C_6$ and Fe_2Ti forms, the Fe_2Ti initially being in a relatively fine dispersion so that some hardening is observed, but overageing is very rapid due to the rapid growth of Fe_2Ti.

It is interesting, therefore, to determine the creep resistance of several of the structures which can be produced in this steel and show how the high temperature properties are influenced by structural features. The details of the heat treatments used and the rupture lives obtained after testing at 11 tons/in² at 625°C are given in Table II. The creep curves to rupture are shown in Fig.13b and the low strain region is shown more clearly in Fig.13c. The initial microstructures produced by the different heat treatments are shown in Figs.14a–g. The stages of tempering represented by these tempering treatments can be seen from the tempering curves which are given in Fig.13a.

In the solution treated condition (Fig.14a) $M_{23}C_6$ precipitated during testing giving a rupture life of 538 h and a ductility of 11·2%. The realization of latent creep due to the precipitations of $M_{23}C_6$

TABLE II Effect of precipitation treatment on the rupture strength of 8%Cr-Mo-Ti steel, 11·0 tons/in² at 625°C

Steel comp.	0·07%C, 0·53%Mn, 0·85%Si, 8·42%Cr, 2·89%Mo, 1·18%Ti						
Heat treatment	1050°C, ½h, AC	1050°C, ½h, AC + 5h, 850°C AC	1050°C, + ½h, AC, + 20h, 850°C AC	1050°C, + ½h, AC + 72h, 550°C, AC	1050°C, ½h, AC+ 200h, 550°C, AC	1050°C, ½h, AC+ 1h 750°C, AC	1050°C, ½h, AC + 100h,750°C AC
Time to rupture	538·2	19·2	18·0	651·2	895·3	22·7	2·8
Elongation on 1in, %	11·2	24·7	22·2	3·1	2·8	29·4	29·8
Reduction of area, %	59·2	74·3	72·7	9·9	10·4	78·0	69·9

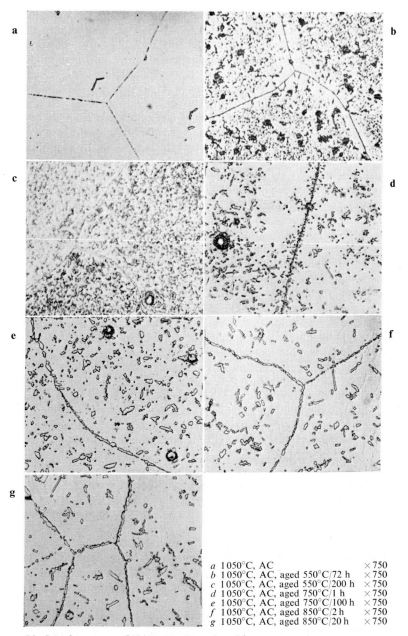

a 1 050°C, AC   ×750
b 1 050°C, AC, aged 550°C/72 h   ×750
c 1 050°C, AC, aged 550°C/200 h   ×750
d 1 050°C, AC, aged 750°C/1 h   ×750
e 1 050°C, AC, aged 750°C/100 h   ×750
f 1 050°C, AC, aged 850°C/2 h   ×750
g 1 050°C, AC, aged 850°C/20 h   ×750

14 *Initial structures of 8%Cr–Mo–Ti steel used for rupture testing*

gave a relatively small transient creep of about 0·5%, but the rapid ageing of the precipitate aggravated by the straining causes the latent creep resistance to be rapidly lost, and the curve shows an increasing rate of straining with increasing time. This loss of the latent creep resistance also gives a reasonable ductility level, but the dispersion hardening still preserves a high strength. Ageing for 72 h at 550°C (Fig.14b) gives maximum ageing due to $M_{23}C_6$ and the precipitate is presumably initially coherent. This gives slightly worse transient creep (0·9%) but the growth of the particles seems to be slower. A much increased strength is observed (rupture life 651 h), but the ductility is very much lower. This low ductility is no doubt due to very heavy strengthening of the matrix and some denudation at the grain boundaries, leading to intercrystalline fracture. Overageing for 200 h at 550°C (Fig.14c) gives a heavily dispersion hardened structure, and the rupture life increases further to 895 h although the transient creep is only of the same order as when precipitation occurs during testing. This confirms that, as with the $2\frac{1}{4}$%Cr–Mo steel described in the previous section, a coherent precipitate does not give such high strength as a very heavily dispersion hardened structure. The ductility also is lower.

Ageing for 1 h at 750°C (Fig.14d) gave a slightly increased hardness and a precipitate of fine Fe_2Ti and $M_{23}C_6$. These precipitates grew rapidly during testing and the strength had been greatly reduced to 23 h. This was probably also due to loss of solid solution hardening by Ti in the matrix. Further ageing for 100 h at 750°C (Fig.14e) accentuated this effect and a rupture life of only 3 h was obtained. The ductilities were high at 29–30% owing to the lack of strengthening of the matrix by precipitate and also to loss of solid solution hardening by Ti. No latent creep was realized because it has been shown[11] that when Fe_2Ti is present, much less subsequent precipitation of $M_{23}C_{16}$ occurs due to the reduced Ti content of the steel.

Precipitation of Fe_2Ti after ageing for 2 and 20 h at 850°C (Figs. 14f and g) produces large plates of Fe_2Ti which do not exert much dispersion hardening effect and very considerably reduce the solid solution hardening of Ti in the matrix. This results in a complete loss of creep resistance, to give rupture lives of 22–24 h. There is again no realization of latent creep during testing because the Ti concentration has been reduced to a level below that required to allow $M_{23}C_6$ to precipitate. Due to the higher ageing temperature the solubility of Fe_2Ti will be slightly higher than at 750°C so that the rupture strength is slightly better than obtained in the lowest life test after ageing at 750°C.

These results indicate again that best creep resistance is obtained with a heavily dispersion hardening matrix rather than coherent precipitation, possibly due to the greater stability of the structure. On the other hand, if dispersion hardening is not very marked, the loss of solid solution hardening may give very poor creep resistance, and the changes in the composition of the matrix may make it impossible to realize any latent creep resistance by eliminating the possibility of precipitation occurring during testing.

3. Work has been carried out to test the effect on rupture strength of initial precipitation in a 12%Cr steel. The rupture tests were carried out at 500°C and the 100 h rupture stress was determined. This is a short time criterion and at longer time or higher temperature the differences between the initial conditions would be less marked. Details of the initial conditions and the rupture strengths and ductility are given below:

Steel composition	0·12%C–0·57%Mn–0·20%Si–11·40%Cr			
Heat treatment	1050°C, AC	1050°C, AC T.500°C, 4 h	1050°C, AC T.550°C, 10 h	1050°C, AC, T.700°C, 4 h
Tensile strength, tons/in²	96·4	96·2	56·0	42·2
Stress for rupture in 100 h, tons/in²	30·0	28·0	22·5	18·0
Elongation, %	9·5	13	18·5	22

The initial structures are shown in Fig.15 together with the structures near to the fracture after testing for 100 h at about 550°C. In the initial 1050°C AC condition, the structure consisted of auto-tempered martensite containing many Fe_3C precipitates (Fig.15a). During testing, much latent creep was obtained due to precipitation of Cr_7C_3 in the matrix and also overageing of the precipitate occurred whilst the Fe_3C largely transformed to Cr_7C_3. This precipitation during testing gave good creep resistance with a 100 h rupture stress of 30 tons/in², but the ductility was very poor (9·5%) owing to the precipitation and strengthening which occurred during the test.

Initial ageing at 500°C for 4 h produced some secondary hardening due to precipitation of Cr_7C_3 and a reduced amount of Fe_3C (Fig.15b). The rupture strength was slightly lower than obtained with the martensite condition and the ductility was slightly improved. Considerable overageing occurred during testing with growth of the matrix precipitate of Cr_7C_3 and the Fe_3C present in the initial structure largely transformed to Cr_7C_3.

265

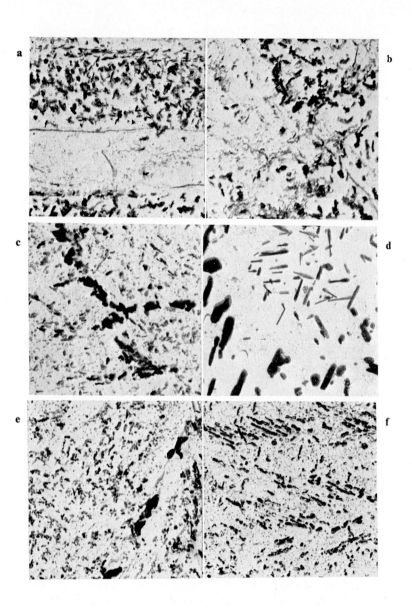

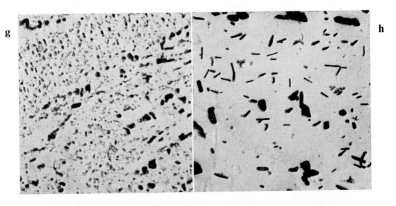

g   h

a 1 050°C, AC, before testing
b 1 050°C, AC, tempered 500°C/4 h, before testing
c 1 050°C, AC, tempered 550°C/10 h, before testing
d 1 050°C, AC, tempered 700°C/4 h, before testing
e 1 050°C, AC, near to fracture after testing
f 1 050°C, AC, tempered 500°C/4 h near to fracture, after testing
g 1 050°C, AC, tempered 550°C/10 h near to fracture, after testing
h 1 050°C, AC, tempered 700°C/4 h near to fracture, after testing

15 *Effect of heat treatment on the microstructures of 12%Cr steel, before and after rupture testing at 500°C*   ×15 000

Ageing at 500°C for 10 h had produced a marked overageing (Fig.15c) and the dispersion hardening was not at a maximum either as shown by the initial tensile strength. Testing caused further overageing and because the dispersion hardening was not very marked originally and also because there was now little possibility of realization of latent creep, the rupture strength was reduced to 22·5 tons/in², although the ductility was considerably increased at 18·5%.

Still further overageing at 700°C for 4 h (Fig.15d) decreased further the dispersion hardening and also reduced the solid solution hardening so that, with the loss of all but minor latent creep realization, the rupture strength was reduced to 18 tons/in² and the ductility was higher still at 22%. During testing little change in the structure was observed, as expected due to the greater stability.

As stated previously, in short time low temperature testing, the creep resistance often reflects the initial strength either at room temperature or during tensile testing at the rupture test temperature and this relationship is shown in Fig.16b for these tests. In longer time tests or at higher test temperatures the strengths of each condition would gradually approach each other. An interesting

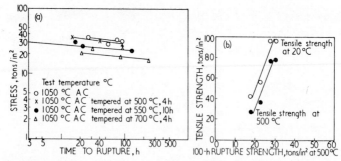

16 a *Effect of initial structure on rupture strength of 0·1%Cr–12%Cr steel*
 b *Relationship between tensile strength and 100 h rupture strength of 0·1%C–12%Cr steel*

feature which was observed in the specimens which altered structurally during the rupture test was that near to the fracture where there was very heavy deformation, the carbides formed during test were generally smaller, than those at positions remote from the fracture where the strain had been less. This comparison in microstructures is shown in Fig.17. It seems therefore that applied deformation can retard or inhibit the growth of precipitating phases.

Considerable mention has been made of the latent creep resistance which can be realized either by precipitation or by dislocation atmospheres of solute atoms being produced during testing.

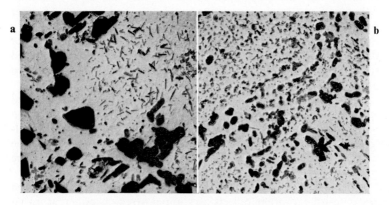

 a 1050°C, air cooled; tempered 550°C/10 h Structure after testing remote from fracture
 b 1 050°C, air cooled; tempered 550°C/10 h Structure after testing near to fracture

17 *Effect of strain on the structures produced during rupture testing a 12%Cr steel at 500°C*   × 15 000

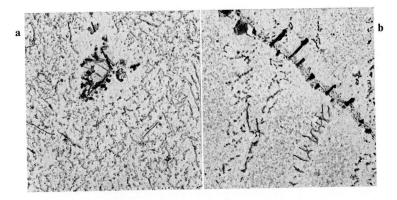

a precipitation of NbC on dislocations
b precipitation of NbC on dislocation pile-ups at grain
boundaries

18 *Precipitation of carbides along dislocations in stainless steel* ×15000

If a precipitation takes place during straining during test, the precipitated particles often form along the dislocation lines as shown in Fig.18. This mode of precipitation is particularly effective in improving creep resistance, although it may reduce the creep ductility because the precipitates are formed where they will most hinder dislocation movements and therefore the creep deformation will be markedly reduced. One method by which such precipitates can be made to occur before testing or service is by warm working the material in the temperature range of precipitation.

Dislocation atmosphere effects and grain boundary segregates

These two phenomena are only different manifestations of the same process because grain boundaries can be regarded as arrays of dislocations. Due to the strain fields around dislocations, solute atoms will segregate to the dislocation and relieve the strain. This applies particularly to interstitial elements such as C, N, and B, but can also apply to substitutional atoms as Glen[14] has shown. By segregating at dislocations the strength of the material can be increased by a dislocation locking process and this can be maintained at temperatures up to the temperature at which the dislocation atmosphere evaporates, so that creep resistance can be improved by this means. When segregation occurs at a grain boundary the effect is often to alter the creep resistance of the boundary regions and this often leads to an increased creep ductility.

The effect of Si and Al additions to mild steel provides a good

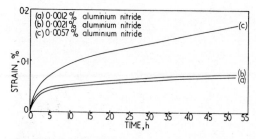

19 *Effect of precipitation of nitrogen as aluminium nitride on the creep curve of mild steel*

example of the effect of N segregating to grain boundaries and dislocations. In Al-killed steels, the precipitation of AlN reduces the active N content and lowers the creep resistance. This is shown in Fig.19 where the creep curves are shown for steels with differing amounts of active nitrogen remaining in the steel. It can be seen that the effect is mainly confined to second stage creep rather than on primary creep, indicating that it is nitrogen segregated at grain boundaries which is affecting the creep strength.

The effect of precipitation of Si_3N_4 in Si-killed mild steels is also very similar. If after normalizing, the steel is tempered at 600°C the N and C are precipitated as shown in Fig.20a. After tempering up to 10 h not much N and C are precipitated and the creep curve shown in Fig.20b confirms that the creep resistance is high. With further tempering up to 100 h the C and N are rapidly precipitated and the creep resistance is markedly decreased.

The following figures show the effect of active C and N contents on the primary and second stage creep:

Tempered °C h	Active C, %	Active N, %	Primary strain, %	Second-stage strain, %
600 1	0·00095	0·0022	0·05	0·02
600 3	0·001	0·0026	0·05	0·02
600 10	0·001	0·0015	0·05	0·02
600 30	0·00045	0·00045	0·08	0·07
600 100	0·00025	0·00030	0·10	0·33

It can be seen that removal of the C and N is by far the most effective on second stage creep indicating that the major effect is due to C and N at the grain boundaries. Removing C and N, however, also increases the primary creep strain indicating that some dislocation atmospheres of these elements are formed at the dislocations within the grains but that the effect is much less than the grain boundary segregation effect. Recent electron microscope evidence has also shown that the precipitates of either AlN or Si_3N_4 can be observed in the structure (Figs.21a, b).

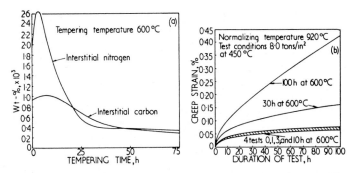

20 a *Effect of tempering at 600°C on amount of C and N in interstitial solid solution in Si-killed mild steel*
b *Effect of tempering at 600°C on creep properties of Si-killed mild steel*

Similar effects, for example, of B improving the creep resistance of austenitic steels have also been experienced[13] but whether this is due to the inherent effect of B or to an improved ductility giving rise to improved creep rupture properties is not certain.

Rupture ductility

Glen[14] has recently given a very full exposition of ductility effects in high temperature testing and it is intended here to draw attention to some of the structural features leading to low rupture ductility and the initiation of intercrystalline cracks.

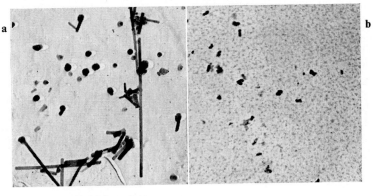

a aluminium nitride
b silicon nitride

21 *Precipitation of aluminium nitride and silicon nitride in mild steel*   × *15 000*

271

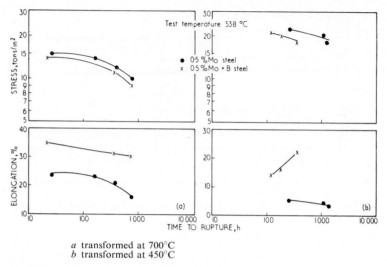

a transformed at 700°C
b transformed at 450°C

22 *Effect of boron on rupture ductility of ½%Mo steel*

Low rupture ductility is invariably accompanied by intercrystalline fracture, which is the result of the grain boundaries being weaker than the grains. The higher strength of the grains may be due to inherent creep strength by solution hardening or a precipitation hardening effect, or to the realization of latent creep resistance by a precipitation effect or dislocation atmospheres. The weakening of the grain boundary regions can be due to a complex series of causes such as localized deoxidation, larger grain boundary carbides, or segregational effects.

Some steels, for example ½%Mo ferritic alloys are very prone to low ductility and intercrystalline cracking, but it has been found that additions of B improve the ductility markedly. Specimens of ½%Mo and ½%Mo–B steels were transformed at 700°C and 450°C to produce polygonal ferrite and bainitic structures respectively in both steels and the rupture properties were determined at 538°C. The curves are shown in Figs.22a and b. The rupture strengths of each steel were very similar, the bainitic condition being stronger than the ferritic condition. The major difference, however, was the marked improvement in ductility in the B Steel. Boron is known to segregate to grain boundaries where it may have two effects. By its presence in the grain boundary region it may retard the overageing and denudation process which can lead to grain boundary weakness. It may also increase the creep resistance of the grain boundary region, thus reducing the difference in strength between the grain boundary and the matrix.

The initiation of intercrystalline cracks has always been of interest. One theory has been that the condensation of vacancies at the grain boundaries causes voids which open into cracks during straining. Direct evidence of this is not yet available but indirect evidence is available. For example, intercrystalline failure is more prevalent at high temperatures where the concentration of vacancies is in any case high, and electron microscope observations on thin films[15] have shown that grain boundaries provide a sink into which vacancies can diffuse as shown by the lack of dislocation loops in the vicinity of grain boundaries.

Another theory which is now well substantiated[11] is that if the matrix becomes precipitation hardened, the relative strength of the grain boundaries is reduced and intercrystalline cracking results. Just how this occurs is not certain but it may be that dislocations can pile against a grain boundary, producing a sink which then opens out by grain boundary sliding into a crack. Possible evidence for this is shown in Fig.23a, in which dislocations have piled against a grain boundary and caused cracking, the dislocations being shown by precipitates of NbC. The sliding of the grain boundary, which is indicated by the dislocation array, can also be seen. Another mechanism is local grain boundary denudation. This is shown in Fig.23b and may be the result either of grain boundary precipitates with a resulting lack of solute atoms in a zone around the grain boundaries, or a lower number of nuclei for precipitation near to the grain boundary because it is acting as a vacancy sink. Strain will concentrate in the softer denuded region and give rise to cracking, a typical effect being shown in Fig.23c.

It has also been observed that large grain boundary carbides can generate dislocations, (Fig.23d), and this may also be a mechanism by which much local deformation can occur and lead to cracking. Finally, during grain boundary sliding the larger grain boundary carbides themselves may be fractured as shown in Fig.23e, which represents a 12%Cr steel tested at 500°C. The disruption of continuity between the matrix and the carbide may well leave a void which can nucleate an intercrystalline crack.

All these possible mechanisms therefore need consideration in interpreting results involving rupture ductility so that this is a very complex property. Whilst it is obvious that the inter-relation of microstructures with the creep processes which occur in steels at high temperature is of a very complex nature, sufficient evidence has been presented to show that considerable progress is being

273

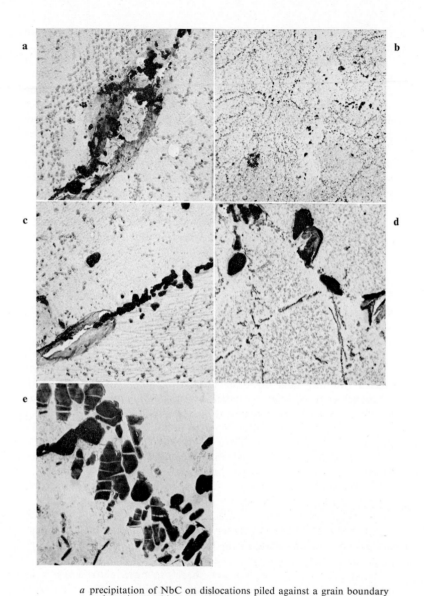

a precipitation of NbC on dislocations piled against a grain boundary
and causing cracking $\times 15\,000$
b local grain boundary denudation $\times 3\,000$
c cracking associated with grain boundary, showing denudation
      $\times 15\,000$
d dislocations generated by large $M_{23}C_6$ carbides at grain boundaries
      $\times 15\,000$
e grain boundary carbides fractured by boundary sliding $\times 15\,000$

23 *Microstructural features associated with intergranular cracking*

made in disentangling the many factors which are operative. Although much of this work is at present qualitative, and cannot be used to make quantitative predictions, sufficient information is available to clarify considerably the structural requirements for high creep resistance, and this means that much useless exploratory work can now be avoided in developing improved properties. The attainment of improved properties, however, becomes more difficult as the strength of steels are improved nearer to their theoretical maximum, especially when an adequate level of ductility is required to be maintained.

ACKNOWLEDGMENT

The authors would like to thank Mr F. H. Saniter, o.b.e. Director of Research, The United Steel Companies Ltd, for permission to publish this paper.

REFERENCES

1. J. GLEN and J. D. MURRAY, in 'Symposium on steels for reactor pressure circuits', *ISI Spec. Rep.* no.69, 1961.
2. F. R. LARSEN and J. MILLER: *Trans. ASME*, 1952, **74**, 765.
3. J. H. HOLLOMAN and L. D. JAFFE: AIME Metals Technology, 1945, Sept.
4. J. GLEN: *JISI*, 1958, **190**, 114–135.
5. M. G. GEMMILL and J. D. MURRAY: *Iron Steel*, 1953, **27**, 347–350.
6. J. W. MARTIN and G. C. SMITH: *J. Inst. Met.*, 1954–55, **83**, 417.
7. H. C. CROSS and J. G. LOWTHER: *Proc. ASTM*, 1940, **40**, 125.
8. J. IVERNEL: *Rev Nickel*, 1957, **23**, (2), 31–35.
9. W. E. LEYDA: 'International Conference on creep-resisting steels', Düsseldorf, 1960.
10. M. G. GEMMILL and J. D. MURRAY: *Iron Steel*, 1956, **29**, 150–152, 173–177.
11. M. G. GEMMILL *et al.*: *JISI*, 1956, **184**, 122–144.
12. J. GLEN: ASTM Spec. Tech. Pub. 128, 1952, 184.
13. G. T. HARRIS, in 'Precipitation processes in steels', *ISI Spec. Rep.* no.64, 1959, 295.
14. J. GLEN: *JISI*, 1958, **190**, 30–39.
15. K. J. IRVINE *et al.*: *ibid.*, 1960, **196**, 166–179.

The structure and properties of 1%Cr– 0·5%Mo steel after service in CEGB power stations

L. H. Toft, B.Sc., A.I.M., A.C.T (Birm.),
and Ruth A. Marsden, L.I.M.

*The effects of service conditions on the structure and pro-
perties of 1%Cr–0·5%Mo steel superheater tubes have been
examined. Tubes from CEGB power stations that have been
operating with steam at temperatures in the range 454–518°C
for times up to 100000 h have been used in this investigation.
The results of stress/rupture tests at 565° and 510°C for
times up to about 10000 h have shown a relationship between
rupture strength and the degree of carbide spheroidization
and precipitation. The various stages of spheroidization and
precipitation occurring during service have been classified.*

INTRODUCTION

THE 1%Cr–0·5%Mo steel is extensively used in CEGB power stations
for superheater tubes and headers. The first time it was used to a large
extent was in 1938 in the construction of the superheater tubes and
headers in two Loeffler boilers at Brimsdown. At that time these
boilers were among the most advanced in the UK. Since then, this
steel has been used in a large number of boilers producing steam at
temperatures of 454°C and above. It is most widely used in the final
sections of superheaters producing steam in the range 482–518°C.
Operating experience has been mostly satisfactory and where failures
have occurred they have usually been due to 'overheating' of the component above its designed operating temperature and/or excessive
corrosion.

The properties and structure of this steel have been studied[1,2]
previously but there are few data available concerning its properties
after long service. This investigation concerns the structure and
properties of 1%Cr–0·5%Mo steel superheater tubes that had been
in service under different operating conditions for various lengths
of time. Information of this kind, relating mechanical properties to

The authors are with the Materials Division, Central Electricity Research
Laboratories, Leatherhead.

service history, will lead to more efficient use of the material in future applications, and the study of associated structural changes will help in the understanding of creep processes.

Preliminary results of a detailed study of the Brimsdown super-heater referred to above, have previously been reported.[3]

DETAILS OF TUBES INVESTIGATED

Fourteen lengths of superheater tube that had been in service, and a piece of new tube, were supplied by various Generating Divisions. Tubes were chosen which had been in service for various times up to 100 000 h in stations operating with final steam temperatures of 454°C and above. Most of the tubes were taken from positions that were as near as possible to the superheater outlet header, where the metal temperature could not only be related more closely to the final steam temperature, but would also have been higher than elsewhere in the boiler.

The tubes used in this investigation conformed to the percentage composition range specified for superheater tubes in BS.3059·1958, which is as follows:

C 0·12 max., Mn 0·40–0·70, Si 0·10–0·60, Cr 0·70–1·10, Mo 0·45–0·65
S 0·05 max., P 0·05 max.

The results of analyses on samples taken from the tubes are shown in Table I. The diameters and wall thicknesses of all the tubes together with the details of the stations and boilers from which they were removed, are given in Table II.

The hoop stresses in the tube walls due to steam pressure, calculated using the 'thick cylinder' (Lamé) formula or the 'thin cylinder' (mean diameter) formula, were less than 2 tons/in², except

TABLE I Chemical Analyses

Identification mark	Station and boiler	Analysis, % C	Si	Mn	S	P	Cr	Mo
TS	'New tube'	0·08	0·46	0·44	0·023	0·025	0·96	0·50
VP	Battersea 16	0·06	0·48	0·39	0·023	0·020	0·87	0·52
VO	Battersea 17	0·07	0·53	0·44	0·020	0·012	0·88	0·44
TT8	Brimsdown 2A	0·14	0·18	0·56	0·036	0·040	0·86	0·42
BT9	Brimsdown 2A	0·15	0·18	0·52	0·033	0·032	0·86	0·40
BB9	Brimsdown 2A	0·16	0·16	0·50	0·034	0·024	0·87	0·50
TW	Carmarthen Bay 3	0·09	0·54	0·46	0·026	0·016	0·99	0·47
TR	Carmarthen Bay 8	0·08	0·49	0·38	0·018	0·029	0·94	0·60
TL	Carmarthen Bay 17	0·09	0·55	0·50	0·021	0·027	0·99	0·57
VA	Goldington 2	0·05	0·24	0·40	0·023	0·029	0·81	0·53
VT	North Tees C2	0·10	0·42	0·38	0·021	0·028	0·90	0·53
VH	Norwich 12	0·05	0·26	0·50	0·023	0·014	0·92	0·59
TV	Staythorpe 3	0·06	0·53	0·38	0·022	0·022	0·81	0·56
VS	Stella North 4	0·07	0·49	0·42	0·021	0·024	0·92	0·45
TP	Upper Boat 13	0·11	0·39	0·50	0·022	0·034	0·88	0·58

TABLE II Service details and dimensions of 1%Cr–0·5%Mo steel superheater tubes

Identification mark	Station and boiler	Final steam conditions lb/in²	°C	Operation time, h	Average tube dia. in	Average wall thickness, in	Hardness, VPN Header end	Remote from header end	Structural classification
TS	'New tube'	...	...	...	2·25	0·280	168–174 *171†*	169–177 *172*	A
VP	Battersea 16	1 420	518	11 770	2·50	0·320	150–160 *156*	154–160 *157*	D
VO	Battersea 17	1 420	518	7 279	2·50	0·320	154–162 *156*	150–167 *157*	B
TT8*	Brimsdown 2A	2 000	504	100 000	2·063	0·243	165–180 *175*	148–171 *159*	D
BT9*	Brimsdown 2A	2 000	504	100 000	2·063	0·239	127–144 *138*	127–152 *138*	D–E top F bottom
BB9*	Brimsdown 2A	2 000	504	11 000	2·063	0·275	157–176 *167*	167–182 *174*	A–B top C bottom
TW	Carmarthen Bay 3	940	496	24 732	2·25	0·250	141–148 *145*	140–147 *144*	D
TR	Carmarthen Bay 8	940	496	13 736	2·25	0·245	177–185 *180*	171–180 *175*	C top D bottom
TL	Carmarthen Bay 17	950	482	5 316	2·25	0·256	167–179 *174*	172–183 *178*	B
VA	Goldington 2	625	471	6 785	2·125	0·200	144–152 *148*	142–149 *146*	C
VT	North Tees C2	950	504	29 437	2·25	0·246	137–144 *140*	157–175 *163*	C
VH	Norwich 12	675	468	35 050	1·625	0·216	141–162 *153*	143–160 *154*	C
TV	Staythorpe 3	950	496	23 500	1·75	0·177	135–143 *139*	136–142 *139*	E
VS	Stella North 4	950	496	5 934	2·00	0·285	138–145 *142*	138–150 *141*	A top B bottom
TP	Upper Boat 13	650	454	95 253	2·25	0·240	173–180 *177*	160–166 *164*	B

All the tubes, except those marked*, were removed from positions as near as possible to the outlet headers.
† Figures in italics indicate average.

in the tubes from Battersea and Brimsdown. The calculated stresses based on the nominal initial dimensions in the latter tube which carried steam at the highest pressure of 2000 lb/in² were about 3·3 tons/in². When superheater tubes are put into service the wall thickness is chosen to allow for a factor of safety in terms of permissible stress and for wastage of the thickness by corrosion. During a large part of the life of most tubes there is very little creep, and it only begins to occur at a significant rate when the strength properties have decreased as a result of prolonged heating or the wall thickness has been reduced by an appreciable amount. It is probable that most of the tubes examined had suffered little creep strain. The emphasis of the present work was to assess the change in properties after prolonged heating in service and to relate these to the microstructural changes which had occurred, rather than to study the factors which confer the initial creep resistance.

TEST PROCEDURE AND RESULTS
Structural examination

Sections from the outlet header end of each tube were metallographically examined under the optical microscope.

The structure of the new tube consisted of ferrite and unresolved pearlite, while the sections of the used tubes showed varying degrees of carbide spheroidization and of dispersion of carbide away from the original pearlite areas. Differences were also observed in the structure at various positions around some of the tubes. These differences, which were most marked in two of the three tubes from Brimsdown (BB9, BT9), were also marked in the tubes from Stella North (VS) and Carmarthen Bay no. 8 (TR). In each tube the bottom sections showed a greater deterioration of the pearlite than the corresponding top sections. The ferrite grain sizes of the samples examined varied from ASTM 4–5 (BB9) to ASTM 9–10 (TR).

During service, changes in the microstructure of a tube will be dependent on both time and the actual metal temperatures attained by the steel. The specified maximum steam temperature of the boiler cannot be accurately related to the temperature of the steam in any particular tube in the superheater. Variations of up to 55°C have been measured where gas stratification, unequal steam flow in the tubes, or varying degrees of ash deposition have occurred. The deposition of fly ash will also control the difference in temperature both between the tube and the steam and also between the top and the bottom of the tube. This can vary appreciably especially if the tube is subjected to high intensity flame radiation, when the flame side can be 25°C hotter than the far side.

The initial microstructure will depend to some extent on the steel composition and the method of production, but mainly on the final heat treatment it received after fabrication. This is specified in BS.3059 as either normalizing or annealing at 920–960°C so that variations in the morphology of the pearlite will occur. Because of these considerations it was decided to attempt to relate the deterioration of the properties due to service conditions, first, to the degree of spheroidization of the carbides, especially in the pearlite areas, and second, to type and degree of carbide precipitation. Examination with the optical microscope showed that the process of spheroidization could be roughly divided into five stages, and that it was possible to classify the structures of all the tubes, without regard to ferritic grain size. Six micrographs (magnification × 500) have been selected to illustrate the original structure and these stages of spheroidization, and are presented in Figs.1–6. The structural condition of each tube is given in Table II.

279

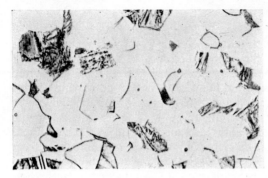

1 *Spheroidization stage A. Ferrite and very fine pearlite. Microstructure of new tube (TS) ×500*

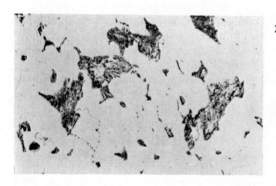

2 *Spheroidization stage B. First signs of carbide spheroidization, usually accompanied by precipitation at the grain boundaries. Microstructure of tube from Carmarthen Bay boiler no. 17 (TL) ×500*

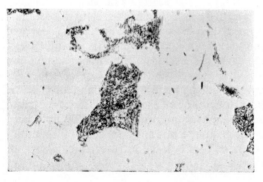

3 *Spheroidization stage C. Intermediate stage. Appreciable spheroidization of pearlite, but some carbide plates still evident. Microstructure of tube from North Tees C, no. 2 boiler (VT) ×500*

280

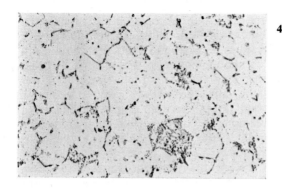

4 *Spheroidization stage D. Spheroidization complete, but the carbides are still grouped in a pearlitic pattern. Microstructure of tube from Carmarthen Bay boiler no. 3 (TW)*
×500

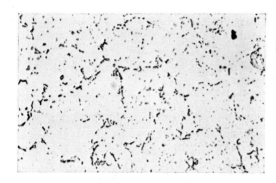

5 *Spheroidization stage E. Carbides are dispersed, leaving little trace of original pearlitic areas. Microstructure of tube from Staythorpe boiler no. 3 (TV)* *×500*

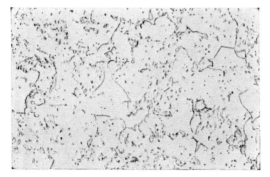

6 *Spheroidization stage F. Size of some of the carbide particles has increased markedly due to coalescence. Microstructure from Brimsdown no. 2A (BT9) ×500*

Specimens from all the tubes were also examined with the electron microscope using carbon extraction replicas. The carbides present were identified by selected area electron diffraction analysis. Specimens from both the top and the bottom of the tubes from Brimsdown (BT9), Carmarthen Bay (TR), and Stella North (VS), were examined because of the differences found in the structures at various positions around these tubes. In general the degree of spheroidization observed optically could be related to the amount of carbide precipitation in the ferrite and to the changes in the nature of the carbides that are present both in the pearlite and the ferrite grains as revealed by the electron microscope. However, the degree of precipitation and breakdown of pearlite do not always reach the same stage simultaneously. For example, the specimen from Norwich (VH) showed very little precipitation in the ferrite grains, as in stage A, although in some of the pearlite areas the Fe_3C particles had spheroidized and transformed to Cr_7C_3 and Mo_2C as in stage D. The stages of spheroidization and precipitation are described in Table III.

TABLE III   **Stages in carbide spheroidization and precipitation in $1\%Cr–0.5\%Mo$ steel superheater tubes**

Stage	Spheroidization	Precipitation
A	Typical of the structure of a new tube, consisting of ferrite and a very fine pearlite.	The carbide present in the pearlite areas is Fe_3C. Evidence of molybdenum carbide particles (Mo_2C) beginning to precipitate in the ferrite grains (up to $0.1\ \mu m$).
B	The first stage of carbide spheroidization usually coinciding with the appearance of small particles of carbides at the grain boundaries.	Small particles of both chromium carbide (Cr_7C_3) and molybdenum carbide (Mo_2C) (up to $0.2\mu m$) present in the ferrite. (particles of Cr_7C_3 also probably present at grain boundaries but not identified).
C	An intermediate stage of spheroidization, showing more distinct signs of carbide spheroidization in the pearlite areas, but some carbide plates still evident. Increased carbide precipitation within the ferrite grains and at the grain boundaries.	Medium-sized particles of Cr_7C_3 and Mo_2C (up to $0.5\mu m$) present in the ferrite.
D	Spheroidization of the carbides is virtually complete, but they are still grouped in the original pearlitic pattern.	Some Fe_3C particles have transformed to Cr_7C_3 and perhaps Mo_2C. The particles of Mo_2C and Cr_7C_3 in the ferrite have further increased in size (Mo_2C up to 1 μm).
E	Spheroidization is complete and the carbides are dispersed, leaving little trace of the original pearlite areas.	The pearlite areas have dispersed and the Fe_3C particles have completely transformed to Cr_7C_3 and Mo_2C particles. The Mo_2C and Cr_7C_3 precipitates are large in size (Mo_2C up to $1.5\mu m$).
F	There is a marked increase in the size of some of the carbide particles, partly due to coalescence.	The pearlite areas are completely dispersed. The amount of Mo_2C present throughout the structure has decreased to form areas of the complex metal carbide M_6C. This metal carbide is molybdenum rich, but contains both chromium and iron. Some new grains of ferrite may also have been formed.

Mechanical properties

Hardness tests

The hardnesses of the sections varied from over 180 VPN to less than 130 VPN and are shown in Table II. There is obviously no consistent relationship between hardness and service conditions. For example, the tube from Goldington (VA) which had been in service carrying steam at 471°C for 6 785 h, had an average hardness of about 147 VPN, whilst the tube from Carmarthen Bay no. 8 (TR), which had carried steam at 496°C for 13 736 h, had an average hardness of 180 VPN.

There was little difference in the average hardnesses obtained from the two ends of each length of tube, except in the sections taken from one of the tubes from Brimsdown and the tube from North Tees which showed differences of 16 VPN and 23 VPN respectively. Variations in hardness of over 20 VPN were apparent around some of the tubes, the lowest hardness values being obtained at the bottom of the tube section. The hardness values suggested that most of the tubes that were used in this investigation were in the normalized condition when they were put into service. The new tube was in the normalized condition.

Tensile tests

Tensile tests were carried out on Hounsfield no. 12 specimens machined from the tube wall thickness at the steam outlet end of five of the tubes which had been in service, and from the new tube. Specimens, which were tested at room temperature and at 565°C, were machined from five tubes chosen because the hardness and microscopical examinations indicated that they had suffered the greatest deterioration in structure during service.

The results of the tests are presented in Tables IV and V for the tests at room temperature and 565°C respectively.

TABLE IV   Hounsfield tensile test results at room temperature

Identification mark	TS		VP		TT8		BT9		TW		TV	
Station	'New tube'		Battersea 16		Brimsdown 2A		Brimsdown 2A		Carmarthen Bay 3		Staythorpe 3	
Service conditions	..		1 420 lb/in², 518°C 11 770 h		2 000 lb/in², 504°C 100 000 h		2 000 lb/in², 504°C 100 000 h		940 lb/in², 496°C 24 732 h		950 lb/in², 496°C 23 500 h	
Position of test specimen	Top	Bot-tom	Top	Bot-tom	Top	Bot-tom	Top	Bot-tom	Top	Bot-tom	Top	Bot-tom
UTS, tons/in²	32·4	32·8	33·0	32·2	37·2	35·0	29·8	28·2	31·0	30·8	29·6	28·4
Elong., %	35	35	34	35	28	30	40	40	37	35	37	42
R of A, %	64	68	75	75	68	70	72	70	75	77	76	80

TABLE V Hounsfield tensile test results at 565°C

Identification mark	TS		VP		TT8		BT9		TW		TV	
Station	'New tube'		Battersea 16		Brimsdown 2A		Brimsdown 2A		Carmarthen Bay 3		Staythorpe 3	
Service conditions	...		1 420 lb/in², 518°C, 11 770 h		2 000 lb/in², ʒ04°C, 100 000 h		2 000 lb/in², 504°C, 100 000 h		940 lb/in², 496°C, 24 732 h		950 lb/in², 496°C, 23 500 h	
Position of test specimen	Top	Bottom	Top	Bottom	Top	Bottom	Top	Bottom	Top	Bottom	Top	Bottom
UTS, tons/in²	27·0	27·2	17·6	16·0	20·2	18·8	15·6	14·4	16·0	17·2	15·8	14·8
Elong., %	31	31	41	48	32	33	48	47	45	43	48	46
R of A, %	72	75	76	79	78	78	80	79	78	80	78	78

The tubes from Staythorpe (TV) and Brimsdown (BT9) which had the lowest average hardness values (139 VPN and 138 VPN respectively) had the lowest tensile strengths at both room temperature (28·2 to 29·8 tons/in²) and 565°C (14·4–15·8 tons/in²).

The tensile strength of the new tube (TS) was 32·6 tons/in² at room temperature and 27·1 tons/in² at 565°C. Results quoted[4] for material in the normalized condition are 34·4 tons/in² at room temperature and 26·9 tons/in² at 565°C.

Stress rupture tests

The stress rupture properties of all the tubes were determined at 510° and 565°C using Denison $\frac{3}{4}$-ton machines at stress levels which resulted in fracture in times of up to 10 000 h.

A number of test pieces of 1in gauge length and 0·126in dia. were machined from the wall thickness of each of the fifteen tubes listed in Table II. Specimens having a smaller diameter than that of standard miniature test pieces (0·1785in), had to be used because of the insufficient thickness of some of the tube walls. The test pieces, which were machined from the steam outlet end of each tube, were numbered so that the exact position of each test piece was known.

The results obtained on the new tube (TS) were compared with some published results on 1%Cr–0·5%Mo steel in the form of bar[2] and with rupture results obtained from the material from the top of a tube from Brimsdown (BB9) and with that from Stella North (VS). Both of these tubes had similar structures in this position to that of the new tube (stage A). The results of the rupture tests at both 510° and 565°C on each of these materials were in good agreement.

The results obtained on the remaining twelve tubes have been divided into three groups, according to their structures. The results from the tubes whose structures were in stages B and C are classed

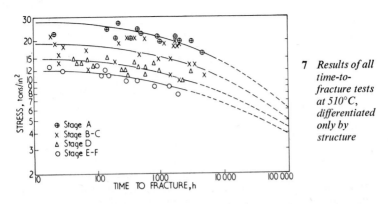

7 *Results of all time-to-fracture tests at 510°C, differentiated only by structure*

together, those in stage D form a separate group, and those in stages E and F form the last group. It was found to be most convenient to group the results together in this way, because they then fell into comparatively narrow scatter bands. Grouped in this way all the results obtained at 510° and 565°C are shown in Figs.7 and 8 respectively. Whilst the results obtained from the tubes having structures in stages B and C and stage D overlap to some extent, those from stage A all lie at the top of the band and those in stages E and F all lie at the bottom of the band.

It was noted previously that two tubes from Brimsdown (BT9 and BB9), and those from Carmarthen Bay no. 8 (TR) and Stella North (VS), showed variations in structure around the tube sections. These variations did not affect the stress rupture results obtained from specimens machined from various positions around the

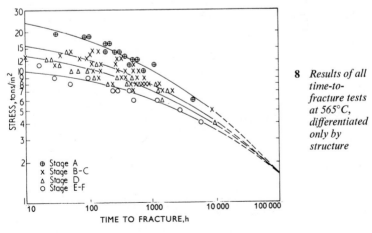

8 *Results of all time-to-fracture tests at 565°C, differentiated only by structure*

285

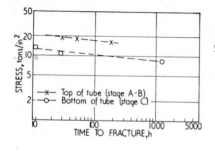

9 *Effect of specimen position on the relationship between stress and time-to-fracture in tests at 565°C (1050°F) on one of the tubes from Brimsdown (BB9)*

tube from Carmarthen Bay no. 8 (TR) and from one of those from Brimsdown (BT9), but both these tubes had reached a fairly advanced degree of spheroidization at both top and bottom positions. However, the material at the top of the other two tubes (Stella North (VS) and Brimsdown (BB9)), had not started to spheroidize, although the material at the bottom of these tubes had spheroidized to some extent. In these two tubes the stress rupture results obtained at 565°C on specimens from the bottom material were consistently worse than those obtained from the top material. The stress/time-to-fracture relationship for the specimen which showed the greatest effect (BB9) is shown in Fig.9. Insufficient results were obtained at 510°C to allow any effect of specimen position to be shown.

The ductility obtained at fracture on each test piece was assessed by measuring the elongation on a 1in gauge length. The results which were classified in the same way as the rupture strength values, are shown in Figs.10 and 11. There is a greater amount of scatter in the ductility results than in the rupture strength results, and it tends to

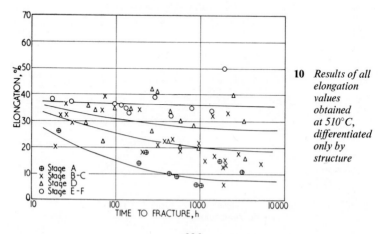

10 *Results of all elongation values obtained at 510°C, differentiated only by structure*

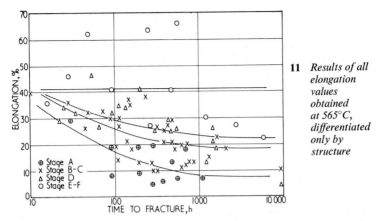

11 *Results of all elongation values obtained at 565°C, differentiated only by structure*

become greater as the degree of carbide spheroidization and precipitation increases. However, this is mainly due to the large amount of scatter found in the Brimsdown tube (BT9) which showed the greatest deterioration in structure. The effect of increasing carbide spheroidization and precipitation is to increase the elongation values which are obtained for a given fracture time. For each type of structure, except stages E and F, the ductility tends to decrease with increasing time-to-fracture.

Despite the scatter in the elongation results, the values obtained from the tests at 565°C on material from the bottom of the tube from Stella North (VS) and one of those from Brimsdown (BB9), had on average about 8% higher elongation value than those from tests on material from the top of these tubes.

DISCUSSION

As stated previously the microstructure of the tubes cannot be very reliably related to the service conditions in the boilers from which they were removed, mainly because the actual metal temperature histories are not known. However, for the purposes of schematic representation (Fig.12), the steam temperatures at the outlet headers

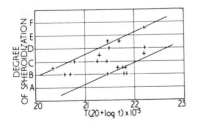

12 *Relationship between time-temperature parameter $T(C + \log t)$ and degree of spheroidization*

287

and the operating times of the tubes have been combined in the conventional temperature-time parameter,[5] $T(C+\log t)$, where $T=$ steam temperature (degrees Absolute), $t=$ the operating time, and $C=20$. The expected trend is clearly shown although the scatter band is wide.

Therefore, if the deterioration in structure and properties of a tube is to be reliably related to service conditions, the true metal temperature history of the tube must be measured whilst it is in service. At Brimsdown power station the temperatures of the tubes used to replace those removed for examination (BB9, BT9, and TT8) were measured over a period of six months. These measurements showed that metal temperatures of above 565°C were attained for longer periods in a tube in the middle of the superheater than one at the top. A temperature gradient was also shown to exist around each tube from top to bottom. These measurements explain the differences found in the microstructures of the tubes BB9, BT9, and TT8.

The microstructural changes which occur in the $1\%Cr–0·5\%Mo$ steel during service are carbide spheroidization and precipitation. They appear to occur independently but proceed together, and each usually reaches a given stage at the same time.

These changes in structure may be summarized as follows:

Ferrite areas	Precipitation and growth of Cr_7C_3 and Mo_2C particles	Formation of M_6C and new grains of ferrite.
Pearlite areas	Spheroidization of Fe_3C and change in composition to Cr_7C_3 and Mo_2C.	

The changes that occur in the structure of $2\frac{1}{4}\%Cr–1\%Mo$ steel during tempering have been studied by Baker and Nutting[6] and some of the effects noted by these workers have also been observed in the present investigation. The formation of recrystallized grains of ferrite resulting from the complete breakdown of pearlite (or bainite in the $2\frac{1}{4}\%Cr–1\%Mo$ steel) is one of the features apparent in the work on both steels.

Although it has not been possible to correlate very precisely the service conditions with the results obtained from the stress rupture tests, it has been shown that a close relationship exists between rupture properties and the microstructural changes that occur in $1\%Cr–0·5\%Mo$ steel superheater tubes in service, and that there is a consistent decrease in rupture strength with increasing carbide spheroidization and precipitation.

The main factor affecting the creep strength of a low-alloy ferritic steel is the nature of the carbides precipitated in the ferrite because the carbides prevent the movement of dislocations through the ferrite grains. It has been suggested[7] that the creep strength is highest just before the carbides lose coherency with the matrix and grow to form larger particles. However, Glen has shown[8] that the creep rate in 0.5%Mo steel that has been heavily tempered can decrease during straining, that is the material can still be strengthened. It has not been possible in the present rupture tests to measure creep strains accurately because only small specimens could be used. There was evidence of molybdenum carbide particles in the ferrite grains in the tube which had not been in service. Obviously, therefore, the carbides were already beginning to lose their coherency with the matrix. If this tube is typical of new material, it is probable that superheater tubes made from 1%Cr–0.5%Mo steel are not strengthened to any significant extent during service life. It is possible to postulate that if the matrix is strengthened by the pre-precipitation of carbides, this is being counteracted by the loss of coherency of precipitates, the growth of precipitates already formed, and to a less extent by the spheroidization of carbides in the pearlite areas. The results obtained show that the strength decreases as the size of the precipitated alloy carbide particles increase.

There is a marked difference in the decrease in rupture strength during various stages of carbide spheroidization and precipitation. For example, it will be seen from Fig.8 that the stress required to give a rupture life of $1\,000$ h at $565°C$ is about 10 tons/in² for new material, but decreased to $7\frac{1}{2}$ tons/in² for material having a structure in stages B or C. However, the stress required to produce rupture under the same conditions in material having a structure in stage D is 7 tons/in², and in stages E or F, about 6 tons/in². The rupture strength decreases more during the first stage of carbide spheroidization and precipitation, which is probably when most of the carbides lose coherency with the matrix, than during the other subsequent stages of structural change. The rates at which the structural changes occurred in the tubes used in these tests could not, of course, be assessed.

In a similar programme of work in which the effect of service on the structure and properties of mild steel superheater tubes has been studied, no relationship has been found between the stress rupture properties and the degree of carbide spheroidization. The scatter bands for both the mild steel and 1%Cr–0.5%Mo steel superheater tubes are shown in Fig.13. It is apparent that even the weakest 1%Cr–0.5%Mo steel tube had better stress rupture properties than any of the mild-steel tubes. The chromium–molybdenum steel in this 'weak' condition probably contains no coherent precipitates and most of the carbides present will be in the form of fairly large and widely spaced particles which will have comparatively little

289

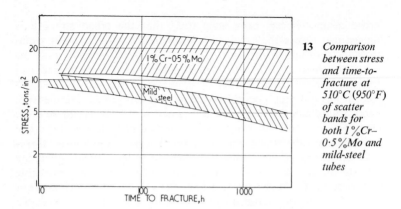

13 *Comparison between stress and time-to-fracture at 510°C (950°F) of scatter bands for both 1%Cr–0·5%Mo and mild-steel tubes*

effect on creep strength. It is probable, therefore, that the weakest chromium–molybdenum steel has better creep strength than the best mild steel because of the solution hardening effects of chromium and molybdenum. Although it has been considered that solution hardening in austenitic steels is of minor importance[9] it may be of greater importance in ferritic steels.

It is difficult to distinguish between the effects of carbides and solution hardening. Furthermore, little is known of the effects of carbide morphology on creep strength, and of the relationship between carbides and the remainder of the structure. In order to understand these relationships it is obviously desirable to study both the constitution and form of carbides and their effects on deformation processes.

No stress rupture tests were carried out for longer than 10000 h, but the stress rupture lines shown in Figs.7 and 8 have been extrapolated to 100000 h using the Manson-Haferd[10] method of extrapolation. At 565°C the stress rupture lines for each type of structure meet at a stress of about $1\frac{1}{2}$–2 tons/in² at 100000 h. At 510°C the extrapolated stress rupture lines do not meet, but tend to converge, falling to stresses in the range 4–6 tons/in² at 100 000 h. These extrapolated values are lower than those estimated by Glen[1] using a different method of extrapolation and may be a little pessimistic. Glen's estimates of stresses to cause rupture in 100000 h at 565° and 510°C were $2\frac{1}{2}$ tons/in² and 7 tons/in² respectively.

As previously mentioned the stresses due to steam pressure in all the tubes investigated, except those from Battersea and Brimsdown, were less than 2 tons/in². The calculated stresses in the tubes from the latter station were about 3·3 tons/in². Therefore, the strength of the material is probably adequate in most superheaters providing the tubes do not continually operate with metal temperatures of the order of 565°C and that no severe thinning of the wall occurs due to corrosion.

There are two ways in which the stresses present in a superheater tube during its service life can affect its subsequent stress rupture properties. First, if the stresses in a tube wall are great enough to cause the material to creep appreciably in service, the stress rupture life in subsequent laboratory tests at the service temperature and stress may be shortened. This is obviously a very complex problem, for it must be remembered that the stresses in a tube in service are predominantly circumferential, while the stresses applied to the material in stress rupture tests are longitudinal with respect to the tube.

Second, creep may accelerate or retard the precipitation of the carbides[11] and therefore the properties may deteriorate at a faster or slower rate than in the absence of stress. However, there is evidence[12] that in a $2\frac{1}{4}\%$Cr–1%Mo steel, stresses of up to $2\frac{1}{4}$ tons/in^2 have no effect on microstructure providing the tertiary stage of creep is not reached. The stress in the walls of the 1%Cr–$0\cdot5\%$Mo steel tubes carrying steam at a pressure of 950 lb/in^2 was less than 2 tons/in^2 and the small amount of strain produced probably had no significant effect on the rate of carbide precipitation in this steel.

The stress in the Brimsdown superheater tubes carrying steam at 2000 lb/in^2 was about $3\cdot3$ tons/in^2, and the metal temperatures were probably in the range 510–565°C for most of the time while peak temperatures of up to 589°C occurred from time to time. These conditions obviously caused a significant amount of creep to occur during 100 000 h in service and may also have affected the rate of carbide precipitation and consequently, the properties of the material. In the test at a stress of 4 tons/in^2 at 565°C on the tube BT9, which had a structure in stages E to F, failure occurred after 5900 h. This result does not, however, clearly indicate whether or not the strain that occurred during service life in the circumferential direction had appreciably affected the stress rupture life of the material in the longitudinal direction.

The grain sizes of the tubes investigated varied from ASTM 4 to ASTM 10 but careful inspection of the detailed results provided no evidence to suggest that this variation had a significant effect on the stress rupture properties of the steel.

The ductility values obtained in the stress rupture tests appear to depend firstly on the stage of deterioration of the structure and secondly on the rupture stress. There is an overall increase in ductility as the structure changes from stage A to F as shown in Figs. 10

and 11, which corresponds to decreasing rupture strength. Then in each stage (except stages E and F) the ductility tends to decrease with increasing time to fracture, that is, with decreasing stress. As mentioned earlier it is unlikely that a significant amount of creep occurred in most of the tubes during service. The increase of ductility with service time (for a given stress rupture life) is what might be anticipated as a result simply of the effect of prolonged heating on the microstructure. In each individual stress rupture test there is obviously again a progressive change in microstructure, but nevertheless the mechanisms leading to failure (such as intergranular cavitation) also develop and tend to curtail ductility. It is interesting to speculate that in tests of long duration (low stress) the fracture process develops more rapidly than the change in microstructure.

The minimum elongation values (measured on a 1in gauge length) were obtained on the new tube, and in tests of up to 1 095 h duration at 565°C were in the range 5–8%. A value of 4% was also obtained on the tube from Carmarthen Bay no. 3 (TW–stage D) for a specimen which fractured in 9 200 h at 565°C and 4 tons/in². Although this value is below the level of 5%[13] which is normally accepted as satisfactory for most applications, it may, of course, rise during extended service as the microstructure deteriorates. Unfortunately it is not yet known how much ductility is required in a component such as a superheater tube in the presence of complex stress systems. Further work is also required to relate structural changes to ductility in longer-time rupture tests.

CONCLUSIONS

The microstructural changes which occur in $1\%Cr-0\cdot5\%Mo$ steel superheater tubes during service have been studied. The changes that occur in the ferrite and pearlite areas in the structure may be summarized as follows:

Ferrite areas	Precipitation and growth of Cr_7C_3 and Mo_2C particles.	Formation of M_6C and new areas of ferrite.
Pearlite areas	Spheroidization of Fe_3C and change in composition to Cr_7C_3 and Mo_2C.	

The results of stress/rupture tests at 565° and 510°C for times up to about 10000 h have shown that the strength properties of a tube decreased as the degree of spheroidization of the cementite in the pearlite increased, and as the amount and size of the alloy carbides that precipitated in the ferrite increased. The strength properties were poorest when the complex carbide, M_6C, was present in the structure. Relatively low stresses are normally present in the walls of $1\%Cr-0\cdot5\%Mo$ steel superheater tubes carrying steam at 950 lb/in^2 or less, and therefore even after the properties of a tube fall to this minimum level, they are probably adequate if the tube operates under normal conditions.

The deterioration in the structure and properties of a particular tube depended upon the length of time that it had been in service, and to some extent on the temperature of the steam it had carried. It was, however, more closely related to the prevailing metal temperature. Long times and high temperatures produced the greatest deterioration in both structures and properties. The decrease in the stress rupture properties of a tube is most marked during the first stage of structural deterioration, that is, during the initial stages of carbide spheroidization and precipitation which may occur early in its service life.

ACKNOWLEDGMENTS

This paper is published by permission of the Director of the Central Electricity Research Laboratories, Leatherhead.

The samples of the superheater tubes were provided by a number of Divisions, and thanks are due both to the divisional metallurgists and the station staffs concerned for their co-operation.

Most of the analyses of the samples were carried out in the Divisional Laboratory of the North Eastern Division, and preliminary metallographic examinations were carried out in the Metallurgical Laboratory of the South Wales Division.

The temperature measurements were carried out by Mr M. E. Peplow and the stress rupture tests by Mr J. Hacon, both formerly of CERL.

The examinations with the electron microscope were carried out at the Aeon Laboratories.

REFERENCES

1. J. GLEN: *JISI*, 1955, **179**, 320–336.
2. 'The effect of notching on the rupture characteristics of $0\cdot5\%Mo$ and $1\%Cr-Mo$ steels', BEAIRA Report no. J/E/T 203.
3. L. H. TOFT and D. E. WETHERLY: 'Examination of a $1\%Cr-0\cdot5\%Mo$ steel superheater from Brimsdown power station after 20 years in service', International Discussion on the long-time performance of high temperature steels, Düsseldorf, June 1960.
4. 'Data on creep and heat resisting steels', published by The United Steel Companies Limited.
5. J. H. HOLLOMAN and L. D. JAFFE: *Trans. AIME*, 1945, **162**, 223–249.
6. R. G. BAKER and J. NUTTING: *JISI*, 1959, **192**, 257–268.
7. J. D. MURRAY, in: 'Precipitation processes in steels', *ISI Spec. Rep.* no. 64, 1959, 285–291.
8. J. GLEN in discussion: *JISI*, 1959, **192**, 293–297.
9. J. GLEN and J. D. MURRAY, in: 'Symposium on steels for reactor pressure circuits', *ISI Spec. Rep.* no. 69, 1961

10. S. S. MANSON and A. M. HAFERD: 'A linear time–temperature relation for extrapolation of creep and stress rupture data' Nat. Advisory Com. Aeronautics, Tech. Note 2890, 1953.

11. V. B. NILESHWAR and A. G. QUARRELL: 'Precipitation processes in steels', *op. cit.* 259–271.

12. K. F. HALE: *Metal Treatment*, 1959, **26**, 145–153, 160.

13. W. F. BROWN and G. SACHS: Nat. Advisory Com. Aeronautics, Tech. Note 2433, August 1951.

Some factors affecting the creep rupture performance of a 3%Cr–Mo–W–V steel at 550°C

J. D. Hodkin, A.Met., A.I.M., L. G. Finch, Ph.D., B.Met., and E. W. Colbeck, M.A., F.I.M.

The results of long-time creep tests on a 3%Cr–Mo–W–V steel in various conditions of heat treatment are discussed and a correlation is shown between the creep properties of wrought bar and the size of the ingot. The effects of a notch on the rupture properties of the steel have been investigated and it has been found that notch-strengthening or notch-weakening may occur, depending on the condition of heat treatment of the steel and on the stress and duration of the test. The occurrence of intergranular cracks within the gauge length of plain creep specimens has been noted, particularly at the longer durations, and experiments have been carried out which appear to indicate that this effect does not arise from intrinsic embrittlement of the grain boundaries.

INTRODUCTION

THE DEVELOPMENT of land-based gas turbine installations and other long-term high-temperature equipment has led in recent years to intense interest in the metallurgy and application of creep resisting steels. The high initial cost of equipment, labour, and materials dictates the requirement that many components must be capable of lasting for ten years or more. At the same time, the economic factor also demands increased operating efficiency and this immediately poses problems of higher operating temperatures and stresses. In striving to meet these requirements the metallurgist and engineer have encountered novel problems and it is the purpose of this paper to draw attention to some of the metallurgical features and to the attempts which are being made to define and overcome them. Thus the designer may at least be better armed with data on which

Mr Hodkin is research manager, high-temperature properties section, Dr Finch is research controller, and Mr Colbeck is metallurgical and research director, Hadfields Ltd, Sheffield.

to base a realistic compromise between the required and the less desirable features of the steel's behaviour.

A modern ferritic creep-resisting steel is designed with regard to two basic precepts. First, strengthening of the matrix by the formation of a solid solution of one or more metals in another, and second, precipitation hardening. To a certain extent the composition of the matrix is determined by the requirements of hardenability, and control of the creep, or deformation, is exercised principally by controlling the mode and rate of precipitation, both by an appropriate choice of chemical composition and by heat treatment.

Previous work on 3%Cr–Mo–W–V steel, carried out by Wood and Rait[1] and Colbeck and Rait[2] showed the effect of composition and heat treatment on the creep properties and drew attention to the importance of carbide-forming elements. The steel was initially developed for jet aircraft turbine discs and the results of their investigations were based essentially on tests of short durations, generally 1 000 h or less. A few long-time tests were carried out to substantiate the short time data but these were concerned only with the conventional creep properties. Subsequently, investigations have been carried out with particular emphasis on the long term properties of the material in both plain and notched conditions and greater attention has been paid to long term rupture ductilities.

MATERIAL

The steels used in Part I of these investigations were obtained from production casts and represent a variety of ingot sizes ranging from 7 to 15in, measured across the flats. Their compositions are listed in Table I. In each case, the ingots were partly forged and samples from these blooms were then reheated and forged into 1in dia. bar. The effect of a number of heat treatments is discussed in the text but in every instance the first thermal cycle on the black bar was that

TABLE I Chemical compositions of casts investigated and summary of results obtained after 300 and 1 000 h at 550°C, stress 16·5 tons/in²

Heat treatment: 1150°C ½ h, AC/1060°C, ¾ h OQ/700°C, 4 h, AC

Cast no.	Ingot size, in	Chemical composition, % C	Si	Mn	Cr	Ni	Mo	W	V	Total plastic strain, % 300 h	1 000 h
J 5884	15	0·22	0·46	0·30	2·75	0·24	0·57	0·56	1·00	0·802	1·32
P 1803	15	0·22	0·41	0·43	2·51	0·26	0·44	0·54	0·83	0·802	1·22
F 9182/2	11	0·21	0·43	0·31	2·62	0·15	0·80	0·43	0·95	0·57	0·95
F 6631	9	0·24	0·46	0·28	2·55	0·11	0·92	0·40	0·91	0·392	0·577
F 5896	7	0·22	0·41	0·13	2·55	0·17	0·81	0·48	0·86	0·35	0·50
F 6630	9	0·25	0·49	0·33	2·57	0·11	0·88	0·41	0·88	0·298	0·45

Note: Casts J and P, basic electric, cast F, basic high-frequency.

TABLE II   Composition of large basic-electric ingots

| Cast no. | Chemical composition, % | | | | | | | |
	C	Si	Mn	Cr	Ni	Mo	W	V
P.1122 ⎫ Z.770 ⎬ *	0·20	0·46	0·35	2·43	0·28	0·85	0·45	0·74
L.3003	0·20	0·49	0·29	2·55	0·17	0·86	0·49	0·89

* Combined cast

of a normalizing treatment from 1150°C. The individual heat treatments, which were carried out before the final machining of the specimens, are mentioned as they arise.

In Part II of the text a particular experiment is described which concerns the effect of altering the load during the course of a creep test. For this purpose material was machined directly from two large forgings from a pair of 44in octagonal ingots of basic electric steel. The compositions of these ingots are listed in Table II.

PART I   TESTS ON WROUGHT BAR MATERIAL
The effect of cast-to-cast variations

It has long been recognized that the properties of a particular quality of steel may vary slightly from one cast to another, although the chemical compositions lie within closely specified limits. A study of these effects has been made using six separate casts. From each of these, test specimens having a 5in parallel gauge length and 0·505in dia. (0·2in² cross-sectional area), were prepared from 9in lengths of 1in dia. wrought bar which had previously been heat treated in the following manner:

Normalized   1150°C, ½ h, air cooled
Hardened   1060°C, ¾ h, oil quenched
Tempered   700°C, 4 h, air cooled†

†Henceforth, an abridged notation, e.g. 1150°C, AC/1060°C OQ/700° C, AC will be adopted for the heat treatments.

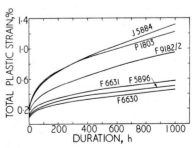

1 *Creep results on 1in dia. wrought bar from six separate casts of 3%Cr–Mo–W–Vsteel, stress 16·5 tons/in², 550°C. Treatment: 1150°C AC/1060°C, OQ/700°C (4 h) AC*

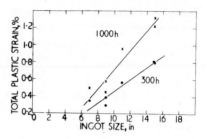

2 *Relationship between ingot size and creep properties, stress 16·5 tons/in², 550°C. Treatment: 1 150°C, AC/1 060°C, OQ/700°C (4 h) AC*

The results which were obtained after the application of a creep tensile stress of 16·5 tons/in² at 550°C for a duration of 1 000 h are shown in Fig.1. The chemical compositions of the various casts and the total plastic strains observed after 300 and 1 000 h of testing are listed in Table I. With the exception of the manganese and molybdenum contents, the chemical compositions all lie within segregational variations of one cast of steel. Whilst the higher molybdenum casts show the better creep properties, there appears to be no significant correlation between other variations in chemical composition and the results obtained during testing. On the other hand, when the total plastic strains after 300 and 1 000 h duration are plotted against the original ingot sizes, as in Fig.2, a marked correlation is observed and the creep properties are seen generally to decrease with increasing ingot size.

The two extreme casts, F5896 and J5884 (insufficient material was available from cast F6630), were used to provide skeleton design curves for 1 % total plastic strain with durations up to 5 000 h, the results of which are shown in Fig.3. These data show that the differences in stress required to give 1·0% strain in a given time become more marked with increased durations.

Effect of heat treatment on creep and rupture properties at 550°C

Stress rupture properties for cylindrical specimens after four variations of heat treatment are shown in Fig.4. These tests were carried out on specimens prepared from the cast denoted P1803 in Table I.

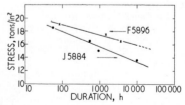

3 *Design curves for 1·0% total plastic strain at 550°C; extreme casts of Fig.1*

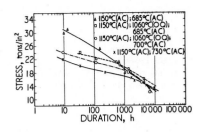

4 *Effect of heat treatment on the stress rupture properties at 550°C (cast P1803)*

The 1150°C AC/685°C AC treatment was designed initially to give optimum short time (300 h) creep properties for aircraft turbine applications. Increasing the tempering temperature to 730°C brought about a reduction in creep properties but improved the room temperature ductility and impact values. The 1150°C AC/1060°C OQ/700°C AC treatment, previously established by Wood and Rait,[1] was found to give the desired properties in large forgings in which a room temperature tensile strength of 45–55 tons/in² and good room temperature ductility values were required.

It will be noticed that the curves do not show the straight-line characteristics so frequently associated with stress/log-duration plotting. At the outset, considerable differences in the stress required to cause rupture exist between the various treatments but these differences become less significant with longer durations: for example the stress difference for rupture in 10 000 h is somewhat less than 2 tons/in². The introduction of an oil quenching treatment from 1060°C is seen slightly to improve the long-term rupture properties in the case of material tempered at 685°C.

The effect of heat treatment on the rupture properties of specimens containing a circumferential V-notch (60° notch, 0·25 mm root radius) is shown in Fig.5. These results are considered in greater detail later in the text.

In order to compare creep properties, the stress to give 0·2% total plastic strain was selected as the criterion. This value was chosen because many of the specimens which had received the

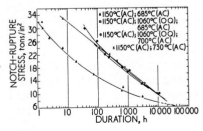

5 *Effect of heat treatment on the notch–rupture properties at 550°C (cast P1803)*

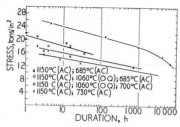

6 *Design curves for 0·2% total plastic strain; various conditions of heat treatment (cast P1803)*

treatment designed to give optimum rupture strength (300 h basis) fractured even before 0·5% strain had occurred. (The problem of low rupture ductility will be discussed later when considering the effect of heat treatment on notch sensitivity.) The results of this comparison are illustrated in Fig.6 which shows the 1150°C/685°C treatment to be superior as regards creep properties at least for durations up to 10000 h. It will be noticed that the introduction of the 1060°C oil quench significantly reduces the creep properties.

Effect of heat treatment on embrittlement and notch sensitivity

The phenomenon of 'embrittlement' of creep-resisting steels, after prolonged periods of testing under an applied stress at elevated temperatures, has been recognized for many years. A further interesting effect is the weakening, or strengthening, which accompanies the introduction of a notch.

Generally, creep tests are carried out on smooth cylindrical specimens having carefully designed radii at the junction between the parallel test length and the heads, so that fracture will be predisposed to take place within the test length. Tests have none the less been known to fail prematurely at the point of fixture of an extensometer or in the threads, although the base of the threads is generally of much greater cross-sectional area than that of the actual test length. Many such failures have not only occurred in brittle material (as determined by a room-temperature impact test) but also in materials which were known to possess good ductility at the outset of the tests.

Perhaps the first indications of this type of embrittlement occurring under actual service conditions are to be found in an early report by Bailey[3] concerning the brittle and premature failure of boiler flange bolts, although these were designed with large safety factors.

During the 30 years which have elapsed since this occurrence, similar types of failure have arisen and have been reported by Reincke[4] and others in Germany. Numerous investigations have also been carried out on the embrittlement and notch sensitivity of heat resisting steels in the United States. In a survey on heat-resisting steels, Sachs and Brown[5] concluded that all the steels which they investigated were subject to embrittlement or 'creep damage' under an applied stress at 500°C. The magnitude of this effect was found to vary widely and to depend markedly on the composition of the alloy. The effect of notch dimensions has been investigated by Newman et al.,[6] and Davis and Manjoine.[7] These investigations have shown that a notch may either strengthen or weaken a material and that the degree of strengthening or weakening is determined not only by the chemical composition of the material but also by the dimensions of the notch.

The effect of notches and multi-directional stress systems and the importance of notch effects when considering turbine blade materials and their 'fir tree' root fixing, has been described in detail by Siegfried.[8]

Investigations on 3% Cr–Mo–W–V Steel at 550°C

For the present investigations a circumferential V-notch possessing an included angle of 60° and a root radius of 0·25 mm was machined at the centre of cylindrical specimens of 2in gauge length. (In the case of the 1150°C/1060°C/685°C series of treatments a 5in gauge length was used). This gave an effective cross-sectional area at the root of the notch of 0·1in² in a specimen having an initial diameter of 0·505in (0·2in² cross-sectional area). The stresses for the notched tests were calculated on the minimum cross-sectional area.

The ratio r/d is about 0·027, where r=root-radius of notch, and d=reduced diameter of cylindrical bar below notch. This gives an elastic stress concentration factor of about 4, which is considered to be more severe than would normally be encountered in practical turbine engineering design. This value is unlikely to remain true under conditions where the material behaves plastically at elevated temperatures and is offered as a guide only.

The results of notch tests in the four conditions of heat treatment already mentioned (shown in Fig.5) are super-imposed on the curves for plain specimens (Fig.4) in Figs. 7–10. Rupture elongation values and design curves for total plastic strains up to and including 1·0% have also been added. Under notched conditions no appreciable difference in the duration required to cause rupture has been found between the two treatments which incorporated an oil quench from 1060°C and that of straight normalizing and tempering at 730°C. Allowing for a small degree of scatter, a single curve would suffice to describe the properties for these three treatments.

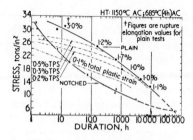

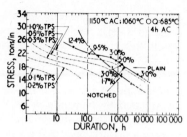

7 *Notch–rupture characteristics at 550°C. Treatment: 1 150°C AC/685 C (4 h) AC (cast P1803)*

8 *Notch–rupture characteristics at 550°C. Treatment: 1 150°C AC/1 060°C OQ/685°C (4 h) AC (cast P1803)*

Considering first the heat treatment for optimum short time properties, i.e. 1 150°C AC/685°C AC, Fig.7 shows that the presence of a notch considerably reduces the life of the specimens at all times up to 10000 h and by a moderate amount of extrapolation this weakening is likely to continue to at least 50000h, when the two curves probably cross at a stress of about 6 tons/in². At all durations, the rupture ductilities for the corresponding plain specimens were exceptionally low. All the tests failed before 1·0% extension had occurred, as measured by the extensometer, and the longer term tests failed before the specimen had undergone 0·3% total strain. Even the rupture elongation values of 1% may be rather optimistic as large errors can arise in fitting the ends of the broken specimens together for the purpose of measurement.

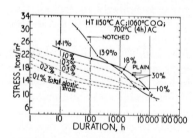

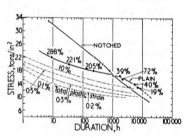

9 *Notch–rupture characteristics at 550°C. Treatment: 1 150°C AC/1 060°C OQ/700°C (4 h) AC (cast P1803)*

10 *Notch–rupture characteristics at 550°C. Treatment: 1 150°C AC/730°C (400 h) AC (cast P1803)*

In the normalized, hardened, and tempered condition (i.e. 1 150°C AC/1 060°C OQ/685°C AC) it has been shown that the short time rupture properties are reduced whilst the long term rupture strength is slightly increased (Fig.4). However, if the curves for plain and notched specimens are superimposed a marked notch strengthening is observed for durations up to 170 h (Fig.8) thereafter, the steel is notch-weakened. No 'restrengthening' of the notched tests is apparent, the curves becoming virtually parallel. If such a restrengthening or recovery of notch strength does take place it must occur in excess of 100 000 h duration at a stress of about 6 tons/in².

The introduction of an oil-quenching treatment considerably improves the short term rupture ductilities of the plain specimens and slightly improves the long term values, although the latter are still of a low order. Even in the test of long duration (4 433 h), 1·0% total plastic strain was recorded 1 500 h before rupture occurred.

Increasing the tempering temperature to 700°C shows further improvement in rupture ductilities for durations up to about 100 h and the onset of notch-weakening is displaced to about 400 h, as shown in Fig.9. Extrapolation of the curves in excess of 10 000 h suggests that the slightly higher tempering temperature will result in a further period of notch strengthening after about 12 000 h.

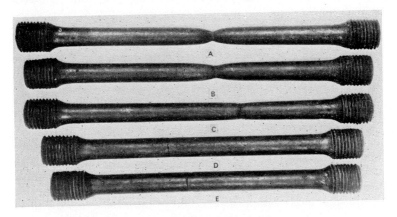

Specimen A	22 tons/in²;	9 hours;	28·8% elong.
B	20 ,,	; 34 ,, ;	22·1 ,,
C	18 ,,	; 221 ,, ;	20·5 ,,
D	15·5 ,,	; 2 123 ,, ;	7·2 ,,
E	13 ,,	; 6 842 ,, ;	1·9 ,,

11 *Series of fractured plain creep specimens (cf. plain curve of Fig.10). Treatment: 1 150°C AC/730°C (4 h) AC*

In the most ductile, but less creep resistant condition (i.e. after the 1150°C/730°C treatment) a marked notch-strengthening is observed for durations up to about 1100 h (Fig.10). Subsequent notch-weakening in this case is accompanied by a much greater fall in the corresponding rupture elongation, from 28·8% after 9 h to less than 2% after 6842 h. At intermediate durations (1000 to 5000 hours) the elongations show a slight improvement on those exhibited for similar durations by specimens in the 1150°C AC/ 1060°C OQ/700°C AC heat-treated condition. Unlike the 1150°C AC/685°C AC treatment, all the specimens displayed more than 1·0% total plastic strain before failure and it again appears that notch strengthening may occur after about 50000 h at a stress of 6·0 tons/in², as was the case with the lower tempering temperature (i.e. 1150°C AC/685°C AC).

It is evident from these investigations that the onset of notch-weakening is displaced to shorter durations with decreasing tempering temperatures (cf. Figs.7 and 10, 8 and 9). The introduction of a hardening treatment delays the onset of notch-weakening, improves the notch strength and also improves the rupture ductility values for plain specimens (cf. Figs.7, 8, and 9).

Photographs of the plain test-pieces from the 1150°C AC/730°C AC series of tests are shown in Figs.11–13; this series has been illustrated because it shows clearly the transition from an exceptionally ductile condition to one of negligible rupture ductility as the duration of the successive tests increased.

Rupture ductility values for the four treatments which are under discussion are plotted against duration to rupture in Fig.14. The onset of notch weakening is indicated on the three curves which show initial ductile fractures. In each case, the onset of notch weakening is associated with a rupture elongation of 9%.

Notch-rupture tests at 500°C

It is of interest briefly to compare the foregoing results with some notched tests which have been carried out at a temperature of 500°C, using specimens in the 1150°C AC/1060°C OQ/700°C AC condition. These results are illustrated in Fig.15 and show notch strengthening at all stress levels within the duration of the tests. From the trend of these values it appears that notch weakening is unlikely to arise in less than 20000 h. The rupture elongation value of 6% for the un-notched test at 22 tons/in² lies considerably below the rupture elongations of about 9% which were associated with the onset of notch sensitivity of specimens having an identical heat treatment but tested at 550°C.

304

12 *Etched section through fracture of specimen A (Fig.11)* × 7

13 *Etched section through fracture of specimen E (Fig.11)* × 7

Comparison of 'creep embrittlement' and room temperature impact properties

The fall in rupture ductility from initially high values for short-time tests to very low values for durations of the order of 5000 to 10000 h, indicates that an 'embrittling' mechanism is operative. Embrittlement was also disclosed by impact tests carried out at room temperature on Izod test pieces machined from the gauge length of the broken creep rupture test pieces. These results are shown graphically in Fig.16 and irrespective of the short-time values, these being dependent on the initial heat treatment, all the long-term impact values are of a fairly low order, the best of these being 5 ft lb after 3800 h duration for the 1150°C/1060°C/700°C heat-treated material.

14 *Relationship between creep duration and rupture elongation at 550°C; various heat treatments. (cast P1803)*

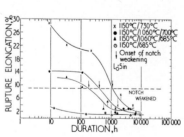

15 *Notch rupture characteristics at 500°C. Treatment: 1 150°C AC/1 060°C OQ/700°C (4 h) AC (cast P1803)*

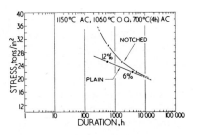

16 *Relationship between creep rupture duration at 550°C and room temperature impact properties of the fractured specimens*

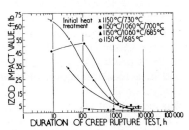

These specimens were examined metallographically using the picric acid–zephyran chloride etch as a check against temper embrittlement; there was no significant response.

It is unlikely that there will be an immediate theoretical relationship between the rupture ductility and the impact value, as the one represents inter- and the other essentially trans-granular fracturing.

PART II TESTS ON LARGE ROTOR FORGINGS

A number of tests carried out on material machined directly from the peripheries of two rotor forgings, produced from 44in octagonal ingots of 20 tons weight (*see* Table II) appear to confirm that the decrease in rupture-ductility with increased duration is not due to an 'embrittlement' of the metal. It is noteworthy that the rupture properties of this material were very similar to those of the 1in dia. bars used in the earlier investigations, though the latter had received a relatively immense forging reduction from the original ingots.

17 *Creep rupture properties of two large rotor forgings at 550°C*

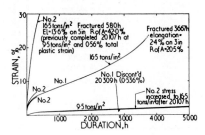

The two lower curves in Fig.17 show the creep behaviour for the first 5000 hours of long-term creep tests conducted at a stress of 9·5 tons/in² at 550°C for 20000 h (20000 h specification tests).

The results of short-time tests conducted at a stress of 16·5 tons/in² (300 h specification tests), one of which was allowed to proceed to rupture, are also shown. On the basis of these comparisons the results from the two forgings are considered to be sufficiently similar to indicate that they possess almost identical properties.

In order to ascertain whether the material had in fact become embrittled during the 20000 h duration, the stress on one of the tests was increased at this stage to 16·5 tons/in² (300 h specification) and the specimen was allowed to proceed to rupture. This increase in stress resulted in a much higher creep rate, failure after a further 580 h, a local reduction of area (necking) of 42% and a rupture elongation of 13·6% on a 5in gauge length. The original test which was carried out wholly at 16·5 tons/in² fractured after 3667 h, with a reduction of area of 20·5% and a rupture elongation of only 2·4% on a 3in gauge length. Although these gauge lengths are not identical, sufficient evidence is presented to show that the material had undergone a peculiar softening rather than embrittlement.

Softening may reasonably be expected to influence the creep rate, but an analysis of the initial 20000 h period did not show the anticipated increase and the rate of deformation remained virtually constant from 2000 to 18000 h. Between 18000 and 20000 h a small fluctuation of rate occurred but the effect was transient and appeared to signify the formation of a few intergranular cracks whose presence was subsequently confirmed. A summary of the creep rate data is presented in Table III.

TABLE III Summary of creep rate data

Time, h	Creep rate, %/h at $9\frac{1}{2}$ tons/in²
0–1500	Primary creep
2000	$2\cdot38 \times 10^{-5}$
4000	2·38 ,,
6000	2·38 ,,
8000	2·44 ,,
10000	2·30 ,,
17000	2·32 ,,
18000	2·04 ,,
19000	2·18 ,,
20000	Stress increased to $16\frac{1}{2}$ tons/in²

We thus have a condition of constant creep rate terminating in enhanced ductility when an additional load is applied.

It is of interest that the second test, discontinued after 20000 h, was subjected to ambient temperature impact tests which showed a decrease from 15 ft lb for the original heat-treated condition to 8 ft lb after 20000 h of creep. Thus the conventional impact test does in fact disclose a form of embrittlement.

Extrapolation of the 20000 h tests on a strain/log time basis indicated that failure should not occur in less than 40000 h. It is anticipated that had these tests been allowed to continue to rupture relatively low values of ductility and residual impact energy would have been obtained. In order to confirm this view a further test which has so far completed 28000 h and registers 1·04% strain is being allowed to continue to fracture.

Metallographic examination of the differentially loaded creep specimen disclosed a few internal intergranular cracks. These had apparently developed during the period of steady creep and whilst they may possibly contribute to reduced impact properties they showed no particular tendency to propagate in the accelerated creep test, which broke with enhanced ductility and an essentially fibrous type of fracture.

PART III METALLOGRAPHICAL EXAMINATION

Samples of bar representing the range of ingot sizes which was studied in these investigations were examined metallographically in order to determine whether there was a consistent structural alteration. The mean separation of the banding (as disclosed by Le Chatelier's etching reagent) was determined on each sample, but the uncertainties in these determinations were great and correlation with the size of the original ingot was unconvincing. An attempt to establish a systematic correlation with the non-metallic inclusions in the sections was also unsuccessful.

Sections from the un-notched creep specimens were prepared for microscopical examination after the creep tests were completed. Microstructures corresponding to the shortest and longest of the creep tests on material in the 1150°C AC/685°C AC condition are shown in Figs.18a and b. There are no outstanding differences in microstructure between these specimens, both of which show clearly defined carbide particles along the prior austenite grain boundaries and sparsely distributed carbide particles within the grains. No intergranular micro-cracks were observed along the gauge length other than immediately adjacent to the fracture which, in every case, was intergranular.

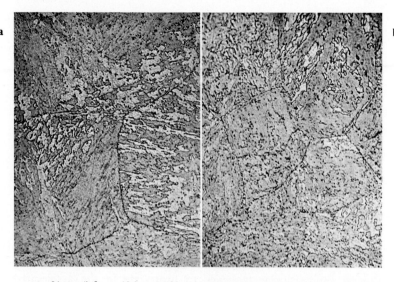

a   31 tons/in²;   13 h;   3 % elongation on 5 in
b   13   ,,   9 195   1·1 %   ,,   ,,

18   *Microstructures of fractured creep specimens. Treatment: 1 150°C AC/685°C*
(4 h) AC   × *500, reduced photographically* × ⅔

A similar structure with well defined grain boundaries and intergranular carbide particles was seen after increasing the tempering temperature to 730°C, Fig.19a. The structure near to the fracture of a test of 9 h duration at 22 tons/in² was considerably elongated and this is shown in Fig.19b. No internal cracks, other than immediately adjacent to the fracture, were observed in specimens which fractured after 9 and 34 h, but intergranular cracks within the gauge length of the specimens appeared and increased in number with greater durations to rupture. These cracks all lay approximately perpendicular to the principal tensile stress direction and many were confined in length to only one grain boundary, terminating at points where the grain boundary turned towards the direction of the principal tensile stress. Chains of etch-pits were noticeable in many of the uncracked grain boundaries, denoting a condition of incipient cracking. A typical example, from a position remote from the primary fracture and after a rupture duration of 2 123 h, is shown in Fig.19c. This specimen has been selected for illustration because it shows clearly that a considerable proportion of an apparent long-term ductility may arise from the summation of numerous internal cracks, as distinct from elongation of the

310

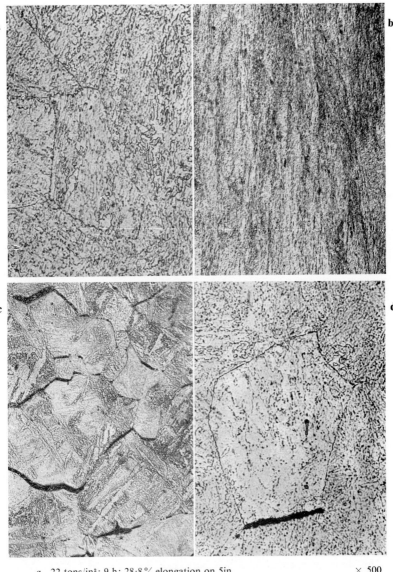

a   22 tons/in²; 9 h; 28·8% elongation on 5in   × 500
b   22 tons/in²; showing structural distortion near to fracture   × 100
c   15·5 tons/in²; 2 123 h; 7·2% elongation on 5in; position remote from fracture
                                                            × 100
d   15·5 tons/in²; detail of intergranular crack   × 500

19   *Microstructures of fractured creep specimens. Treatment: 1 150°C AC/730°C*
(4 h) AC, reduced photographically about × ⅔

grains. No perceptible distortion is recognizable within the grains though rotation has clearly occurred. Figure 19*d* shows how intergranular cracking may be confined by the unfavourable orientation of grain boundaries.

X-ray crystallographic examination of electrolytic extracts from this series of specimens showed the principal carbide phase to be vanadium carbide (of almost constant lattice parameter, 4·17Å) together with small amounts of the chromium carbide Cr_7C_3. According to Krainer[18] the lattice spacings obtained for the vanadium carbide correspond to a solute content of about 15 at-% of molybdenum. Chemical analyses of extracted carbides (e.g. Colbeck and Rait[2]) have shown small amounts of both tungsten and molybdenum to be present and the carbide is most probably a complex solid solution of the type (W, Mo, V) C.

The microstructures of the test pieces which had been normalized, oil quenched, and tempered at 685°C (i.e. 1150°C/1060°C/685°C) differed from the previous series which had simply been normalized and tempered in that the grain boundaries were generally more difficult to identify; presumably due to their relative freedom from grain boundary carbide particles. A few cracks were observed in these specimens after rupture durations in excess of 111 h. However, no cracks were observed in the specimen which fractured after 1616 h. This observation remains unexplained but the effect probably accounts for the anomalous impact result of 42 ft lb shown in Fig.16. A few cracks were observed in the specimen which failed after 4433 h. The structure observed in the test of least duration ($33\frac{1}{2}$ h) from this series is shown in Figs.20*a* and *b* and that of the longest test (4433 h) in Figs.20*c* and *d*. From Fig.20*d* it will be seen that the introduction of the oil-quenching treatment has suppressed to a very large extent the precipitation of intergranular carbides.

The optical microscope has of course great limitations as regards the resolution of fine details. Accordingly, specimens from the 1150°C AC/730°C AC treatment, which showed the transition from an exceptionally ductile short-time fracture to one of low long-term ductility, were selected for electron microscopical studies: these are described below

Electron microscopical examination

The series of specimens which had been heat treated 1150°C AC/730°C AC were electrolytically polished and etched. Carbon extraction replicas were prepared and the electron micrographs of test pieces which fractured after 9, 221, 1711, and 6842 h are shown in Figs.21*a–d* respectively.

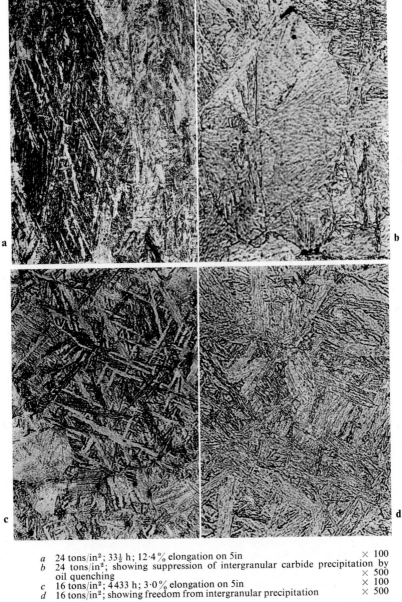

a 24 tons/in²; 33½ h; 12·4% elongation on 5in   × 100
b 24 tons/in²; showing suppression of intergranular carbide precipitation by
    oil quenching   × 500
c 16 tons/in²; 4433 h; 3·0% elongation on 5in   × 100
d 16 tons/in²; showing freedom from intergranular precipitation   × 500

20 *Microstructures of fractured creep specimens. Treatment: 1150°C AC/1060°C
OQ/685°C (4 h) AC, reduced photographically about × ⅔*

313

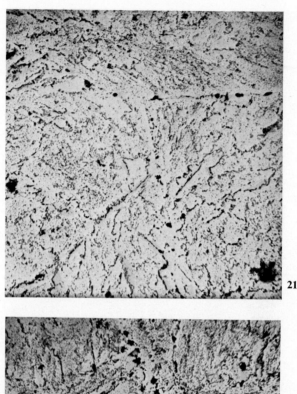

21a

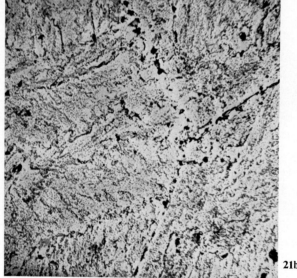

21b

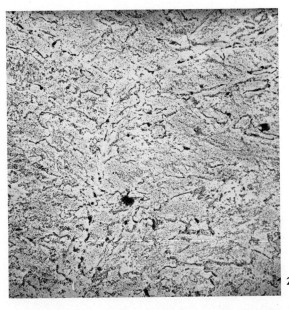

21c

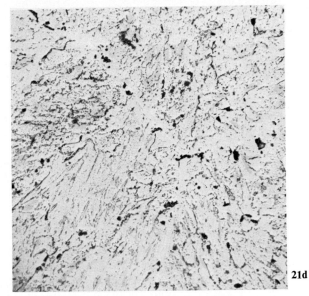

21d

a	22 tons/in²;	9 h;	28·8%	elongation
b	18 ,,	221 ,,	20·5	,,
c	16·5 ,,	1711 ,,	3·9	,,
d	13 ,,	6842 ,,	1·9	,,

21 *Electron micrographs of extraction replicas from series of creep tests at 550°C*
Treatment: 1150°C AC/730°C (4 h) AC ×5000

In each case the structures comprise large chromium carbide particles at the grain boundaries and a fine dispersion of small particles, most probably vanadium carbide (V_4C_3) throughout the grains. There was slight preferential precipitation of carbides at the sub-grain boundaries. The matrix immediately bordering the grain boundaries was essentially free from precipitates, at all stages of testing. There did not appear to be any outstanding differences between these structures despite the extensive differences of rupture-duration and ductility. The most dense precipitation occurred in the micrograph of the 1711 h specimen whilst agglomeration of the finer precipitates appeared to have commenced after 6842 h. These effects were, however, of such a subsidiary character as to raise the question of reproducibility in preparation of the replicas.

DISCUSSION OF RESULTS

The observation that the creep properties of bar material were so closely dependent on the size of the original ingot was a rather unexpected outcome of the investigations. The mechanism underlying this behaviour is likely to be extremely complex and it is to be expected that metallic micro-segregation (coring of the original dendritic pattern) will play a notable part, as also may the size and distribution of non-metallic inclusions. Metallographic comparison of bar specimens representing the various sizes of ingot failed to supply sufficient evidence on which to base a factual explanation. From a design point of view, however, the effect may warrant consideration in cases where the application requires the use of an unusually large ingot.

It has been shown (Fig.4) that the initial heat treatment of the steel has a marked effect on the short-time creep rupture properties. The treatment (1150°C AC/685°C AC) which gives the optimum short-time rupture strength leads to an inherently low ductility and this is considered to derive from the combination of a continuous chain of grain boundary carbides (Cr_7C_3) with intra-granular stiffening by finely dispersed V_4C_3, as illustrated in Fig.18. This low ductility is noticeable at all test durations whether these be of the order of a few hours or as long as 10000 h and is associated with low notch-strength.

An improvement of the short-time rupture ductility is brought about by increasing the tempering temperature to 730°C (i.e. 1150°C AC/730°C AC) but this enhanced condition deteriorates progressively with increasing duration of testing and, at the same time, the creep properties are less satisfactory. With notched specimens however, the increase in tempering temperature brings about a

316

marked improvement in the rupture strength, at least for durations up to about 50000 h (Fig.5). At the same time, the onset of notch-weakening is displaced to longer durations and there is evidence of a recovery of notch strength at lower stresses. A similar behaviour is noticed if normalizing is followed by an oil-quenching treatment. The manner in which the additional oil quenching improves the notch strength for a given tempering treatment will be seen by comparing the 1150°C AC/685°C AC and the 1150°C AC/1060°C OQ/685°C AC treatments which are shown in Fig.5. Increasing the tempering temperature of the oil-hardened specimens again improves the rupture ductility at short and intermediate durations, but the values do not attain those of specimens tempered at 730°C after normalizing only.

Carbon replicas of the series of creep specimens which showed the greatest transition from ductile to brittle fracture with increasing duration of testing were examined by electron-microscopy, but this approach did not disclose any notable alteration of the structure during the course of creep. As regards the optical microstructure, the effect of the various heat treatments is seen principally in the distribution of the grain boundary carbides, the more nearly continuous carbide networks being generally associated with the poorer ductilities. For a stated tempering temperature, oil quenching markedly improves the ductility and there is a corresponding suppression of grain boundary precipitation (cf. Figs.18 and 20). Continuous grain boundary films were present after normalizing and tempering at 685°C and may be partly responsible for both the poor initial ductility and the improved creep resistance, though the less heavily tempered matrix must obviously contribute to these effects.

An outstanding feature of all the long-term tests has been the occurrence within the specimens of small intergranular cracks, whose presence has been detected even at considerable distances away from the position of the final fracture; a typical example is shown in Fig.19c. An alternative means of representing creep data is that of the log strain/rate method of plotting (details of the method and its usefulness have been described by Glen[9]) and a selection of creep curves from the longer term tests are plotted in this manner in Fig.22. It will be noticed that the later stages of these curves are characterized by large numbers of fluctuations of the rate at which the deformation proceeds. It may also be pointed out, although the justification is admittedly slight, that the fluctuations become more conspicuous with increased duration of the test (cf. the 1711 h and 9195 h curves of Fig.22). In the investigations carried out by Glen, gradual changes of rate occurred and these

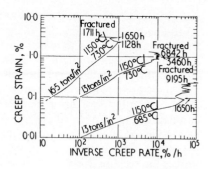

22 *Logarithmic plot of creep strain and inverse creep rate for three tests at 550°C*

he ascribed to the precipitation of carbides during the course of the tests. In the present instance, the changes are much more abrupt and it seems probable that they correspond to the formation of the numerous intergranular micro-cracks to which reference has been made. The strain/rate method of plotting appears, therefore, to offer a notable advantage by emphasizing details of the onset of the fracturing process which are not readily discernible in the conventional long-term creep curve (cf. Figs.22 and 23). The occurrence of intergranular cracking has been recorded by numbers of investigators[10,11] and the theory has been advanced that it arises from the diffusion of vacancies to the intergranular positions.[12,13] This simple concept has been analysed in detail by McLean[14] who subdivides intergranular cracks into those which commence at grain corners and others which develop by link-up of grain-boundary cavities. In each circumstance, stress concentrations are the favoured nucleating force but whereas the growth of the grain corner defects is predominantly a stress effect, that of the purely boundary defects may be significantly assisted by diffusion transport of vacancies.

It is well recognized that a creep-resisting steel derives much of its peculiar property from the fact that it is not initially in an equilibrium condition. The formation of alloy carbides by diffusion is a lengthy process and the choice of alloying of this class of steels is made with deliberate intent to promote protracted carbide reactions. X-ray crystallographic examination of electrolytic residues has

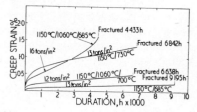

23 *Long term creep curves for 3%Cr–Mo–W–V steel at 550°C*

318

confirmed the predominant carbide type throughout this series of tests to be V_4C_3 and a similar conclusion was reached by Baker and Nutting[15] who examined unstressed samples of the steel after various normalizing and tempering treatments. Chromium carbide also was detected in the present tests and metallographic examination showed it to be located particularly at the large angle grain boundaries, with lesser amounts at those of the sub-grains. At these positions it may be expected to affect the initial mechanical properties of the steel and also to supply a fixed contribution to the creep strength, but the particles were large and incoherent and it seems unlikely that their effect would change greatly during the course of creep. The amount of these carbides accounted for only a small fraction of the total chromium content, most of which was retained in solid solution in the matrix. Vanadium, on the other hand, favours fine intra-granular carbide precipitation which initially is coherent with the ferritic matrix, and its continued precipitation during the course of creep will cause re-stiffening of the grains until the supersaturation has been substantially relieved. Under these circumstances the intra-granular strains which arise continually from the slip processes will be transmitted to positions within the grain boundaries as cumulative stress concentrations and misfits. It seems inevitable that a continuous process of this type must favour rupture at the boundaries and accumulated vacancies or misfits may well provide the foci from which this rupture finally develops; the presence of etch-pits in many of the grain boundaries of Fig.19c is suggestive of this process. Elsewhere on this micro-section various stages of the sequence of growth and coalescence of cavities to form distinct cracks were to be seen, as also was the grain corner type of crack.

Figure 19c also depicts extensive intergranular cracking accompanied by perceptible grain rotation and it appears at first sight that the steel is displaying simultaneously the characteristics of both brittleness and ductility. Pronounced intra-granular stress relaxation must, however, have followed the observed cracking and it is suggested that the consequent renewal of glide has facilitated grain rotation without further loss of intergranular cohesion, possibly by the process of polygonization. An additional consequence of intra-granular relaxation is evidenced in Figs.19c and d by the blunted ends of many of the cracks which terminate at unfavourably oriented grain boundaries; in order to accommodate this terminal strain, boundary sliding must have occurred, again indicating that there has not been an intrinsic embrittlement of the structure.

While the rupture ductility commonly falls as durations increase, at relatively long durations (low stresses) a fresh effect frequently makes its appearance and the rupture ductility begins to recover. This behaviour has been illustrated particularly clearly by Brown et al.[16] and by Glen.[17] From the trend of the present series of tests it is believed that this point is reached at durations of the order of 10 000 h and support for this view is forthcoming from current work at higher temperatures (650° and 600°C) in which the values of creep ductility are showing minima at times of 700 to 1 500 h.

The behaviour of a specimen on which the stress was increased after an initial period of steady testing (Fig.17) is of particular interest. This alteration markedly affected the manner of deformation and the specimen proceeded to fracture with enhanced ductility, exceeding that of a fresh sample tested throughout at the higher stress. It is evident, first, that the initial period of creep (20 000 h at $9\frac{1}{2}$ tons/in²) had not created intrinsic embrittlement of the grain boundaries; secondly, that within the matrix an alteration had occurred such that triggering by an increase of the applied load permitted enhanced glide. Yet before increasing the load the initial creep was proceeding steadily without any indication of an increased rate (Table III). An explanation based simply upon softening of the matrix by over-ageing is not compatible with the steady rate of the initial creep but it appears feasible to explain the behaviour by the additional consideration of precipitation of carbides at critical lattice sites during the course of deformation. In this manner a spatial network of 'locked' dislocations would be built up, contributing additional strengthening during the steady-state creep. At the close of the 20 000 h period, supersaturation of the matrix with readily diffusible alloy atoms would have been largely relieved and, in these circumstances, the increased load would re-activate the immobile dislocations with little opportunity for renewal of the locking mechanism. The freshly loaded comparison specimen, on the other hand, would be exposed to the entire supersaturation of the tempered but otherwise unaged matrix, and it is probable that its deformation would not only be restricted by the more active centres for VC/V_4C_3 precipitation but also by other 'short-term' carbides residual from the prior heat treatment.

It is interesting to consider the implication of this effect, since it apparently provides a 'safety valve' in the specific eventuality of accidental overloading. In this particular circumstance, the reserve of ductility is evidently available even though the steady state creep may be destined to low rupture-ductility.

Throughout these considerations attention has been directed particularly towards the carbide (or corresponding nitride) type VC/V_4C_3 as this has been conspicuous in each heat treated condition.

When considering dislocation locking, this view of the precipitation phenomena is undoubtedly over simplified. To close on a speculative note the writers consider that small amounts of tungsten, molybdenum, and chromium are probably also present as exceedingly fine specific carbides, whose formation stems from dislocation interactions at sites adjoining dissolved alloy atoms. In this manner, relatively minor thermal activation would suffice to displace alloy atoms into the dislocation network and the further acquisition of carbon (or nitrogen) atoms should present no difficulty. On the other hand, the growth of these precipitates would be severely restricted by the low diffusivities of the alloy atoms, and the problem of detection may readily exceed the capabilities of the X-ray diffraction method.

SUMMARY

1. It has been found that the creep properties of wrought bar vary systematically with the size of the original ingots, particularly at the longer creep durations.

2. The initial condition of heat treatment of the steel may markedly affect the short term creep properties, but these differences become less noticeable with longer durations (i.e. lower stresses). The heat treatments which give the better initial rupture ductilities lead to the highest notch rupture strengths at durations of about 10000 h.

3. The introduction of a notch is found to bring about short term notch strengthening in most cases. With increasing duration the notched and plain creep curves finally cross and the steel becomes notch weakened. The extent of notch weakening is apparently greater for those heat treated conditions which show the lower plain rupture ductilities. The onset of notch weakening has generally occurred at durations corresponding to a rupture elongation of about 9% (gauge length=10×dia.) and is displaced to shorter durations as the tempering temperature is reduced. For a stated tempering treatment notch sensitivity is reduced by the introduction of an oil-quenching treatment before tempering.

4. Rupture elongations fall progressively with increased duration of testing (i.e. lower stresses). There are indications that this effect may attain a minimum and, at extremely long durations, experience a recovery.

5. Internal intergranular cracking at positions remote from that of the final fracture has been associated with all the long term tests and the number of these cracks is seen to increase with duration of testing. This mode of cracking has been studied theoretically by numbers of investigators and the nature of the present investigations

has not been such as to throw direct light on this problem. It is believed, however, that stiffening of the grains by continued precipitation of carbides during the course of the creep test will favour this type of breakdown.

6. Overloading of a specimen after a protracted period of steady state creep, during which a few intergranular cracks had formed, appeared to confirm that there had been no intrinsic embrittlement of the grain boundaries. This specimen continued to deform with enhanced ductility, leading to the interesting speculation that the steel possesses a reserve of ductility which can be tapped in the specific circumstance of accidental overloading.

ACKNOWLEDGMENTS

The authors wish to express their gratitude to Dr J. M. Cairney, Dr B. J. Piearcey, Mr C. V. Mills, and to other colleagues in the Research Department of Messrs Hadfields Ltd for their assistance in the experimental investigations; also to the Metallurgical Department (Sheffield University) for kindly providing electron microscopical facilities.

REFERENCES

1. G. WOOD and J. R. RAIT: *Iron Coal Trades Rev.*, 1949, **158**, 221–281.
2. E. W. COLBECK and J. R. RAIT, in 'Symposium on high-temperature steels and alloys for gas turbines', *ISI Spec. Rep.* no.43, 1951.
3. R. W. BAILEY: *Proc. IME*, 1928, **144**, 417–452.
4. F. REINCKE: Mitt *Verein. Grosskessel*, 1937, **65**, 338–359.
5. G. SACHS and W. F. BROWN: 'Symposium on strength and ductility of metals at elevated temperatures, 1952', ASTM Spec. Tech. Pub. no. 128, 1953, 6.
6. D. P. NEWMAN et al.: *Proc. ASTM*, 1953, **53**, 677–689.
7. E. A. DAVIES and M. J. MANJOINE: 'Symposium on strength and ductility of metals at elevated temperatures, 1952', 67, *op. cit.*
8. W. SIEGFRIED: *JISI*, 1947, **156**, 189–207.
9. J. GLEN: *ibid*, 1958, **189**, 333–343.
10. A. H. SULLY: 'Metallic creep', 1949, London, Butterworth.
11. 'Symposium on creep and fracture at high temperatures, 1954', Proceedings, 1956, London National Physical Laboratory.
12. C. Crussard and J. Friedel: *ibid.*, 243–262.
13. J. N. GREENWOOD: *JISI*, 1954, **176**, 267–269.
14. D. McLEAN: 'Symposium on vacancies and other point defects in metals and alloys,' Inst. Metals Monograph and Report Series no. 23, 1959, 159–198.
15. R. G. BAKER and J. NUTTING: 'Precipitation processes in steels', *ISI Spec. Rep.* no 64, 1959, 1–22.
16. W. F. BROWN et al.: ASTM Spec. Tech. Pub. no 128, 1953, 25.
17. J. GLEN: *JISI*, 1955, **179**, 320–336.
18. H. KRAINER: *Arch. Eisenhütt.* 1950, **21**, 33–41.

The variability of the creep resistance of mild steel

N. P. Allen, M. Met., D. Sc., F.I.M., F.R.S., and
L. M. T. Hopkin, Ph.D., A.R.S.M., A.I.M.

It has been widely accepted that the creep resistance of mild steel is governed by the amount of nitrogen held in solution in the ferrite which in turn is affected by the aluminium content. The results of past NPL work are not consistent with this view. Further investigation has shown that the creep resistance of high purity iron is unaffected by the presence of 0·015% in solid solution at the creep test temperature of 450°C. The creep resistance of these materials is markedly inferior to that of commercial mild steel, indicating that nitrogen content is not the controlling factor. Transmission electron micrographs of commercial mild steels of low and high aluminium contents in a condition immediately before loading in creep tests reveal no precipitates on disclocations which might be expected to confer creep resistance. It is concluded that the effect of aluminium is not yet known.

INTRODUCTION

THE VARIABILITY of the creep resistance of mild steel has been known and studied for many years, and for the purposes of control the phenomenon may be considered to be well understood. The primary cause of variability is the addition of excessive amounts of aluminium to the steel during the finishing stages, and the amounts which are excessive depend to some extent upon the quantities of oxygen and nitrogen present in the steel when the addition is made. Steels to which no aluminium has been added, or to which the aluminium additions have been sufficiently cautious, exhibit a relatively high standard of creep resistance and their creep resistance is not very greatly affected by variations of thermal and mechanical treatment. This is not to say that their creep resistance cannot be altered, for all ferritic steels will become weaker if heated sufficiently long at a

Dr Allen is Superintendent, and Dr Hopkin is Principal Scientific Officer of the Metallurgy Division, National Physical Laboratory, Teddington, Middlesex.

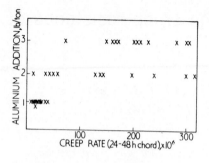

1 *Effect of aluminium additions on low-carbon steel superheater tubes. Tests at 8 tons/in² at 450°C*

temperature just below the critical range, and all steels will have their creep resistance improved by cold work, provided the temperature at which their creep is tested is kept sufficiently low; but special steps have to be taken to alter their creep resistance appreciably. Steels to which large additions of aluminium have been made, on the other hand, have a relatively low standard of creep resistance, and their creep resistance is deeply influenced by a number of factors that do not seriously affect aluminium-free steels.

This relative insensitivity of low aluminium steels was well illustrated in a series of tests on low carbon steel superheater tubes, reported by Herbert and Jenkinson.[1] Three steels were made identical in all respects except for the final aluminium additions, which were respectively 1, 2, and 3 lb of aluminium per ton. Tubes of each steel were tested in 12 different conditions,* and the creep rates, in a standard test under 8 tons/in² at 450°C, were as shown in Fig.1. These were short time tests, but there is ample evidence that similar differences would have been shown in long time tests.[2]

The relative insensitivity of aluminium-free steels is also illustrated in Fig.2 plotted from data in the extensive papers by Jenkins and Tapsell.[3] In the diagram a comparison is made between the creep rates of two mild steels, to which respectively 0·3 and 2·3 lb/ton of aluminium had been added, after they had been normalized at 1100°C, and reheated for 15 min to the temperatures indicated. The low-aluminium steel was practically unaffected by the heat treatment, but the high aluminium steel lost significantly in creep resistance on being heated to 600°C, was very seriously affected at temperatures between 800° and 950°C, and gradually recovered on heating to higher temperatures.

* Each steel was received in three conditions: as-pilgered, hot reduced, and cold drawn. Tests were made in the as-received condition and after the following heat treatments: 675°C 15 min AC, 925°C 15 min slow cool to 500°C in 5 h AC, and 925°C 15 min AC.

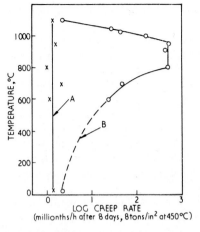

A   0·3 lb Al/ton, 0·17%C,
    0·72%Mn, 0·20%Si,
    0·001 sol.Al, 0·004% total N
B   2·3 lb Al/ton, 0·16%C,
    0·46%Mn, 0·005%Si,
    0·024% sol.Al,
    0·003% total N

2 *Effect of heat treatment following
normalizing from 1100°C*

This behaviour has suggested that in the high-aluminium steel
something is precipitated between 600° and 900°C, which causes a
lowering of the creep resistance, and that the precipitate is redis-
solved above 900°C. The suggestion is strengthened by the fact that
the creep resistance of the high-aluminium steel is lowered by slow
cooling from 1100° to 600°C, whilst that of the low-aluminium
steel is practically unaltered (Fig.3). Nevertheless, the creep resistance of the low-aluminium steel is lowered by prolonged heating
around 650°C, which eventually brings about spheroidization of the
carbides.[3]

It is probable that these effects of aluminium additions, which
were first noticed in low-carbon mild steels for tubes, are found in

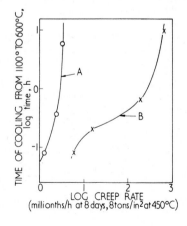

A   0·3 lb Al/ton
B   2·3 lb Al/ton

3 *Effect of rate of cooling*

low-alloy steels generally. In the recent symposium on steels for reactor pressure vessels, the same general behaviour was reported in plate steels of high manganese to carbon ratio,[4] though the creep resistance of the 1.5% Mn steels is generally somewhat higher than that of the older mild steels with about 0.5% Mn. Table I contains some hitherto unpublished data by Jenkins, showing that 0.5% Mo steels containing 0.01% or more of soluble aluminium may have unusually high creep rates in the normalized condition, may be sensitive to the normalizing temperature in the same way as mild steels, and also be unusually sensitive to prolonged heating at 650°C. Pearson and de Lippa[5] also noted that the addition of aluminium to Ni–Mo steels resulted in a deterioration of creep resistance.

In view of the known grain refining effects of aluminium additions, it was natural to attempt to associate the loss of creep resistance with the decreased austenitic grain size, but exhaustive experiments failed to establish any clear connection between the microstructure of the steel, as revealed by the optical microscope, and the creep

TABLE I   **Analyses and Creep Resistance of 0.5% Mo Steels**

			Weight %		
Element	FHA_{1-3}	FZW	HKD_{1-11}	KPB	LFK
C	0·11	0·09	0·18	0·15	0·23
Cr	0·16	0·28	0·086	0·086	0·08
Mo	0·52	0·49	0·51	0·53	0·45
V	nil	<0·01	0·002	nil	0·008
Al (sol)	0·002	0·039	0·0035	0·010	0·0015
Al (insol)	<0·001	0·005	<0·001	0·015	<0·001
N_2 Vacuum fusion	0·006	0·006	0·004	0·003	0·003

		Creep rate in millionths per hour at 200 h in tests at 550°C, 9 tons/in²			
As received	22	1·8	5·2	32	1·9
N 925°C	6	21	4·5	40	1·5
N 975°C	9	4·3	1·7	20	4·0
N 1100°C	...	2·1	2·8	4·0	3·9
1100°C+60 days 650°C	...	>4000	50	>4000	80
N+14 days 625°C	68	>4000	15	>4000	27

resistance. On the other hand, the suggestion that the formation of a precipitate is concerned has received support from the observation that aluminium nitride can be detected in aluminium-killed mild steel, and is taken into solution when the steel is heated to the temperature to which it must be heated in order to improve its creep strength. Bardgett and Gemmill established a relationship between the creep resistance and the aluminium nitride content of one of the steels studied by them.[6]

More recently the view has been offered, and widely accepted, that the creep resistance of mild steel is governed not by the amount of aluminium nitride present in the steel but by the amount of nitrogen held in solution in the ferrite,[7] and the curve shown in Fig.4 has been put forward as representing the relationship between the 'active nitrogen content' (that is, the total nitrogen minus the nitrogen present as aluminium nitride, or in the case of alloy steels, as other insoluble nitrides capable of being extracted from the steel) and the creep rate as observed between the 24th and 48th hour of a test under a stress of 8 tons/in^2 at 450°C. It is therefore of interest to look back at some of the older work to see how far it can be explained in terms of this relationship.

Difficulties arise immediately on account of the variations of testing procedure that, for good reasons, have been adopted at different times during past years, but the effects of these variations can often be reasonably closely estimated. The total nitrogen contents of the steels, and their soluble aluminium contents are generally available, and though the aluminium nitride contents have not been determined, progress can be made on the assumption that if the steel has been

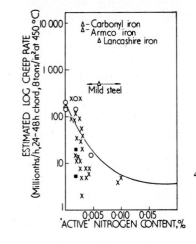

X Jenkins and Tapsell
O Herbert and Jenkinson
△ Jenkins and Mellor

4 *Effect of active nitrogen on creep resistance*

heated to a high temperature and fairly rapidly cooled the majority of the nitrogen will be in solid solution, whereas if it has been normalized at a temperature about 900°C an amount of nitrogen equal to about one tenth of the amount of soluble aluminium will have been precipitated as aluminium nitride, as was found by Bardgett and Gemmill. [6]

In this way the points represented by crosses in Fig.4 have been obtained from the work of Jenkins and Tapsell, and those represented by circles from the work of Herbert and Jenkinson. The distribution of points is not adequately represented by the curve: clearly steels containing between 0·002 and 0·003% of active nitrogen may have any creep rate between 2 and 300 millionths per hour under the specified conditions.

The points represented by triangles are obtained from a paper by Jenkins and Mellor, [8] and relate to samples of Swedish Lancashire iron, Carbonyl iron, and Armco iron, which were of low carbon content (about 0·02%). No aluminium will have been added to the Swedish Lancashire iron and the Carbonyl iron during manufacture. It is likely that aluminium was added to the Armco iron, but its oxygen content was so high that no soluble aluminium can have been present. The nitrogen in these samples (which was appreciable) was therefore in solid solution in the active form. The creep tests were not in every case made under 8 tons/in² at 450°C, but sufficient tests at 450°C were made to permit a fairly close estimate of the behaviour under 8 tons/in², and in every case the creep rate was extremely high. It may be considered unfair to compare irons of low-carbon and manganese contents with ordinary mild steels, but at least these results show that the strengthening effect of nitrogen in solid solution in ferrite is negligible compared with that of quite ordinary quantities of carbon and manganese.

The pure iron made in recent years at NPL has very low creep resistance, and one creep curve is available, made at 2·5 tons/in² at 550°C, on an iron containing 0·01%N. This is compared in Fig.5 with that of a similar iron low in nitrogen, tested under the same conditions. The complete analyses of both irons are given. At this temperature the nitrogen would certainly have been in solid solution, and it appears that under these conditions of testing the dissolved nitrogen has very little effect.

These results give reason to question the emphasis that has recently been placed on the effect of dissolved nitrogen on the creep strength of steel, and in view of the importance of this matter a fuller investigation of the influence of dissolved nitrogen in ferrite has been undertaken. Two 50-lb ingots of iron were made in the

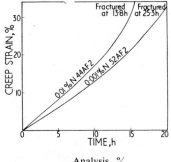

5 *Effect of nitrogen in solid solution, $2\frac{1}{2}$ tons/in² at 550°C*

	Analysis, %				
	52AF2	44AF2		52AF2	44AF2
C	0·002	0·004₃	Cr	0·001	ND
Si	0·003	0·003	Cu	0·004	ND
S	0·005	0·003₆	Al	0·002	0·004
P	0·001	ND	O₂	0·0046	0·001₃
Mn	<0·005	ND	N₂	0·0016	0·01
Ni	0·007	ND	H₂	<0·000005	<0·000005

NPL vacuum induction furnace, one of which was cast under a low pressure of hydrogen, giving material of the normal standard of purity obtained in NPL iron, containing 0·0013%N, whilst the other was exposed before casting to nitrogen under $\frac{1}{2}$ atm pressure, with the result that the nitrogen content of the ingot was 0·015%. Both ingots were rolled to $\frac{5}{8}$in dia. bar, normalized at 950°C and subjected to creep tests under stresses of 2, 4, and 6 tons/in² at 450°C. The results of these tests are shown as log strain/log time curves in Fig.6, from which it is seen that again there is no significant difference in the creep resistance of the nitrogen-free and nitrogen-containing material. At 450°C the whole of the nitrogen in both samples would have been in solid solution, and it is impossible to avoid the conclusion that this quantity of nitrogen in solid solution has very little effect on the creep strength of pure iron.

Both these samples of iron were substantially weaker than either aluminium-free or aluminium-treated mild steel at 450°C. For comparison typical creep curves of each type of mild steel under 8 tons/in² at 450°C are given in Fig.6, and show that aluminium-treated steel has about the same creep rate under 8 tons/in² as pure iron under 4 tons/in² (curve *A*) whereas aluminium-free steel has a substantially lower creep rate (curve *B*). The strength of mild steel at 450°C must be attributable principally to factors other than nitrogen.

The creep resistance represented by curve *B* in Fig.6 can be attained in mild steel without the addition either of aluminium or of

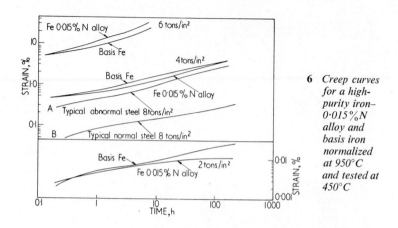

6 *Creep curves for a high-purity iron–0·015%N alloy and basis iron normalized at 950°C and tested at 450°C*

nitrogen, so that neither aluminium nor nitrogen is essential for this strength. Nevertheless, it is clear that when precipitation of aluminium nitride occurs, it is accompanied by a loss of creep resistance and it is of great interest to know how this loss of creep resistance comes about.

The optical study of the microstructure provides no explanation, since it has been well established that steels of equal grain size and pearlite structure but of different aluminium content may have widely differing creep resistances, and it seems reasonable to conclude that the pearlite network, though it may well contribute to the creep resistance of the steel, is not involved in the characteristic differences between aluminium-containing and aluminium-free steels.

Examination in the electron microscope by the transmission technique has as yet been equally unhelpful. At a magnification of ×45 000, precipitated particles can be seen in a normalized aluminium-containing steel of low creep resistance, which are not seen in a corresponding aluminium-free steel (Figs.7 and 8), and these are probably aluminium nitride. They are few and fairly widely spaced, and apparently would neither help nor appreciably hinder the passage of a dislocation. There is no difference between the two steels either in the spacing of the dislocations or in the quantity of precipitate associated with the dislocations. Indeed, evidence of the presence of precipitates other than the isolated particles found in the aluminium-containing steel is entirely lacking. This is true whether the steels are examined as normalized or after an additional 17-h heating at 450°C which typically precedes the application of load in the creep test, and this is significant, for the difference in creep

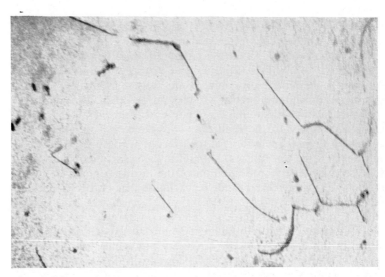

7 *Transmission electron micrograph of aluminium-bearing steel for which results are given in Figs.2 and 3. Normalized from 950°C and heated at 450°C for 17 h*

×45000

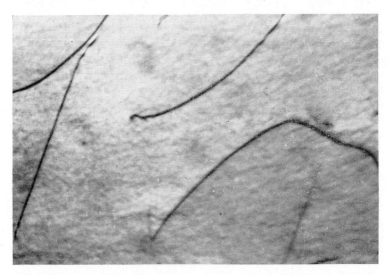

8 *Transmission electron micrograph of aluminium-free steel for which results are given in Figs.2 and 3. Normalized from 950°C and heated at 450°C for 17 h*

×45000

resistance between the two types of steel is perceptible immediately on loading, and certainly before the creep strain is as much as 0.1%.

It is to be concluded that the creep resistance influenced by the precipitation of aluminium nitride is due either to elements in solid solution in the ferrite, or to precipitates so small that they are not seen under a magnification of $\times 45000$, i.e. less than 10^{-6} cm dia.

If elements in solid solution are concerned, the effects cannot be attributed simply to the reduction of the nitrogen or aluminium content of the solid solution, for the effect of nitrogen by itself is not sufficiently large, and the reduction of the aluminium content of the solid solution due to precipitation of the nitride is relatively insignificant. The possibility cannot be excluded that nitrogen, in combination with some other constituent, such as carbon, silicon, manganese or aluminium, might have an effect on the creep resistance of the solid solution entirely different from that exerted by nitrogen alone. In this case it would be necessary to assume the presence in the solid solution of complexes of nitrogen with the second element and to assume also that these complexes, though few in number, are exceptionally powerful in retarding the movement of dislocations.

If small precipitates are concerned, an explanation of the influence of aluminium can be reached on the basis of the assumptions that the effective precipitates are nitrides, that they are smaller and more effective if formed near the creep testing temperature than at 800–900°C, that amounts of nitrogen of the order of 0.002% are significant, and that the function of soluble aluminium is to ensure that not even this small amount of precipitate nitrogen can be present unless the steel is cooled fairly rapidly from a temperature of the order of 1100°C. The figures for the effect of aluminium on the solubility of nitrogen in iron given in Table II, calculated by Kubaschewski, show that aluminium may be expected to have the desired effect. The table also shows that quantities of nitrogen of the order of 0.002% would not be expected to be precipitated from pure iron at 450°C, but that they might be precipitated if as little as 0.2% Si were present. This might have a bearing on the great difference between the creep resistance of pure iron and that of mild steel. But it is also possible to think that the effective precipitates are carbides and that the influence of precipitated aluminium nitride is principally to modify the form in which the carbide is precipitated by a nucleating action similar to that which Bain has demonstrated in the formation of pearlite nodules in imperfectly quenched aluminium-killed steels.[9] A theory of this kind would be consistent with the fact that the higher creep resistance is always obtained in mild steels of low nitrogen content when the aluminium content is low.

TABLE II Influence of aluminium, silicon, and manganese on the solubility of nitrogen in iron (calculated by Kubaschewski)

Concentration of solute	Precipitate	Nitrogen content of α or γ solid solution, wt-%			
		450°C	650°C	950°C	1150°C
Pure iron	Fe_4 N	0·04	0·23	...	...
0·001%Al		$2·2 \times 10^{-13}$	$8·5 \times 10^{-9}$	$4·5 \times 10^{-4}$	0·016
0·01%Al	Al N	$2·2 \times 10^{-14}$	$8·5 \times 10^{-10}$	$4·5 \times 10^{-5}$	0·0016
0·1%Al		$2·2 \times 10^{-15}$	$8·5 \times 10^{-11}$	$4·5 \times 10^{-6}$	$1·6 \times 10^{-4}$
0·2%Si	Si_3 N_4	$4·8 \times 10^{-7}$	$1·4 \times 10^{-4}$	$9·8 \times 10^{-2}$	0·59
0·5%Si		$2·4 \times 10^{-7}$	7×10^{-5}	$4·8 \times 10^{-2}$	0·3
0·5%Mn	Mn_4 N	0·032	...	...	...
1·5%Mn		$4·1 \times 10^{-4}$	...	...	...

All these possibilities are involved, and unsupported by experimental evidence, but simple explanations will not meet the known facts. It must be admitted that the true cause of the influence of aluminium on the creep resistance of mild steel is not yet known. Experiments on the influence of the variables concerned on the directly observed rate of movement of dislocations under constant stress are much to be desired.

ACKNOWLEDGMENT

The work described has been carried out as part of the general research programme of the National Physical Laboratory and this paper is published by permission of the Director of the Laboratory.

REFERENCES

1. D. C. HERBERT and E. A. JENKINSON: *Trans. NE Coast Inst. Eng. Ship.*, 1953, **69**, 27–44.
2. A. I. SMITH et al.: *Inst. Mech. Eng.* Preprint Aug. 1960.
3. C. H. M. JENKINS and H. J. TAPSELL: *JISI*, 1952, **171**, 359–371.
4. K. J. IRVINE and J. D. MURRAY, in: 'Symposium on steels for reactor pressure circuits', *ISI Spec. Rep.* no.69, 1961.
5. T. F. PEARSON and M. Z. DE LIPPA: *ibid.*
6. W. E. BARDGETT and M. G. GEMMILL: *JISI*, 1955, **179**, 211–219.
7. W. E. BARDGETT: Institution of Metallurgists refresher course, 1957.
8. C. H. M. JENKINS and G. A. MELLOR: Unpublished work.
9. E. C. BAIN: *JISI*, 1938, (II) 33P–56P.

Discussion 3

The six preceding papers were presented and discussed at this session.

Mr J. Johnson (AEI Manchester Ltd): The papers, admirably and concisely presented, constituted between them a mental meal which requires some time for digestion and even more for assimilation. The range is wide. It covers the carbon–manganese steels, some low alloy creep-resisting steels, and austenitic materials. In consequence, the paper presents a useful cross-section of the materials with which the engineer, working in the fields of high steam or gas temperatures, must clothe his future designs.

In a number of instances, it is clearly stated, and in others it can be inferred, that the information at present available provides more questions than answers. It is well to remember that, since these are materials currently going into service under conditions of maximum exploitation of their creep strength, all those questions relating to long-term creep ductility will have been answered favourably or unfavourably within the next two decades.

The paper of Toft and Marsden is welcomed for its attempt to correlate the behaviour of materials in service with experimental creep results, and we must hope that more such papers will be forthcoming, perhaps with more specific knowledge of the initial conditions of the material than was, understandably, available in the present case.

It is important to realize that this work, covering 100 000 h of service life at temperatures above 450°C, could not have been undertaken earlier, but it is equally important that we should grasp the opportunity for further excursions of this kind from now on. We can only hope that material from redundant plant, carrying the marks of 100 000 h in service, will not be allowed to escape full examination.

Evidence of embrittlement of the steels as would be shown by low elongations even at comparatively short rupture times seem to be absent and there is evidently no serious damaging effects from strain-induced precipitation in these steels in service. Toft and Marsden have attributed this to the low stresses imposed on superheater tubes in service, but this is a controversial point.

Glen and his associates have made available useful data on the effect of long-time tempering on silicon-killed steels, and the times involved are disconcertingly realistic in terms of tempering or stress-relieving cycles likely to be used. Does this point to the need for more stringent control of silicon content or are we to demand minimum contents of nitrogen in specifications for this type of steel, or of such minor constituents as normally come within the general term of residuals?

From the comfortable acceptance in the paper by Glen and his associates that the reduction in creep strength of steels containing excessive amounts of aluminium is related to the loss of active nitrogen, and from Irvine's assertion that it is the precipitation of aluminium nitride at the grain boundaries that affects the creep strength of aluminium-killed steels, we have the contrary opinion of Allen and Hopkin that the active nitrogen content is not a major factor in determining the creep rate in carbon–manganese steels, and that, in fact, the effect of variation of nitrogen content on pure iron is negligible in the absence of other factors. We might question the justification of Allen and Hopkin in bulking the data given in Fig.4 of their paper, where the variation in creep rate for a given content of nitrogen is greater than the cast-to-cast scatter for a steel of one specific type.

Allen and Hopkin accept the possibility that the role of nitrogen may be in forming complexes or nitrides with other minor constituents in the steel as coherent precipitates. This would emphasize the need, as was pointed out by Glen, for experimental techniques that permit the study of precipitates earlier than the stage at which they come within the present range of the electron microscope.

The long-term creep behaviour of 3%Cr–Mo–V–W steels must be of vital interest to design engineers interested in relatively large forgings, adequate room temperature strength and creep resistance, in applications which will demand a much longer life than that for which the steel has previously found application.

A number of questions are raised by this interesting and provocative paper. What were the hot tensile properties of the samples from the ingots used in Part 2? It is notable that the differences in creep strain at 300 h are all associated with the magnitude of the initial strain.

What is the explanation of the effect of ingot size on the creep properties? How far do they expect us to extrapolate the curve in Fig.2 towards the ingot sizes likely to be in use for heavy engineering applications?

Is the behaviour of the material for a 44-in dia. ingot anomalous? The implication in the results reported is of an ingot size effect which remains as an inherent property independent of subsequent forging operations or of heat treatment. It is noticeable, incidentally, that the molybdenum content varies over a 2:1 ratio in these casts and is approximately in the inverse order of ingot size. In fact, a reasonably convincing picture of creep strain dependency with molybdenum content could be plotted with no anomalous behaviour attributed to the large ingot material. This is of course an over-simplification: is the conclusion in the paper equally over-simplified?

What must we make of the statements facing each other on pages 306 and 307? The first accepts an indication that an embrittling mechanism is operative; the second a confirmation that the decrease in rupture ductility with increased duration is not due to embrittlement.

We are interested in all evidence of embrittlement with these steels. They originated in Germany where they are at present regarded with great suspicion because of their long-term low ductility and the deterioration of impact strength. These characteristics are related to the initial tensile properties and presumably to the initial structure.

It is interesting to see that, at all durations, we have low ductility and low impact after the 1150°, 685°C treatment, but not after tempering at 730°C, which has the best ductility and impact for short-term creep.

It is noted that on both optical and electron micrographs the structure is described as well defined grain boundaries with marked grain boundary carbides, and a fine dispersion of vanadium carbide in the matrix. Why, then, the explanation of low ductility at all times of the 685°C tempered material in terms of this combination?

It would be interesting to know if Hodkin et al. have done any work on specimens aged without stress at 550°C before creep testing in order to throw more light on the unexpected ductility in the specimen tested at 16·5 tons/in² after previously being tested for 2 000 h at 9·5 tons/in². The creep ductility on such specimens would be enlightening.

In connexion with the paper by Kirkby and Truman, the authors are frank in their assessment that the present data are controversial and pose many questions, but one cannot resist the feeling that more has been extracted from the data than is justified. Further evidence provided by Truman in his presentation suggests that they are, in fact, extending their results beyond 1000 h. This would in fact be the information needed to justify the belief that the curves in Figs. 9–12 do continue downwards as drawn. It would be more difficult to explain a similarity in behaviour of pipe material treated at 1050°C with bar material treated at 1350°C, which would largely discount the possibility of a similar mechanism of solution as is accepted for the short-term ductility pattern.

Dr K. J. Irvine (The United Steel Companies Ltd): I should like to refer to the paper by Allen and Hopkin, which seems to be in conflict with our own work. The main point is stated in their introduction as follows: 'It has been widely accepted that the creep resistance of mild steel is governed by the amount of nitrogen held in solution in the ferrite, which in turn is affected by the aluminium content. The results of past NPL work is not consistent with this view'. However, I am not sure that they are correct in this deduction. I should first like to emphasize that I am talking about mild steel, and I do not think that the work they refer to on pure iron is relevant.

Turning to their results for mild steel, however, it is surely wrong for them to base their conclusions on assumed values on nitrogen. Their paper states 'Although the aluminium nitride contents have not been determined, progress can be made on the assumption that if the steel has been heated to a high temperature, and fairly rapidly cooled, the majority of the nitrogen will be in solid solution, whereas if it has been normalized at a temperature of about 900°C an amount of nitrogen equal to about $\frac{1}{10}$ of the amount of soluble aluminium will have been precipitated as aluminium nitride'. I do not think that they are justified in their assumption and in fact our work shows quite definitely that this assumption is wrong. The fact remains that there has been a considerable amount of work published in the last year by several authors, which shows the controlling influence of the active nitrogen content on the creep properties of mild steel. I feel that any attempt to challenge this viewpoint should be backed by experimental work in which accurate nitrogen contents have been obtained.

Mr J. D. Murray (The United Steel Companies Ltd): In last year's symposium on steels for reactor pressure vessels,* the subject of carbon steels was given a good airing. The conclusion from that discussion was that the variable creep resistance of carbon steel was due to the variation in active nitrogen content. This was true whether the steel had been killed with either aluminium or silicon or a mixture of the two. At this session we have had a further paper from Glen and his co-workers which confirms this finding. I would repeat that all this evidence has been presented for carbon steel, which implies that the material contains a certain amount of carbon and manganese. Within the making range of these steels, variation in these elements has a minor effect on the creep strength compared with the effect brought about by variation in the active nitrogen content.

Before discussing the NPL paper, it might be advisable to recall the main claims that have been put forward with respect to the nitrogen theory. A paper by Bardgett and Gemmill showed that the creep resistance could be varied by variation of the aluminium nitride content. It should be remembered that, in this case, only one cast of steel was examined in this context and therefore there was a constant total nitrogen content. Consequently, as the aluminium nitride content was increased, the amount of active nitrogen in the steel decreased.

It became clear from subsequent work in which the total nitrogen content

* 'Steels for reactor pressure circuits', *ISI Spec. Rep. No. 69*, 1961.

336

was varied, that there was no relationship between aluminium nitride and creep resistance. Irrespective of the total nitrogen content or the soluble aluminium content, there was a relationship between active nitrogen content and creep resistance.

Probably one of the most important features that has been shown is that the nitrogen effect is dependent upon the strain rate and temperature of the test. At 250°C there is a very marked effect in tensile tests. At 450°C there is no effect in tensile tests and no effect in stress to rupture tests of less than 2000 h duration. Once again, in these latter tests the strain rate is high. It is only in creep tests at 450°C where the strain rate is relatively low that the effect is observed. It is clear from this evidence that there is a critical strain rate at each temperature at which the effect becomes marked, and this behaviour is in keeping with an atmosphere effect. Explanations for the behaviour have been given on this basis. Further evidence for the atmosphere effect have been obtained from microscopical examination with the electron microscope of specimens tested for times up to 40000 h. In this examination no evidence of precipitation has been noted.

On the basis of this work, production casts of carbon steel which has been heavily killed with aluminium have been made. To these casts, an addition of nitrogen was made to give sufficient active nitrogen and thus obtain good creep resistance. This work was described at the last symposium. It was also shown that the creep resistance of this type of steel can be destroyed by thermal treatments that bring about further precipitation of aluminium nitride, thus lowering the active nitrogen content.

Figure 2 of the Allen and Hopkin paper shows how the creep resistance of aluminium-killed steel can be varied by reheating in the range 600–900°C, which is, of course, the temperature range in which the aluminium nitride precipitates most rapidly. There is abundant German work which shows this clearly. The remaining evidence in this paper is put forward to dispose of the nitrogen theory. Unfortunately, this evidence is based mainly on assumptions rather than fact, and in no case is regard taken of the important effect of strain rate. The points included in Fig.4 of the paper have been evaluated on an assumption that after normalizing at 900°C, an amount of nitrogen equal to $\frac{1}{10}$ of the soluble aluminium content will have been precipitated as aluminium nitride. From many chemical analyses of soluble aluminium and aluminium nitride contents, we find that this ratio can vary from $\frac{1}{5}$ to $\frac{1}{45}$. It is not surprising, therefore, that their points did not fall in with the relationship that has been previously given.

This information serves to show how important it is to do detailed chemical analyses in order to determine the active nitrogen contents of all samples. Nowadays, of course, we are using internal friction techniques to get a better measure of active nitrogen content, and our success in this was again indicated at a previous symposium. The absence of detailed chemical analyses or internal friction work is a serious omission from the NPL paper. Because of this omission, it is difficult to make realistic comment about the data presented on pure iron. With respect to the latter work, in many cases, the strain rates and test temperature were too high for the nitrogen effect to be observed, and in the tests where low strain rates were operative, there was an effect due to nitrogen. This is shown at the bottom part of Fig.6. The importance of strain rate cannot be over-emphasized when considering this particular aspect.

In their discussion, Allen and Hopkin considered the effect of nitrogen in the context of solution hardening and precipitation. Solution hardening was

337

dismissed because there is insufficient nitrogen to make any significant contribution. Precipitates *per se* are dismissed because of their absence. They conclude that it is aluminium that is the most important because of its effect on the formation of pearlite. Their main evidence for the latter conclusion is that high creep resistance is always obtained in mild steel of low nitrogen content when the aluminium content is low. We, on the other hand, have conclusively demonstrated that good creep resistance can be obtained where the aluminium content is high provided there is sufficient active nitrogen. It is widely accepted that strain ageing, observed in tensile tests, is associated with the nitrogen content: why then should not a similar mechanism be operative at 450°C, when the strain rate is low, and therefore the dislocation density is also low.

Dr N. P. Allen (National Physical Laboratory): We part company with the other authors at the point where they advance from a demonstration of the importance of the precipitation of aluminium nitride to the conclusion that the creep resistance is effectively dominated by the quantity of soluble nitrogen in the steel. When this opinion was put forward we looked back at our own work to see whether it would account for the results we had obtained, but could not convince ourselves that that was the case. We had the nitrogen and aluminium contents of the steels, and would have been willing to determine the aluminium nitride contents if we had felt that it was worth while. But the amount of aluminium nitride formed is very small, and its determination would have made no difference to the conclusion, so that we felt that the experimental work was not justified.

The great difficulty of this subject is to decide when nitrogen is, or is not, in solution, and for this reason Dr Kubaschewski's estimates were included which show that when 0·2%Si is present the possibility exists that no nitrogen is in solution at the temperature of the creep test. The accuracy of his calculations should not be overestimated, but it is pleasing to see that they are confirmed by some of the results in Irvine's paper. But more precise knowledge on these subjects is necessary.

Having acquired doubts about the importance of soluble nitrogen a few experiments were made to see whether it could be shown that nitrogen in solid solution in iron affected the creep rate and the results were negative. Other results on the influence of nitrogen presented in this symposium are rather curious. In the light of Dr Kubaschewski's calculations, Dr Glen's results can be interpreted as being in fair agreement with Gemmill's curve, but Irvine's results are different. He has measured directly the amount of nitrogen in simple solid solution, by means of damping measurements, and finds that the higher standard of creep resistance is obtained with as little as 0·0015% of active nitrogen present. This is inconsistent with Gemmill's curve, and indicates a need for further investigation.

It may be added that though our results show that dissolved nitrogen has little effect on the creep resistance of pure iron under our conditions of test, they do not exclude the possibility that dissolved nitrogen may have an important effect when a third element is present. We have drawn no firm conclusions about the effect of aluminium, but we notice that when aluminium is not added, a relatively good standard of creep resistance can be obtained in steels of low nitrogen content.

Dr J. Glen (Colvilles Ltd): I would like to remind the audience that the papers for this symposium were restricted to about 3000 words so that it was impossible to give a very full treatment of any aspect of the subject. In our paper it was clearly stated that many factors affect the creep resistance of mild steel. For example manganese is very important. If you test three steels with 0·1, 0·5 and 1·0%Mn the creep rate varies enormously, the higher manganese steel being much better. Thus the test points in Fig.4 of Allen and Hopkin's paper would need to be corrected for the effect of manganese before they could be used to refute the evidence given in another paper.

I would also like to emphasize one other point. Dr Allen has said that nitrogen does not have any effect on the creep resistance. In our paper we have shown that nitrogen has a very big effect on the strain/ageing peak in tensile at 250°C. This I believe is generally accepted by everyone. If a silicon-killed steel is tempered, this strain/ageing peak disappears, whereas in a steel containing no silicon there is little effect due to tempering. This seems good evidence that active nitrogen is removed in the form of silicon nitride, I do not think it necessary to say any more at this stage, but I would like to emphasize that a great deal more work has been carried out since this paper was presented for publication, and none of this work contradicts the view that active nitrogen is very important as regards creep resistance.

Mr H. W. Kirkby (Thos. Firth and John Brown Ltd): There is one thing I have learnt at this discussion which I find very interesting. I was taught at school that nitrogen would not support combustion. This is untrue!

In the case of the paper by Irvine and his colleagues on the subject of grain size, I think the authors tend to dismiss its influence rather lightly. Whilst I agree that grain size plays a secondary rôle in some cases, it may have an important influence in certain circumstances, e.g. under conditions where long life and low stresses operate. In considering the effect of grain size it is very necessary to specify the conditions since the influence of grain size may depend upon the particular criterion used. Thus, in the authors' paper a low strain criterion is used in one instance and a rupture criterion in another part of the paper and with different materials. It is clear that a lot more information is still required before the rôle played by grain size can be accurately determined.

With regard to the niobium-stabilized steels, it is agreed that the effect of solution treatment on creep and rupture resistance should take into account the effect of solubility of the carbide. I still feel, however, that a case could be made out for grain size particularly at the low stress end.

In connexion with the paper by Hodkin and his colleagues, I find it difficult to understand how ingot size can influence creep resistance, as stated by the authors. Whilst we have not submitted material to the particular criterion in question, we have carried out a lot of tests under varying conditions and on material originating from a wide range of ingots. Examination of these data fails to show any effect which could be attributed to ingot size. In addition to this, I do not understand the necessity for using an 1150°C treatment, since all our results are similar to those indicated by the authors. In our case, no 1150°C treatment is used.

Commenting briefly on the paper by Glen, and the controversy which has been raging about the influence of nitrogen, I think it is unfortunate that most of the work on mild steel started, so to speak, half way up the stairs. In talking about mild steel, we are in fact talking about an alloy steel, that is, carbon steel with a number of alloying elements and nitrogen is only one such element.

One fault I find with Dr Glen's paper is in regard to his explanations of anomalous results, which he tries to explain solely in terms of whether nitrogen is in or out of solution. In this respect, the paper appears to be lacking in evidence, though the writer appreciates the difficulty in proving all these cases. It is often

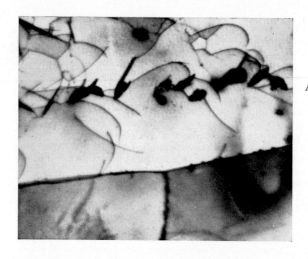

A Precipitate which is holding up the dislocations, presumably formed on the nearby grain boundary which has since migrated ×20000

the anomalous results, however, which provide a lead in explaining certain phenomena and this is the way progress is made. I would suggest, however, that if nitrogen is a factor then its effect, as mentioned earlier, must be taken in conjunction with a number of other things.

Dr **T. Broom** (CERL): I, too, wish to comment on the evidence in the paper by Irvine and his co-workers on grain size effects. First, they assert that the secondary creep rate depends on grain boundary movement and possibly movement in sub-boundaries. Then they report experiments which they suggest indicate that secondary creep rate or rupture is independent of grain size, but their experiments on stabilized austenitic steels are not well conceived. The best way to compare two specimens of different grain size is to have the same amount

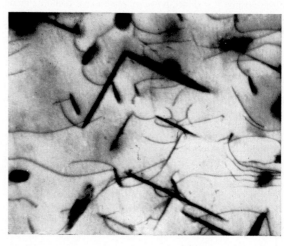

B Acicular precipitate of molybdenum carbide, Mo_2C, showing interaction with dislocations ×20000

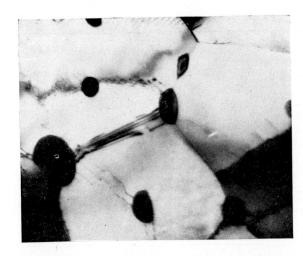

C *Formation of
    subgrains
    between large
    precipitate
    particles*
    × 20000

of niobium in solid solution by taking one specimen to a high temperature, as they did, and then heating at the lower temperature from which the other was solution treated until equilibrium is obtained; one can go on from there with the appropriate experiments.

Later, in three or four places in their paper, they indicate that if something affects secondary creep rate, this is in fact an effect upon a grain boundary and I question what evidence they have for this. Indeed, one would like to see on alloy steels, experiments of the kind that have been done by McLean and others on pure metals in order to establish at particular temperatures, strain rates and stresses, what proportion of deformation is occurring at boundaries and what proportion within grains. They would be difficult experiments but I suggest they would be well worth doing. Perhaps Dr Irvine or one of his colleagues could, from their experience, give some additional evidence on this point.

With respect to the discussion on precipitation and dispersion hardening, beginning on page 259, it would be interesting to know whether the qualitative statements of the authors could be supported by quantitative measurements interpreted according to the idealized model given by Dr McLean on page 32. Such models are of course extremely valuable but I am sure that Dr McLean would agree that it will be necessary to determine experimentally how dislocations move past or through dispersed precipitates.

As an indication that this is becoming possible some new results on one of the specimens described in the paper by Toft and Marsden may be of interest. Thin foils of the Brimsdown steel, which had been exposed to 20 years' service, are being studied by Dr E. J. Langham. Mr A. J. Hall of CERL prepared the foils giving the micrographs in the figures. Dislocations can be seen to be held up by particles in Figs. *A* and *B*. One wonders whether the sub-grains in Fig. *C* are in fact playing an important rôle in determining the creep resistance of this material and whether in fact this is a softer region than the structure shown in Fig. *B*. We do not understand the details of the mechanisms yet, but I think that it is this kind of work, preferably on specimens that have had a better known history than this particular Brimsdown steel, that is going to tell us how precipitates are affecting creep properties.

TABLE 1 Details of steels and analyses

Dimensions, details of manufacture, and heat treatment	Analyses, %						
	C	Mn	Si	Ni	Cr	Mo	Nb (+Ta)
Tube $1\frac{7}{8}$in o.d. $\frac{1}{8}$in wall; extruded 1 220°C and cold drawn; soaked at 1 050°C for 1 h, air cooled	0·09	1·60	0·56	10·9	18·5	...	1·30
Pipe $10\frac{1}{4}$in o.d. $1\frac{1}{4}$in wall, pierced at 1 230°C and hot drawn at 1 230°C and then cold drawn; soaked at 1 050°C for 20 min, air cooled	0·11	1·20	0·45	11·5	18·5	0·09	1·27

These commercial steels are very variable in structure and, of course, if we are going to make any progress we have to carry out many examinations of a similar nature on high-purity materials, but we cannot give 20 years' creep service in the laboratory, and so we must pay some attention to steels in which this variability occurs. I think it is worthwhile to assert my belief that it is this kind of work that is going to help towards some understanding of why the creep resistance is still high in Fig.11a on p.259, after 10–50 h.

Solid solution hardening has been much discussed. I think it is completely misleading for Irvine *et al.* to separate dislocation atmosphere effects from the so-called solid solution hardening effects. For example, the effect of phosphorus is instanced on p.248, but one wonders whether in fact there is segregation to dislocations.

To make a constructive suggestion, arguments about mechanisms of hardening by solid solution may be resolved by detailed tensile tests in which one studies the effects on the yield phenomena of temperature, strain rate, and conditions during arresting or temporarily unloading. I believe that the pattern of work which will lead to useful results in the future should consist of carefully designed mechanical tests correlated with thin film electron microscope work of such high

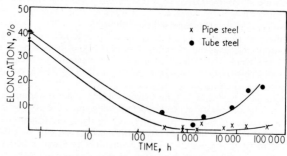

D *Elongation/time curves at 650°C, 18%Cr–12%Ni–1%Nb steel*

342

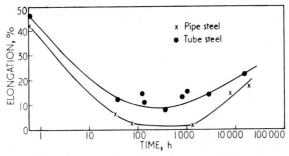

E *Elongation/time curves at 700°C, 18%Cr–12%Ni–1%Nb steel*

quality as to give all the information one requires about orientation relationships and the vexed question of when coherency stops and incoherency begins.

Mr E. A. Jenkinson (National Physical Laboratory): At the NPL we have been carrying out creep tests on pipe and tube material in austenitic 18%Cr–12%Ni–1%Nb steel. Details of our steels are shown in Table 1. The elongation at rupture/log time to rupture diagrams at 650°C and 700°C are shown in Figs.*D* and *E*, respectively. Both the tube and pipe materials at 700°C and the tube material at 650°C show well defined minima in elongation as the time to rupture increases. There is now evidence[1–4] suggesting that the decreasing elongation on these materials is associated with the formation of a fine strain-induced precipitation of NbC on dislocations and that the subsequent increase of elongation occurs when the NbC precipitate becomes coarse. The results obtained during the present work are consistent with these observations except that the elongation at rupture of the pipe steel tested at 650°C showed little tendency to increase even after a test which ruptured in 40726 h although the coarsening of the NbC precipitate appeared much the same as for the tube sample.

It has been shown previously that this minima in the elongation/log time-to-rupture curves is not associated with the formation of the sigma phase.[5]

Figures *D* and *E* also show that at either temperature the elongation minima

TABLE 2   X-ray examination and chemical analyses of residues from the 18–12–1 pipe and tube samples in the 'as received' condition (Residues extracted electrolytically in 10%HCl in alcohol)

Sample	Phases identified by X-ray examination	% Residue	Fe	Cr	Nb	C	Niobium remaining in matrix by difference, %
Pipe	NbC + trace $Cr_{23}C_6$	1·34	1·8	0·9	79·4	9·0	0·21
Tube	NbC	1·34	0·0	1·0	81·5	...	0·21

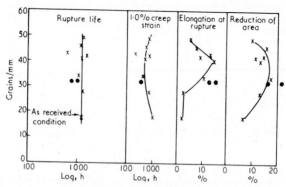

F *Effect on creep properties of refining the grain size of the pipe steel, creep tests at 700°C and 7 tons/in²*

occur in the same time for both pipe and tube samples but that the minimum value of elongation at each test temperature is markedly different for the two samples. This difference in behaviour might be explained if these samples contained different degrees of supersaturation of NbC at the test temperatures. However, Table 1 shows that both pipe and tube samples have similar Nb and C contents, similar thermal history during fabrication and the same final heat treatment of air cooling from 1 050°C. Also, Table 2 shows that similar amounts of residues were extracted from both samples in the 'as-received' condition and that these residues consist essentially of NbC. It can be concluded, therefore, that the degree of supersaturation of NbC at its test temperatures is substantially the same for both pipe and tube samples so that similar amounts of NbC in the two samples should be available for precipitation during creep testing.

Another explanation must be found, therefore, for the marked difference in the minimum values of elongation between the pipe and tube samples. It is believed that the effect is attributable to the difference in grain size between the two samples; the grain size of the pipe sample being 18 gr/mm while that of the tube was 32 gr/mm. To confirm this idea samples of the pipe material were reheated to 1 050°C, given various reductions by forging and rolling with frequent reheating, and then finally heat treated by air cooling from 1 050°C. Grain sizes of up to 50 gr/mm were obtained. The results of creep tests at 700°C made under conditions to give minimum elongation at rupture are plotted against grain size in Fig.F where it will be seen that, initially the elongation at rupture increases with decreasing grain size. Also plotted as circles in Fig.F are the values obtained for the tube sample and it can be seen that there is reasonable agreement with the pipe material of similar grain size. The decrease of elongation of the pipe sample at the finest grain sizes is not understood.

It may be expected that maximum resistance to dislocation movement occurs only when the matrix remains supersaturated so that further precipitation can take place on dislocations which have moved away from their original precipitates. Such a process would be expected to result in strain ageing and indeed tensile tests[6] in the temperature range 600–700°C result in serrated stress/strain curves. Thus, the recovery of ductility for times greater than for minimum ductility may occur not only when the particles have grown beyond a critical size but also when the supersaturation of the matrix disappears. This could explain the result that there is little recovery of ductility in the pipe sample at

344

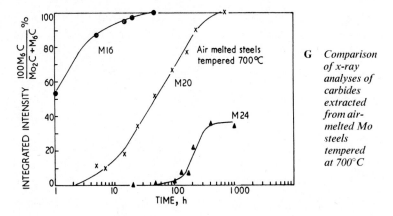

G Comparison of x-ray analyses of carbides extracted from air-melted Mo steels tempered at 700°C

650°C (Fig. D) although the precipitated NbC particles have grown considerably. Since the strains were low in this sample few dislocations are formed to nucleate precipitation so that precipitates can grow whilst sufficient degree of supersaturation remains in the matrix for further precipitation on any dislocations moved from their original positions.

Mr K. A. Ridal (English Steel Corporation Ltd): Many contributions at this symposium have stressed the importance of precipitation during creep. I should like to say a few words about the effect of creep upon precipitation, particularly upon the tempering of alloy steels.

It is generally accepted that prior cold work accelerates precipitation and, in the past, the assumption has been made that creep deformation will also enhance the rate of precipitation. Recent work by Nileshwar and Quarrell has indicated that this is not always the case; in a low-C 9%Cr ferritic steel, creep deformation was found to retard the Cr_7C_3 transformation on creep tempering at 600°C. They have also offered some evidence that the Mo_2C to M_6C transformation is similarly retarded.

Professor Quarrell and I have continued the investigation on the effect of creep on tempering, but we have attempted to refine the experimental techniques for extraction and examination of the carbides so as to obtain more precise information. We confirm that the chromium carbide transformation is retarded by creep at temperatures from 550° to 700°C. However, the magnitude of the retardation is not as great as previously reported. Perhaps too much importance was attached to this effect in the early days.

However, the main course of our investigation has been to obtain more detail on molybdenum carbide transformation in a series of low carbon 3·5%Mo steels. I thought it suitable to give an outline of the results we obtained.

Generally, we found the degree of acceleration increases with higher rates of straining, lower test temperature and slower rates of transformation; which is dependent on the carbon content of the steel.

Much has been said about the effect of trace elements upon creep. In the course of obtaining the results I have outlined, we had cause to make both vacuum- and air-melted molybdenum steels. It seems interesting that the tempering behaviour was markedly affected by what must have been trace elements.

Figure G shows the progress of the molybdenum carbide transformation for a series of air-melted 3·5% molybdenum steels of varying carbon contents,

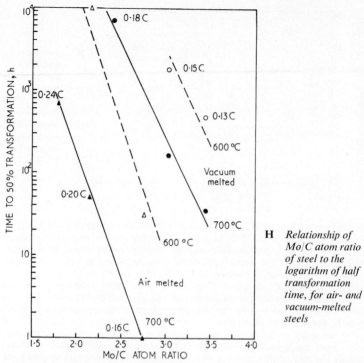

H *Relationship of Mo/C atom ratio of steel to the logarithm of half transformation time, for air- and vacuum-melted steels*

tempered at 700°C. The only real difference in chemical composition is that you have 0·24, 0·20, 0·16%C and the rate of transformation increases with decreasing carbon content.

Figure *H* shows progress of the transformation in a vacuum-melted series of steels tempered at 700°C. This is a similar series but these are vacuum melted steels. The structure is bainitic and the normal composition is the same, 0·18, 0·15 and 0·13%C, and again, with the lowering of the carbon content, there is increased rate of transformation.

Figure *I* is a comparison of the transformation rates for the two series of steels, air-melted and vacuum-melted, tempered at 700°C. The Mo/C ratio is calculated from the composition of the steel and is a measure of the availability of molybdenum atoms necessary for carbide transformation. On the air-melted steels we have plotted time of transformation to atom ratio. If you compare with vacuum-melted steels, you again get a straight line but it is displaced by a factor between 100 and 1000 times.

It is very difficult at the present time to explain this fully. Intuitively, one suspects the cleanness of the steel for the great differences in the rate of transformation, and aluminium, nitrogen and silicon: these are all suspect especially when the air-melted steels were aluminium killed.

I will not try to explain any mechanism for this but I think it is worthwhile mentioning that we are of the opinion that Mo carbide transformation occurs *in situ* and not by separate nucleation process and one could easily see the trace elements acting simply as nucleants.

346

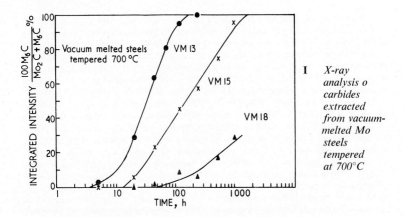

I X-ray analysis o carbides extracted from vacuum-melted Mo steels tempered at 700°C

AUTHORS' REPLIES

Mr **R. J. Truman** (Brown-Firth Research Laboratories): During this discussion only a few comments have been made specifically concerning the paper by Mr Kirkby and myself. I would like to refer back to Mr Johnson's remarks, when he opened the discussion, in which he commented that we had perhaps extracted more from the existing data than is justified, particularly in regard to Figs.9–12. One usually feels compelled to reach some conclusions, or to indicate certain trends, however sparse the actual data. During the course of the presentation of this paper, I did, however, show all further test data obtained since preparing the preprints, and any trends we may have indicated at that time are still valid in view of this later information. Not only have longer time tests been completed, but shorter time tests also, which have given a direct link between the earlier short-time tensile behaviour and the present longer time rupture series. The figures mentioned by Mr Johnson compare the ductility behaviour of 1050°C treated bar and pipe materials. They indicate that 1050°C treated steampipe material behaves like bar material that has received a solution treatment well in excess of 1050°C. We are not trying to infer from this that the ductility of pipe material will remain at a very low level for longer test times, particularly at 700°C when we anticipate that ductility recovery will be apparent reasonably soon. Some data on 18–12–1Nb pipe material at 700°C presented by Mr Jenkinson of NPL have, in fact, shown recovery of ductility at test times somewhat longer than we have completed so far.

In regard to pipe material generally, this is normally regarded as having been solution-treated at 1050°C. It may be more correct to regard this 1050°C treatment as a secondary treatment, rather than a solution treatment, as during fabrication the finishing temperature can be appreciably above 1050°C. This finishing temperature should, in fact, be regarded as the true solution temperature. When we make a comparison with bar material, therefore, it may be more correct to compare 1050°C treated pipes with bar material in the 1350°C condition followed by a secondary treatment of 1050°C, rather than just a high temperature solution treatment only. With the former type of treatment on bar, we have demonstrated that the ductility trends are superior to those obtained from, say, a 1350°C solution treatment only, and may prove eventually to be closely comparable with pipe material.

In regard to Mr Murray's comments, we agree that with this type of steel the niobium carbide/austenite eutectic is reformed on heating to temperatures of the order 1 340–1 350°C, and we did observe a small amount of this eutectic pattern in our test specimens solution-treated at this temperature. We have demonstrated, however, that rupture ductility deteriorates progressively with increasing solution treatment temperature, and that no sudden abnormal change is found after solution treatment temperatures at which this eutectic is formed. Moreover, some of the more recent test data at 700°C have shown that secondary treatments of 850° and 1 050°C cause some improvement in the ductility behaviour of 1 350°C treated bar material, indicating that no permanent deleterious effects appear to result from the formation of small amounts of eutectic structures.

Further confirmation of this was observed in a short time tensile ductility investigation. Again it was shown that increasing solution treatment temperatures, to above that at which the eutectic structure is formed, resulted in a progressive worsening of ductility behaviour with solution temperature. No sudden abnormal change was found at 1 350°C where a small amount of the eutectic structure is formed, or even at 1 375°C where a large amount is formed.

After the 1 350°C solution treatment, we were able to restore completely the ductility behaviour to that of 1 050°C treated bar material, by giving a secondary treatment at 850°C.

From these results, we concluded that the effects arising solely from the formation of a small amount of niobium carbide/austenite eutectic were of a relatively minor order.

Dr **Irvine**, Mr **Murray**, and Mr **Pickering** wrote: Dr Allen raises the point about the analysis procedure for nitrogen and he mentions the agreement between the results obtained by Glen and Gemmill and the inconsistency between these results and those obtained by ourselves. To us this does not seem surprising since the former were obtained by chemical analysis, whereas ours were measured by an internal friction technique. The internal friction technique measures the nitrogen content which is present in interstitial solution. Since this is the nitrogen content which has the important effect on creep properties, however, we consider that our method is preferable.

There is reference by Mr Kirkby and Dr Broom to the effect of grain size. They say that we have minimized the effect of grain size. We think that it should be remembered that our paper attempted to illustrate the most important structural features which have an effect on creep properties and we illustrated these effects by test data which were either our own or which were in the published literature. We differentiated between relatively simple austenitic stainless steels and those containing strong carbide-forming elements. The test data quoted for the simple austenitic stainless steels show that grain size has a practically negligible effect and no one in discussion challenged these results or produced any alternative results to show any different effect. We stated that the position was more complicated in steels containing strong carbide-forming elements, since it is difficult to separate the different effects of grain size and solid-solution hardening. Dr Broom asks for experiments to separate these effects and in this connexion he would find it interesting to study the contribution made by Truman at the recent creep conference in Düsseldorf. He conducted experiments very much on the lines suggested by Dr Broom and these again show the small effect of grain size.

Dr Broom suggests other experiments which would illustrate the effect of grain size as far as grain boundary movement is concerned. We should be quite realistic about this. Work investigating the factors affecting creep properties requires a large amount of test equipment. Any organization, therefore, will naturally concentrate its available test capacity on those topics which it thinks are of greatest importance. Since all of our experience is that grain size has a relatively small effect we have not previously, nor do we intend to concentrate a large amount of test equipment to investigate this variable. Dr Broom, however, represents a large research organization and since he believes firmly in the important effect of grain size, no doubt he will be carrying out the work he has suggested, and we shall be extremely interested to see the results which he obtains.

We were very interested to see the results obtained by Mr Jenkinson on pipe and tube material, since this is a carefully planned and systematic programme of work. In describing the results, all of the emphasis is placed on the difference in the ductility minimum between the two samples, which shows the effect of grain size. We agree that this effect is a real one and should be taken into account. In our opinion, however, the results simply confirm our own viewpoint since the important feature is the marked reduction in ductility which occurs with testing time. In comparison with this major decrease in ductility the variation between the two samples is small. We are interested in the major variable which is the effect of the precipitation process on ductility and we still assert that in comparison with this effect, the effect of grain size is small.

Mr **Toft** and Miss **Marsden** wrote: In his opening comments, Mr Johnson said that the materials discussed in the papers were going into service under conditions of maximum exploitation of their creep strength. This statement assumes that we know precisely the conditions under which various components such as superheater tubes, rotors, turbine blades, etc., operate, and that designers know how the materials they use will behave under these conditions. With few exceptions neither of these statements is true. Even in the comparatively simple case of a superheater tube, it is clear that the stress and temperature systems developed in service are not sufficiently well defined and the designer invariably uses a rupture criterion which includes a safety factor. Until the behaviour of the materials available to him is known over long periods of time, he will not be able to make full use of their potentialities.

Since our paper was presented and discussed, some doubt about the presence of the chromium carbide Cr_7C_3 has been expressed. The identification of this chromium carbide was based upon the knowledge of its morphology in the $2\frac{1}{4}\%Cr-1\%Mo$ steel and it was not positively identified by selected area electron

Table 3   Tensile properties at 550°C, 3% Cr–Mo–W–V steel

Material	Heat treatment	0·2% PS, tons/in²	Max. stress tons/in²	Elong. % 4√L	R. of A. %
1in dia. bar	1150°C, AC/685°C, AC	41·0	46·0	17	53
Cast P.1803	1150°C, AC/730°C, AC	27·9	31·6	21	75
	1150°C, AC/1060°C, OQ/ 685°C AC	38·0	43·0	18	64
	1150°C, AC/1060°C, OQ/ 700°C, AC	27·7	31·0	25	80
Rotors	Not determined				

diffraction analysis. However, as Dr Broom indicated, further work is being carried out on some of the tubes and attempts are being made to identify positively the precipitates and to determine the rôles each of them play in conferring creep resistance.

Mr **Hodkin**, Dr **Finch**, and Mr **Colbeck** wrote: In reply to Mr Johnson, the short-time hot tensile properties of the steel are as shown in Table 3.

It is interesting to note in respect of 1in dia. bar material that the 1150°C, AC/685°C, AC treatment leads to a reasonable level of tensile ductility despite the poor corresponding short-time creep ductility. The relatively poor creep ductility of the 685°C tempered condition, as compared with higher tempering temperatures, seems to us to be in line with normal expectation of the effect of tempering treatments on hardenable ferritic steels. As regards the inter-relation of microstructures and ductility, there was insufficient change in microstructure between the 685° and 730°C tempered conditions to give an indisputable explanation. It seems likely, however, that a higher tempering temperature will lead to progressive spheroidization of the grain boundary carbide, and we would normally expect this to be accompanied by improved ductility.

As we pointed out in the discussion, we were ourselves surprised by the correlation between the creep properties of 1in dia. bar and the size of the original ingot. Although the higher molybdenum contents show generally better creep properties, a plot of the creep properties against ingot size gives a perceptibly closer correlation than does that of creep properties against the molybdenum content and it still seems justifiable to remark that an ingot size effect may be present. Looking more closely at the molybdenum content, two casts (F.5896 and F.9182/2; 7in and 11in ingots respectively) possess almost identical molybdenum contents yet differ markedly in creep strains at 1000 h duration. Since all the ingots relating to Fig.2 were forged to 1in dia. bar, this question may be looked at from the slightly different viewpoint that creep properties are influenced systematically by forging reduction. We certainly would not recommend extrapolation of Fig.2 until a more complete investigation of ingot size effects has been carried out, but it seems necessary to reiterate that this figure applies only to the particular case of forging down to 1in dia. bar: thus a valid extrapolation would still be of no assistance in predicting the properties of a large forging.

Turning to the large rotor forgings, whilst the creep and rupture properties of material machined directly from their peripheries were very similar to those of 1in dia. bars used in the earlier investigations, it is not an easy matter to offer a direct explanation of these observations. We agree that the rotor results fall generally in line with the effect of molybdenum content on creep properties which Mr Johnson implies, but on the other hand the forging procedures, reheating histories, heat-treatment times, and masses of the rotors differ so greatly from the 1in bar material that we hesitate to try to explain their detailed behaviour. It is none the less interesting to note the relative similarity in properties between 1in dia. bars and large forgings and additionally reassuring that almost identical properties can be reproduced in two large components produced from entirely separate casts of steel.

We do not think that the behaviour of the creep test on which the load was increased after a preliminary period (20000 h) of steady-state creep is misleading, as a number of additional specimens (not included in the paper) were subjected to tensile tests at 550°C after being discontinued at various stages of creep and these also have shown a high degree of ductility. The main interest of the result is that it evidently indicates freedom from intrinsic embrittlement of the steel during creep (such, for example, as may be expected from grain boundary carbide precipitation) since there is every reason to believe that these specimens would have broken with low ductility had the creep tests been allowed to proceed to fracture. The reason underlying this behaviour appears to be bound up with the formation of inter-granular cracks during creep. Both nucleation and growth of these cracks are time-dependent effects and if the rate of deformation of the specimen is markedly accelerated then the normal process of plastic flow proceeds at such a rate that the development of the internal cracks is overshadowed and the ductility correspondingly improved.

On page 306 reference is made to an 'embrittling' mechanism and this refers to the form of embrittlement which is disclosed by impact tests. On page 307, however, we refer to embrittlement as indicated by rupture ductility and it is pointed out on that page that there is unlikely to be an immediate theoretical relationship between rupture ductility and impact values. We regret that these alternative usages have led to an ambiguity.

In reply to Mr Kirkby's question regarding the influence of the 1150°C normalizing treatment, in earlier work on this steel it was found that forging temperatures had a distinct influence on the creep and rupture properties; the lower the finishing temperature, the poorer were the results. The high temperature normalizing treatment before hardening and tempering was therefore introduced to overcome variations in previous thermal histories; a net improvement in creep and rupture properties was then obtained due largely to the reduced scatter of results. The high-temperature normalizing ensures solution of the massive carbide phases and promotes more uniform precipitation on subsequent heat-treatment.

REFERENCES

1. K. J. IRVINE et al.: JISI, 1960, **196**, 166–179.
2. R. J. TRUMAN and H. W. KIRKBY: ibid., 180–188.
3. R. N. YOUNGER and R. G. BAKER: ibid., 188–194.
4. N. E. MOORE and J. A. GRIFFITHS: ibid., 1961, **197**, 29–39.
5. A. I. SMITH et al.: Proc. IME, 1957, **171**, 918.
6. 'Steels for use in steamplant operating above 950°F', Publn. J/T 170; 1957, British Electrical and Allied Industries Research Association.